THE YEARBOOK OF
AGRICULTURE 1968

SCIENCE
for
BETTER LIVING

UNITED STATES DEPARTMENT OF AGRICULTURE

UNITED STATES
GOVERNMENT PRINTING OFFICE

FOR SALE BY THE SUPERINTENDENT OF DOCUMENTS
WASHINGTON, D.C. 20402 - PRICE $3.00

Sensing devices on spacecraft and airplanes are being developed to determine crop condition, detect insect and disease damage, and for other purposes. Here, brown soft scale infestation of citrus trees in Texas is detected at early stage with aerial infrared photo. Infested trees below pond are dark, due to absorption of infrared light by sooty mold from infestation.

Infrared aerial photo, *right,* confirms or adds to information in regular aerial color photo, *left.* Varying red shades on infrared photo identify types of mixed hardwoods in California—maple, oak, buckeye, madrone, and bay. In aerial color, identification is difficult. Aerial color film indicates brown grassy areas are dead; green coloration on infrared confirms this. Color film picks up marshy vegetation on shoreline, pink border in infrared shows it is alive.

Chicks hatched in poultry
research at Beltsville, Md.

Experiments in controlled environments have nearly doubled yields of
lettuce, tomatoes, cucumbers, radishes, and other crops. Here, lettuce
produced outside growth chamber is compared with much larger
plant raised under controlled temperature, light, and carbon dioxide.

Biological controls are fast being developed against plant pests. Cinnabar moth was brought from Europe to control tansy ragwort, rangeweed poisonous to cattle. Above is field infested with ragwort—the gold blossoms. Below is same field with foreground cleared of ragwort by cinnabar moth larvae. At top left of next page, closeup shows moth larvae feeding on ragwort, leaving only bare stalks. Cattle, top right, benefit.

Tiny larva of native ichneumon wasp feeds on far bigger larva of the
western spruce budworm, one of the West's most serious forest pests.

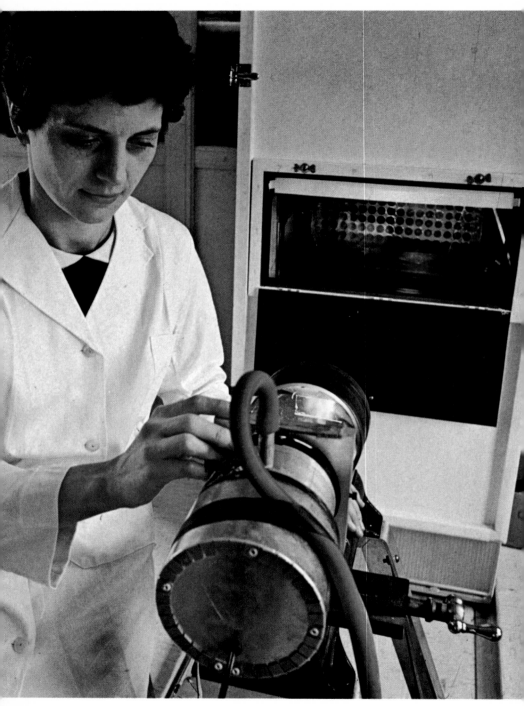

Light of certain intensities and color may "awake" insects from resting state (diapause) at time unfavorable to them, as in winter. Here, scientist adjusts color filter through which light is beamed on diapausing insects. New types of pest control are goal.

In insect control study, mosquito feeds on human blood.

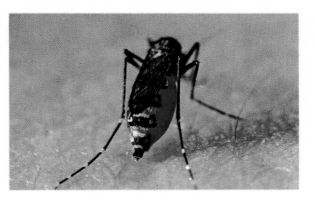

Flies released from cage swarm toward experimental flytrap with ultraviolet lamp as attractant.

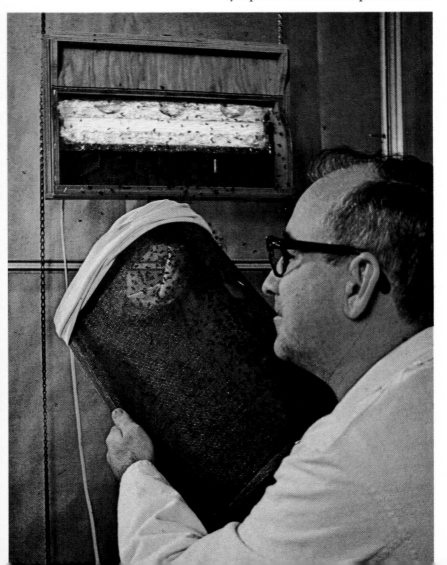

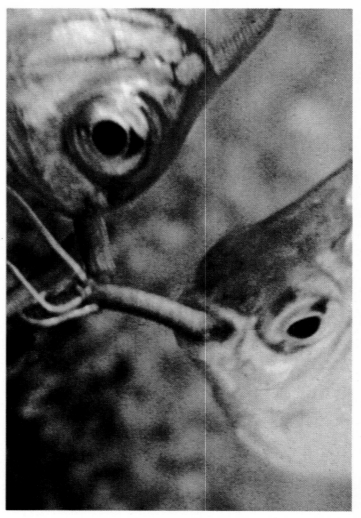

Biological controls are being tested against weeds that infest waterways, curtailing boating and swimming. Here silver dollar fish graze on pondweed.

Flea beetle feeds on waterweed, in Florida.

Physiologist probes secret of how trees make wood. He is providing radioactive carbon to pine tree, so he can trace carbon into chemicals laid down in wood at different times of year. *Below,* female longleaf pine flower.

Crocuses, *top,* herald spring at National Arboretum, America's beautification center.
Rhododendron clusters delight children, *above.*

Mississippi and Florida are among Southern States that have long claimed the magnolia. *Magnolia grandiflora* is one of most popular, and is used in breeding program at Arboretum in its search to widen growing range of this tree.

Blackspot disease spores in waterdrops, *left,* are placed on various types of rose leaves to determine resistance to disease. Traveler, *right,* picks bouquet of crownvetch being used for highway beautification and erosion control. USDA plant scientists have developed crownvetch varieties especially suitable for this job.

Checking precise butterfat content of milk sample.

Bee bred to cross-pollinate alfalfa rests on alfalfa blossom. Heavy pollen deposits on legs indicate it has pollinated hundreds of blossoms.

Petunias and marigolds are moved from greenhouse covered with experimental fluorescent plastic material. Test was made to see if energy is increased in red portion of spectrum, resulting in increased plant growth.

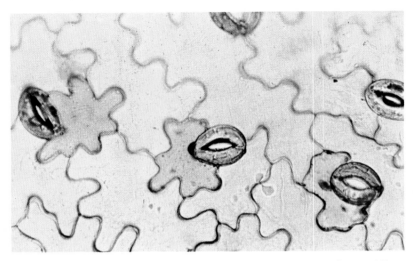

Laughing lips of stomata, microscopic porelike cells on plant leaves. These bean stomata are taking up blue dye in tests made with sealants to cut down on water loss from plants through stomata.

Fluorescent dye stains surface of globemallow leaf, in test to show patterns of herbicide entry into plants. Star-shaped trichomes or leaf hairs are important points of entry. Red light in photomicrograph shows veins.

Model of experimental home built at Forest Products Laboratory. Costs are reduced by wood lamination, prefinished components, and modern adhesive compounds. Only a fourth as many nails are needed.

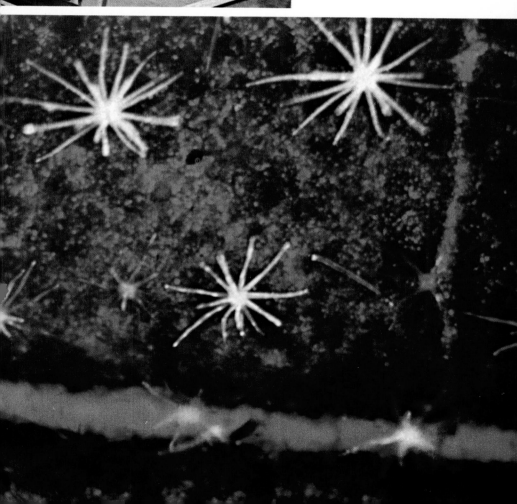

Two sets of twin lambs were born to same ewe 8 months apart. USDA is trying to develop breed of sheep, Morlam, that will stay fairly consistently on 8-month or even 6-month breeding schedule.

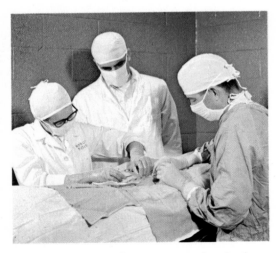

State researchers perform ova transplant in sheep. After conception in one sheep, ova have been transferred to host mother who carries embryo and eventually gives birth.

Dramatic contrast results from selective breeding of hogs for high and low meatiness. Top photo shows cuts from high-fat hog, other photo from low-fat hog. Loin eye area is the cut on upper left in both photos, bacon just below. Hams are at right.

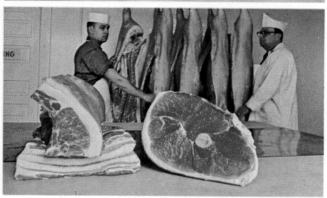

Cowboys round up Hereford heifers used in crossbreeding experiments in Montana.

Brilliant red laser beam, *right*, is used
to automatically guide new types
of farm drainage machines.

USDA chemist hydrogenates a fatty acid in studies at Peoria, Ill.,
to improve soybean oil for salads and cooking.

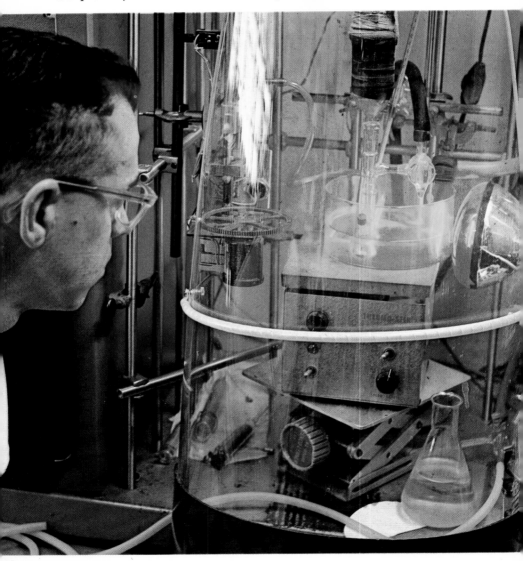

Automation in food packaging:
A radish bagging machine.

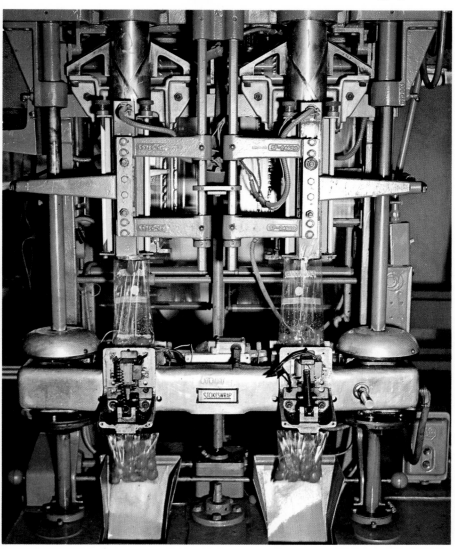

Pineapple is watered in low-rainfall area in Hawaii. Engineering research has led to mechanization of many agricultural operations.

Hydraulically operated lift truck attachment gets final check on test stand. This plant makes cotton handling equipment.

USDA plant breeders are developing new tomato varieties adapted to machine harvesting for use in processed products. The tomatoes all ripen near same time, come from vine easily, and are firm fruited. Two of lines are oblong shaped, which reduces rolling on harvester and lessens bruising.

USDA scientists pluck feather from sandhill crane for chromosome count. Their studies may save whooping crane and other wild birds from extinction. By careful breeding, scientists seek to overcome genes that make a species unable to adapt to changing world. Another potential result: Major improvements in domestic fowl.

Riffle sifter in Alaska stream blows silt from gravel bottom, providing better spawning beds for salmon—a fish crop worth some $116 million annually. Machine was developed by Forest Service and industry research. *Below,* pink salmon egg at 36 days.

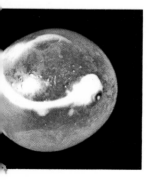

Spacecraft oceanography is new phase of fishery science. This photo by astronauts of southern tip of Florida and the Keys aids studies of pink shrimp nursery grounds. To right of Keys is main flow of Florida current. From this, eddies flow through Keys distributing shrimp larvae into shallow nursery waters.

At 90 feet below surface, fishery technician collects lobsters for use in behavior studies.

New technique for producing oysters. After free-swimming oyster larvae attach to shells or other hard objects, they are put in tank, *above,* and fed artificially. When young oysters have grown so they adhere firmly to hard object, they are taken to natural oysterbeds to grow to adult size.

Machine-washable wool
garments above were developed
through USDA research.

Commercial wash-wear, stretch cottons resulted from government-industry cooperation in research and development.

Wool research starts with sheep. At right, woolly lamb makes new friend.

Inexpensive cotton lace, *left,* made by processes devised by USDA.

Scientists test effectiveness of fire-retardant chemical for forest fire use. Flames blaze high through untreated wood crib fuel bed, *top*, then die down, *below*, on reaching portion treated with chemical.

Preface

JACK HAYES
Yearbook Editor

. . . .

"Science for Better Living"; for you and your family is what you will find in this book, since the theme is agricultural research. We all benefit in our daily lives from that research because it improves the meals we eat, the clothes we wear, our water and air, the wood we build much of our homes with, and the plants and trees that make our surroundings more livable.

The color section gives you an idea of the sweep of that research. Geographically, too, this book covers vast areas. It roams from the United States to Japan, the Philippines, Finland, and points between. Subjects range from the alfalfa bee to the weed-eating sea cow, from balloon logging to WURLAN wool fabric, from a low-calorie cheese to farming by space satellite.

Scientists come to life in these pages. Keith E. Gregory pioneers crossbreeding in beef production. William C. Crow plans markets big enough to feed city areas of 15 million people. B. Jean Apgar, mother of three, determines the structure of a nucleic acid for the first time. Norman E. Borlaug, a foundation man in Mexico, brings short wheats to amazing yield levels.

Mostly we report on research in the last five years or so, although some older landmark achievements are included. Since agricultural research more often than not is cooperative, we describe Federal, State, and industry work.

You may notice that agricultural scientists often are endowed with serendipity, the "gift of finding valuable . . . things not sought for." All it takes is long years developing expertise in a specialty, and a strong streak of sagacity. Then something totally unexpected happens in the lab, and the next thing you know the scientist has figured out a hard-nosed practical use for it. Perhaps a water repellant for paper products, or a flame-resistant finish for fabrics.

George W. Irving, Jr., Administrator of the Agricultural Research Service, served as chairman of the Yearbook Committee. Others on the Committee that planned this book are:

Ned D. Bayley, Director of Science and Education.

Agricultural Research Service—Walter M. Carleton, Earl R. Glover, Edwin R. Goode, Jr., Willis A. Gortner, Sam R. Hoover, Robert B. Rathbone, Eugene P. Reagan, Martin G. Weiss.

Cooperative State Research Service—Bruce F. Beacher, Nelson B. King, Thomas S. Ronningen.

Economic Research Service—Wesley B. Sundquist.

Forest Service—Stephen G. Boyce, William R. Moore, Leon R. Thomas.

National Science Foundation—M. Frank Hersman.

Office of Management Services—Ward W. Konkle.

University of Maryland—Clyne S. Shaffner.

Contents

· · · · · · · · · · · · · · · · · · · ·

CITY AND COUNTRY

NATURAL RESOURCES

GROWING NATIONS AND WORLD TRADE

FOR BETTER LIVING

Scientific Agriculture: Keystone of Abundance

ORVILLE L. FREEMAN
Secretary of Agriculture

. . . .

Tomorrow morning at 3 o'clock in New York City's Hunt's Point market—or in Boston, Chicago, San Francisco, and other large cities—a quiet, friendly, businesslike man will begin moving in and out of the fruit and vegetable stands, checking with food buyers and sellers on the quantity, quality, and prices of commodities offered and sold. He's a USDA market news reporter. Farmers and dealers in farm products use his information daily in operating today's scientific agriculture and keeping a steady supply of food flowing to consumers.

Some hours later in a research lab at Beltsville, Md.—or Philadelphia, New Orleans, Peoria, or one of many other agricultural laboratories around the country—a chemist studies ways to develop new or improved uses for farm products. He's a USDA research scientist. He and his colleagues have already developed commercial penicillin, wash-and-wear cottons, shrink-resistant woolens, concentrated orange and other fruit juices, and hundreds of other products for better living.

In Lewisburg, Ky.—or Shell Pile, N.J., Lovelock, Nev., Centerville, Iowa, or any of thousands of other small rural communities—a local resident conducts a meeting of community leaders working on the problem of expanding job and living opportunities in rural America. He's a USDA field representative of the Farmers Home Administration or the Extension Service.

In an agricultural area of far-off India—or Thailand, Nigeria, Kenya, Brazil, and other foreign lands—a team of scientists and other specialists is helping farmers and government officials to irrigate and drain land, establish market news systems, conserve soil, water, and timber resources, set up credit-cooperative programs, and improve farm productivity and management. They are selected from many USDA agencies to help win the war on hunger.

These are some of *your* public servants in the U.S. Department of Agriculture. They and their colleagues, working with American farmers and American agriculture, keep your market basket filled with food, develop new products for your convenience, play a leading role in revitalizing rural communities, and build better agricultures in poor nations.

But this is not all. They have also helped beyond measure to project this Nation into the first economy of abundance known to man—an economy in which disposable per capita income in 1967 rose to $2,735.

Most of the world's people, unlike most of us, live amid scarcity. Three persons out of four have per capita incomes averaging about $110 per year. In India, the average is only $80—about 22 cents a day.

In these economies of scarcity, most of the people are bound to the soil. Living in villages, in clustered dwellings from which they go to cultivate the fields, they use human muscle supplemented by animal power to do their work. Their agriculture is primitive. The ancient hand sickle, the threshing board, the short-handle hoe, the wooden plow—implements used for thousands of years—are still in common use.

To produce enough food for sustenance is the primary goal, and for many hunger is as constant as their shadow.

Transportation is primarily by foot, animals, or bicycle. The women carry babies on their backs, market baskets on their heads. Most roads are country lanes, sometimes little more than trails.

A high proportion of the people, especially in rural regions, are illiterate. Communication is mainly by word of mouth, neighbor to neighbor.

In an economy of scarcity, life goes on pretty much as it has for 30 centuries.

In an economy of abundance such as ours, *all is change.*

Abundance has enabled us to collapse time and space. It has put us on wheels and given us wings. It makes possible mass education and communication, an increased leisure, extended vacations, hundreds of laborsaving devices, and thousands of gadgets for easier living.

Abundance provides machines to replace, supplement, and extend muscles. Man can literally move mountains, travel at incredible speeds, hear and see events as they occur an ocean span away.

But why us? Why is America, above all nations, far and away the leader in entering the age of abundance?

One reason—undoubtedly the most basic, almost certainly the least recognized—is scientific agriculture.

History clearly shows that the application of research to increase agricultural productivity is the solid base upon which all subsequent economic development rests.

Scientific agriculture in the United States has made and continues to make at least six specific contributions of major importance to this country's economy of abundance.

• It has, in effect, multiplied the

In a primitive agriculture, camel helps till the soil.

Nation's manpower. Scientific agriculture's rapidly rising productivity released millions from farming, thus providing much of the labor force for the continuing industrial revolution. Not only did the rise in productivity make it unnecessary for more people to enter agriculture to supply the food and fiber needs of a growing population; it enabled the actual number of farmers to be steadily reduced.

Almost one-fourth of our people lived on farms in 1937, and 15 percent lived there in 1950. But in 1967, less than 6 percent of the Nation's population was on farms—yet we ate better than ever before.

In 1937, one person employed in agriculture produced enough food and fiber for 10 persons—and in 1950 for 15. But in 1967, he produced abundantly for more than 40 persons.

Agriculture's rising productivity, as a consequence, has made possible the application of a continually rising proportion of the Nation's labor force, including its inventive genius and management, to mill our steel and to generate our electricity; to build homes, schools, office buildings, and factories; to produce cars, television, air conditioners, and computers; to build and sail ships; to make and fly planes; and to man our professions and service occupations.

The scientific and technological progress of our agriculture has been so rapid, however, that the economy has found some difficulty in adjusting to it. Commodity surpluses and rural underemployment have been among the results.

Nevertheless, agriculture's laborsaving contribution has been, and continues to be, a cornerstone of U.S. abundance.

• Scientific agriculture's progress has resulted in sharply lowered food costs relative to income.

This both reduced inflationary tendencies and provided a larger market for industry.

American consumers in 1967 paid out only 17.7 percent of their spendable income for food. In 1960, it was 20 percent—in 1950, it was 22.2 percent—in 1900, about 40 percent.

If U.S. consumers in 1967 had paid for food the same proportion of income as in 1960, they'd have had some $12 billion less to spend on cars, TV's, air conditioning, and vacations. Compared with 1950, the difference becomes $24 billion—compared with 1900, it is at least $120 billion.

• Scientific agriculture sustains our abundance by its steadily growing purchases of goods and services—despite the rapid drop in farm population.

Farm gross income in 1967 was almost $49 billion. Of this, farmers spent about $34 billion for goods and services to produce crops and livestock. Most of the remainder went for the same things that city people buy— food, clothing, drugs, furniture, appliances, and other consumer products and services.

In the mid-1960's, farmers were spending annually about $3.4 billion for new farm tractors and other motor vehicles, machinery, and equipment— providing jobs for 120,000 employees.

They annually purchase products containing about 5 million tons of steel and 320 million pounds of rubber—enough to put tires on nearly 6 million automobiles.

They use more petroleum than any other single industry—and more electricity than all the people and industries in Chicago, Detroit, Boston, Baltimore, Houston, and Washington, D.C., combined.

• Growing exports of U.S. farm products produced by scientific agriculture bulwark the Nation's economy of abundance. In fiscal 1967, foreign markets took $6.8 billion of agriculture's products, absorbing the production equivalent of some 71 million acres. These exports pay wages and interest, buy machinery and fertilizer, storage and transportation, packaging and processing.

Commercial exports or "sales for dollars" in fiscal 1967 totaled $5.2 billion, bringing back to the United States many of the dollars that move out because of defense and aid, tourism, and U.S. investment abroad, thus aiding the overall balance of payments situation.

• Scientific agriculture, the world's number one weapon in the war on hunger, is the basis upon which future world economic development rests.

After World War II, Europe was devastated and the Japanese economy was shattered. Food and fiber from U.S. farms helped them back on their feet. And in the 1960's, Japan became our top dollar customer for U.S. farm products.

Many of the world's people live in underdeveloped areas where agriculture does not produce enough food for them to feed themselves. U.S. exports of grain and other commodities help these nations to meet their immediate needs.

But American agriculture is also the world's biggest "storehouse" and research "factory" for agricultural knowledge. Exporting this knowledge

to improve farm production in food-short countries can contribute immensely to world stability and peace—and to the eventual entry of the entire free world into the age of abundance.

• Scientific agriculture is the keystone of prosperity in rural America. Rural America faces a grave challenge. Following World War II, a mass migration of rural people into the cities drained too many human and economic resources from the countryside. At the same time, it added to the housing, unemployment, congestion, and relief burdens of metropolitan America.

The exodus from rural America was due in part to the agricultural technological revolution. But it was stimulated also by many other factors: Highways that bypassed small towns and brought city stores, doctors, dentists, and entertainment facilities close to rural residents; railroads that stopped serving rural communities; the lure of the city itself.

The exodus is still going on, and this is a problem we must solve. We must restore rural-urban balance.

Fortunately, the tide of outmigration is slowing—and may soon be stemmed as concerted efforts of local people in thousands of rural communities are opening up new economic, social, and cultural opportunities throughout rural America.

Even though only about one in five of our rural people lives on the farm, agriculture remains the core around which the rural economy revolves. It is the biggest single industry, the biggest single source of employment, the biggest single producer of income in Countryside USA.

Working closely with farmers and other rural people, the U.S. Department of Agriculture is helping to stimulate a rural renaissance.

Private enterprise is being attracted to the countryside. Rural people, both

Contour strips sweep across the land in a panorama of scientific agriculture, the keystone to our American economy of abundance.

farm and nonfarm, are taking advantage of government supported opportunities to establish part-time businesses or trades.

Rural communities are acquiring better housing, modern water and sewer systems, and other facilities.

On thousands of farms, picnic and camp sites, riding stables, game and fishing preserves, winter and water sports facilities have become supplementary and even primary sources of income.

The revitalization of rural America now underway is of primary importance to the Nation's continued economic progress.

The age of abundance is obviously the end product of many converging forces. At the base and providing the foundation for all, however, is our productive and efficient scientific agriculture.

For more than a century, the U.S. Department of Agriculture has carried out a large and increasing variety of services which have been largely instrumental in making U.S. agriculture the most productive in the world. These services are well known. They include production and utilization research; conservation of soil, water, and timber; supervised credit to improve farming and family living; programs to extend electric power to almost all farms; measures to support farm prices and income and bring about needed adjustments in supply and demand.

But the Department provides another battery of services directly to all citizens of the United States and in a sense, particularly to urban dwellers. These services, too—though not so well known—have hastened our entry into the age of abundance and steadily contribute to the "better life."

For example, through various food distribution programs, the Department improves diets for the elderly, the unemployed, the disabled, mothers left to rear children alone, and children in schools and institutions.

To assure clean, wholesome meat supplies, USDA inspects all the meat and poultry products which are shipped across State lines.

USDA grademarks on food help consumers get full value for their food dollars.

New or improved foods, cotton, wool, leather, and other agricultural products emerge every year from USDA research laboratories.

New USDA-developed marketing methods—including plans for complete big city wholesale markets—result in a higher food quality, less waste, and consumer savings totaling millions of dollars annually.

USDA educational programs, of special value to the poor and underprivileged, teach people to manage their incomes, buy wisely, prepare more nutritious meals, and to make proper use of credit.

Although the Department is not customarily thought of as a health-protecting agency, it regularly makes immense contributions in this area. Penicillin, dextran, streptomycin, and other wonder drugs all have an agricultural background. Control of cancer, for example, may be aided by a world search now being carried out by USDA to find plants containing substances that inhibit the disease.

USDA plant quarantine inspectors and cooperating customs officials maintain a constant guard at U.S. ports and borders to keep foreign crop and animal pests and diseases from becoming established in the United States.

USDA soil surveys and land use plans help public and private developers and engineers build on sound sites, thus saving taxpayers and individuals many millions of dollars every year.

In the future, such services as these will be increasingly needed not only to meet the demands of a larger population, but also to continue the advance into better living which is the ultimate goal of the age of abundance.

We in USDA have been giving much concentrated thought to our goals in the years ahead. We have expressed these goals in terms of a common theme: AGRICULTURE/2000.

The American of Tomorrow—of the year 2000—will achieve a considerable measure of control over weather and climate. He will employ new sources of energy. He will wipe out most of the presently known diseases. He will increasingly use science in the service of man.

He will substitute additional elements of a manmade environment for that provided by nature. In so doing, he will face a new set of consequences, some favorable, some menacing. Some shadows of the future are already discernible. A few short years ago, we considered air and water to be essentially "free" goods. Because of manmade pollution, pure air and water are now fast becoming scarce goods.

We must anticipate the problems and seize the opportunities of the future.

We must give primary concern to the further conservation and development of natural resources—and this involves devising new methods to prevent pollution.

We must give careful thought and planning to the modification of weather and to biological and chemical control of the environment.

We must build communities for good living—both rural and urban.

We must develop new concepts and technology in transportation and communication.

We must provide new teaching methods and new facilities to provide quality education for all.

Recognizing that leisuretime is a major product of the age of abundance, we must provide new recreational and cultural facilities to take advantage of it.

And finally, we must continue to make new discoveries and applications of science in the production and use of food, fiber, and forest products.

This is the nature of the challenge held out to us by the age of abundance. Agriculture and agricultural science have done much to project us into this age. I am confident that they will continue to convoy us safely in the exciting adventure that lies ahead.

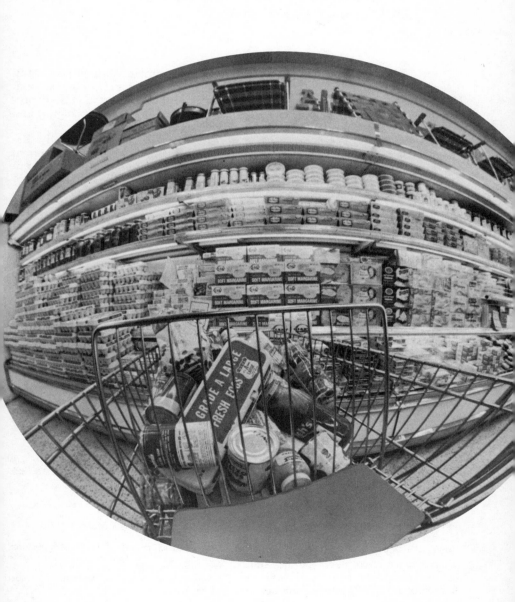

Controlled Environment and the Genies of Growth

WILLIAM A. BAILEY, DONALD T. KRIZEK,
and HERSCHEL H. KLUETER

. . . .

Gigantic advances in technology have been made since the United States launched its first satellite in 1957. Today, we are able to take and transmit color pictures of our own planet from a satellite 18,100 nautical miles above the earth.

Our weather satellites regularly scan the cloud cover from their polar orbit and record temperatures for each part of the earth.

A report on Biosatellite II stated that plants attained 3 days growth in 2 days. In laboratory tests here on earth, however, plants and animals make even faster growth when the critical environmental factors are controlled for maximum growth.

Improved environments, along with reduced infant mortality, improved medical practices, and more food with increased nutritive value have made it possible for the world population to reach more than 3 billion people in 1968. The upward trend in population growth has prompted the U.S. Government to sponsor various research programs on human fertility, conception, and birth rates.

If the present and future population is going to have adequate food, the world's production of food—and especially of protein—must be increased substantially. During the past, application of fertilizers and development of hybrid plants have teamed up to increase the food supply.

Today, we have taken the first steps toward providing controlled environments for more efficient production of

crops and animals. We have also begun to investigate new and unconventional sources of food—fish and oilseed protein concentrates, algae, bacteria, and fungi, as well as leaf protein.

Considerable progress already has been made in the production of animal food through automation and the application of research results of controlled-environment studies. An excellent example is the poultry industry. As a result of research on genetics, egg handling, hatching technology, chicken handling, nutrition, disease control, daily environmental needs of the chicken, poultry house design, and mechanization, the chicken is the most efficient converter of animal feed to human food grown on our farms today.

The large chicken population now in existence has been made possible in large part because of the prolific (240 eggs per year) nature that has

∴   ∴   ∴

WILLIAM A. BAILEY is an Agricultural Engineer with the Livestock Engineering and Farm Structures Research Branch, Agricultural Engineering Research Division.

DONALD T. KRIZEK is a Plant Physiologist with the Vegetables and Ornamentals Research Branch, Crops Research Division.

HERSCHEL H. KLUETER is an Agricultural Engineer with the Farm Electrification Research Branch, Agricultural Engineering Research Division.

All three are on the staff of the Phyto-Engineering Laboratory, an Agricultural Research Service facility at Beltsville, Md., established in 1966 to study the effects of controlled environments upon plant growth.

2

Marketing researcher, *right*, checks condition of grass seeds in experimental germinator at USDA laboratory in College Station, Tex. *Below*, thousands of chicks will hatch within 3 weeks after trayloads of eggs are placed in incubator of hatchery at Blairsville, Ga.

been bred into the domestic chicken. Through the team effort of agribusinessmen, engineers, scientists, and other support personnel, the production of poultry is now so highly organized, mechanized, and controlled that one man can care for 100,000 or more broiler chickens every 9 weeks—or approximately a half million per year.

Most poultry is produced in cooperative or vertically integrated enterprises. Each poultry enterprise has a team of service personnel to aid the scattered growers. The team generally includes: (1) An engineer to handle the problem of environmental control, (2) a physiologist to determine environmental needs of the chickens, and (3) a veterinarian to work out disease control procedures.

The service personnel are backed up by many different types of researchers at university and commercial laboratories. This backup team includes geneticists, pathologists, nutritionists, food technologists, engineers, physiologists, and economists. The investigators are accumulating basic information on effects of environmental factors upon animal growth and development.

Meat production is being made more efficient by studying the effects of temperature, day length, light quality, solar radiation, relative humidity, noise levels, air movement, airborne dust, and pathogens on the physiology of chicken, swine, cattle, sheep, and other animals.

Recent studies suggest exciting food production possibilities will come from farming the ocean, the fresh water ponds, the swamps, and the tidelands for fish and algae. Feed conversion rates up to 1 pound of fish for 1 pound of feed have been reported.

Only chicken broilers approach this conversion rate.

Similar advances are being made in the controlled-environment production of plants. It seems likely that by the year 2000 an increasing number of large growers and farmers will be using controlled-environment facilities for starting or growing their crops.

Special chambers will be used for storing seed, germ plasm, and tissue cultures under conditions of controlled temperature, relative humidity, and atmospheric composition. Propagation chambers equipped with automatic watering and fertilizing devices will be used to start the seedlings, cuttings, and test tube cultures of flowers and fruits. To hasten growth and promote early flowering, the atmosphere in these chambers will be enriched with additional carbon dioxide.

Automated tower greenhouses are already in use for industrial production of vegetables and flowers. The first tower greenhouse nearly 35 feet high was constructed in Austria in 1963. Since then, tower greenhouses up to 134 feet high have been erected.

By building up instead of out, tower greenhouse manufacturers maintain that more space per square foot of floor area is available for growing plants than in the ordinary greenhouse. Use of an artificially controlled environment also makes the plants adaptable to areas of the world where climatic conditions now prevent efficient production.

A continuous chain belt carries the seedlings through a series of climatic chambers and regimes to provide them with the optimum environmental requirements at every stage of growth. Seeds or cuttings are started in one chamber and moved to successive chambers as they mature. When plants mature and are removed, additional plants are started in their place. So the complete production of a crop from seed to harvest is continuously carried out by automatic machinery under controlled conditions.

The tower greenhouse represents only one method of mechanization and one type of controlled-environment facility envisioned in the eventual industrial production of vegetables and flowers. It is also limited to short, sturdy potted plants because of the low clearance between moving racks.

In order to design mechanical and fully automatic controlled-environment chambers and greenhouses for the commercial production of plants,

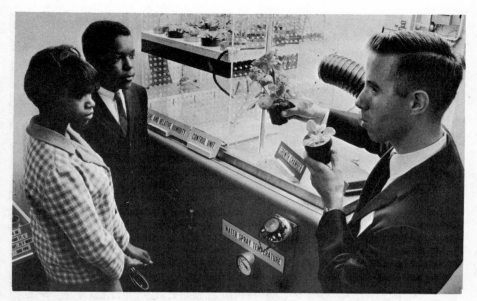

USDA Plant Physiologist Donald T. Krizek explains to high school science students differences between petunias raised in growth chamber, left, and in greenhouse.

designers must rely upon the recommendations of a researcher team of engineers, plant physiologists, horticulturists, and other plant scientists regarding the changing needs of the plant from germination to maturity.

The best combination of environmental factors needed for optimum plant growth are being determined by careful studies carried out in specially designed plant growth chambers in which only a single variable, for example, temperature; or two variables, for instance, temperature and carbon dioxide; or three or more variables, for example, temperature, carbon dioxide, and light intensity, are changed at any one time.

Such studies are now underway in the USDA's Phyto-Engineering Laboratory and in other plant growth facilities throughout the world.

Some of the most exciting work currently being done is carbon dioxide enrichment of the atmosphere.

By increasing the normal concentration of the carbon dioxide in the air some three to five times, researchers have been able to stimulate photosynthesis—the food manufacturing process

in the plant—and to increase the yields of plants.

Studies on carbon dioxide enrichment of greenhouse atmospheres by W. D. Holley and K. L. Goldsberry in Colorado, by C. A. Pettibone and C. L. Pfeiffer in Washington, by S. H. Wittwer and his associates in Michigan, and by D. W. Kretchman in Ohio have resulted in increased yields, improved quality, and accelerated maturity in nearly all flower and vegetable crops studied. Studies conducted in the Netherlands, the United Kingdom, Germany, and in this country show that yields of lettuce, tomatoes, cucumbers, radishes, and other crops under commercial greenhouse production are nearly doubled through the use of atmospheres that are enriched with carbon dioxide.

Experiments now underway on interactions of environmental factors in growth chambers are especially promising. Yields even greater than those obtained in greenhouses have been achieved by growing the plants under controlled conditions using a combination of high carbon dioxide, high day temperature, with relatively high light

5

Cucumber, *top*, and ageratum, *below*, raised for 15 days from seed under varying conditions. Plants at left were grown in greenhouse, others in controlled-environment. Compared with center plants, those on right were exposed to twice the light intensity, five times the carbon dioxide concentration, and 10° F. higher temperature.

Benefits of good postnatal care for plants. Both petunia seedlings are 5 weeks old. Plant on left was grown in greenhouse under natural conditions. Plant on right was raised in plant growth chamber for 18 days under controlled-environment conditions and then moved to greenhouse.

intensity, as well as high nutrient levels, medium relative humidity, and a constant airflow. Lettuce, tomato, and cucumber plants grown in the growth chamber under controlled-environment conditions are superior in size and appearance to those grown in the greenhouse under natural conditions. Bedding plants like petunia, ageratum, and marigold also respond markedly to controlled environments.

Studies now in progress suggest the time to begin controlled-environment treatments is at the seedling stage or even before the young plant emerges from the soil. The carryover effects of good postnatal care for plants are profound. Petunia plants (Pink Cascade) germinated directly in the growth chamber and kept there for 18 days at high day (85° F.) and night temperatures (75° F.) at nearly half the intensity of full sunlight, at five to six

times the normal carbon dioxide concentration, and then moved to the greenhouse, flower in 5 weeks from seed. Those grown in the greenhouse in the winter and early spring under natural conditions take nearly twice as long to flower.

Basic research is underway or being planned to determine the effects of changing the duration, intensity, and quality of light, raising soil and air temperatures, modifying the movement of air across the plants, and increasing the carbon dioxide content of the atmosphere as the plant develops.

Some basic knowledge is already on hand, but further information is needed in order to achieve maximum productivity.

Major advances in lighting technology for growing plants are just ahead. New high-intensity light sources are already being tested for possible use in

7

USDA Plant Physiologist Carl Tubbs measures soil and air temperatures in this controlled-environment installation at Northern Hardwoods Laboratory. Growth requirements of yellow birch and sugar maple seedlings are being studied.

the culture of vegetables and ornamentals in the greenhouse and the growth chamber. Some of these, like the xenon-arc lamp and the carbon-arc lamp, have become popular in the space program where they are used to simulate the intensity and quality of sunlight. Other short-arc lamps like the mercury-vapor lamp, sodium discharge lamp, and the metallic vapor lamp show promise for use in greenhouses and growth chambers when certain intensities and qualities of light are desired. Experimental fluorescent lamps with increased output in the red region of the spectrum are also being tested for growing plants.

New breakthroughs in production of field crops are likely by the year 2000.

The farmer will use computers to determine when to plant, fertilize, irrigate, spray, and harvest his crops. Mulches of various types, underground heating cables, and layers of heat-trapping materials will increase soil temperatures in the fields and enable

the farmer to plant his crops earlier during the year.

Single layers of various films are being tested for use in reducing water loss in the field. Experimental evidence indicates that someday it may even be feasible to spray plants with plastic films and antitranspirants to reduce enormous water losses. No longer need a plant lose much of its water to the atmosphere.

Special breeding programs for tailoring plants to the needs of mechanization are also in progress. Plant breeders at the University of California in Davis and at the USDA Agricultural Research Center in Beltsville, Md., are developing and testing tomatoes that are oblong in shape, have strong skins, and ripen uniformly for harvesting by mechanical pickers.

A variety of chemical and environmental techniques will also be used to hasten flower and fruit development. Tissue culture techniques are already being used for starting disease-free orchids, carnations, and strawberries. In the future, these techniques may also be used for growing food.

Laborsaving chemicals are being tested by agricultural researchers. In the future, chemicals will be used by the commercial grower and homeowner not only to control plant and animal pests, but also to selectively remove lateral or terminal buds, to induce or break dormancy, to shorten plants, and to induce flowering.

By proper manipulation of intensity, duration, and quality of light, temperature, humidity, and atmospheric composition, and by effective use of senescence-retarding chemicals, the storage life of fruits, vegetables, and cut flowers will also be extended. Fresh apples are now available throughout the year because scientists and engineers discovered how to preserve the apple for several months by controlling the temperature and the percentage of carbon dioxide, oxygen, and nitrogen in the atmosphere. Commercial growers have used this information to build controlled-atmosphere storage facilities. Vegetable growers have also been successful in marketing a high-quality product over an extended period of time with similar techniques.

Some crystal gazers predict that someday even grain and fiber crops will be grown in controlled environments. Atomic reactors may be used to supply heat and power and thereby lower production costs.

A team of scientists, engineers, agricultural experts, and economists at Oak Ridge National Laboratory predict that someday nuclear-powered agro-industrial complexes will be developed along coastal areas. These complexes would use reactors capable of desalting sea water and generating a million kilowatts of electricity—essential to mechanized farming, food processing, and maintaining the personnel who operate this complex. They estimate that such a plant could support the production of 2,000 tons of ammonia and 360 tons of phosphorus.

The food factory in this plant would

USDA Engineer Herschel H. Klueter checks electric current used by indoor garden.

Photo story shows how tissue culture technique is used to produce Suwanee variety strawberry plants free of latent-C virus. Virus-infected plants are held in growth chamber, *top, page 11,* heated to 95° F. for 14 to 28 days. Heat seems to prevent virus from moving into tips of plants' runners. Then tiny tip is cut from plant runner, *right.* Tip is placed in jar with sterile nutrient agar for rooting, *below.*

Stem cutting grown in nutrient becomes tiny strawberry plant, *right,* free of virus. At bottom is box of Suwanee strawberries. This variety was developed by USDA, became a favorite of home gardeners, but then almost disappeared from cultivation because of virus.

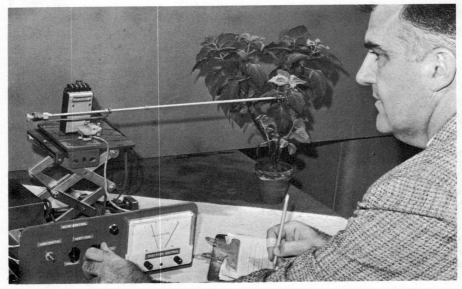

USDA Engineer William A. Bailey operates device to measure plant growth. Instrument determines precisely how fast plant grows—even in dark—by recording its movements. Rod connecting unit to plant is supported by platform that rises automatically to correspond in height with growing plant.

consist of 200,000 acres irrigated and fertilized by the nuclear plant in exactly the right amount based upon careful studies conducted on experimental farms in the area. For a single high-yield grain crop, it is projected that this complex would produce more than a billion pounds of grain annually—enough to feed almost 2½ million people at a caloric level of 2,400 calories per day. In addition, this complex could export enough fertilizer to other agricultural areas (lacking only fertilizer) to cultivate an additional 10 million acres.

The challenge to everyone concerned with agriculture has never been greater. Arable land is being taken over by suburban dwellings. Young people are leaving the farms for the cities. The per capita food production in many countries is decreasing. It seems clear that more food must be produced by fewer people on less land than ever before. Only through the combined efforts of farmers, scientists, bioengineers, and agribusinessmen can we meet this challenge.

For further reading:
American Society of Heating, Refrigeration, and Air Conditioning Engineers, "Environmental Control for Animals and Plants." *ASHRAE Guide and Data Book*, New York, 1966.
————"Environmental Control for Animals and Plants—Physiological Considerations." *ASHRAE Handbook of Fundamentals*, New York, 1967.
Byerly, T. C., *Livestock and Livestock Products*. Prentice-Hall Inc., Englewood Cliffs, N.J., 1964.
Card, Leslie E., *Poultry Production*, 9th edition. Lea & Febiger, Philadelphia, 1961.
Control of the Plant Environment, J. P. Hudson, editor. Proceedings of the Fourth Easter School in Agricultural Science, University of Nottingham, Butterworths, London, 1957.
Environmental Control for Plant Growth, L. T. Evans, editor. Academic Press, New York, 1963.
Food and Agriculture Organization, *The State of Food and Agriculture*. United Nations, Rome, 1966.
Pierre, W. H., and others, *Plant Environment and Efficient Water Use*. American Society of Agronomy and Soil Science Society of America, Madison, Wis., 1966.
Pirie, N. W., "Orthodox and Unorthodox Methods of Meeting World Food Needs." *Scientific American*, Vol. 216, No. 2, New York, February 1967.
Whyte, R. O., *Crop Production and Environment*. Faber & Faber, Ltd., London, 1960.

Resource Survey by Satellite; Science Fiction Coming True

A. B. PARK, R. N. COLWELL, and V. I. MYERS

. . . .

Dr. Robert Wilson, chief agronomist for the Brownhills Land Development Cooperative, decided he had better call his counterpart, Dr. William James, chief forester, for consultation. Together they had responsibility for overall management of 800,000 acres belonging to the co-op. The land was devoted to intensive agriculture and forestry production. There were 500,000 acres of forest land about equally divided between a reforestation project, now some 10 years old, and the remainder on systematic logging and replanting schedule. The 300,000 acres under agricultural production were devoted mainly to irrigation farming, but contained 50,000 acres of range and 10,000 acres of cereal grains.

The two men had very specific duties and responsibilities in their separate fields, but cooperated closely in the range management program. The co-op management had decided that wildlife conservation and cattle production should coexist. This decision required the two men to maintain a very close liaison.

The time was midsummer and a number of management decisions were imminent. It was time to evaluate insect and disease control programs; time to estimate crop production; time to plan the fall logging program; time to check the livestock and wildlife population pressure on the range; time to review the irrigation practices, the need for fertilizer, the available

water, the weather trends; and time to set up the aircraft overflight program for the remainder of the year.

The two men agreed to meet the following day, and Wilson offered to assemble the data and arrange the computer links for the meeting. Although they had been reviewing the satellite and aircraft data periodically, it was time for an indepth review and analysis. Wilson called the Teleservice Section of the Center for Resource Evaluation to arrange for a 6-months' review of the data. He also asked the section to contact the Environmental Science Services Administration (ESSA) for time lapse coverage of weather over the same period and a long-range forecast for this area.

When the two men met in the laboratory early the next morning, Wilson told James that Teleservice had given them 2 hours starting at 10 a.m. The first data they were to receive was the weather. Promptly at 10 o'clock James activated the Teleservice set by punching in a digital

∴   ∴   ∴

A. B. PARK is Assistant to the Administrator, Agricultural Research Service.

R. N. COLWELL is Professor of Forestry, School of Forestry and Conservation, the University of California, Berkeley.

V. I. MYERS is Research Investigations Leader, Remote Sensing, Soil and Water Conservation Research Division, Agricultural Research Service, Weslaco, Tex.

bar which sent a coded signal indicating their transceiver billing number to a computer in the sales and accounting department and opened a clear channel audiovisual two-way link to the Center for Resource Evaluation. Immediately, the ESSA relay opened and the two men were watching a time lapse photographic history of the local weather for several preceding hours. In recent years, ESSA had achieved a zoom lens capability on its synchronous satellites and was now producing high resolution detailed coverage of the regional as well as the global weather.

As the "movie" proceeded, Wilson was recording the data blocks of interest and afterwards ordered the individual images they would need later for their hydrology study. While still in voice communication with the center, he asked for color and color infrared coverage at scales of 1:250,000, 1:50,000, and 1:10,000. For the smallest scale, he requested complete time coverage of the area. He had calculated there should have been six frames during the nine spacecraft orbits in the past 6 months, considering that on three of the days the land could not be seen from the spacecraft because of clouds. As these data were displayed in sequence, one could see the season change from winter to spring to summer.

James ordered the early spring photo which showed the snowpack distribution. They would compare this with radar imagery and ground instruments to verify their previous runoff predictions. Wilson studied all six carefully and selected four dates for specially processed large-scale coverage.

Following this analysis, Wilson asked the center to subject the 1:50,000 coverage to change detection analysis. The dates he selected were fairly recent, and the base coverage against which the other images were to be compared was the commencement of the growing season.

The analysis could be sequential so that a photograph could be compared to the one of the same area taken 21 days later or it could be random so that a photograph could be compared to any other of the same area regardless of when it was taken.

For a given set of coordinates, let us say a 1,000-acre field, a certain latitude of change could be programed as acceptable; for example, the gradual change from green to yellow as grain ripens. Any deviation from this sequence would be printed out in pictorial format so that the analyst not only knew what had happened but where. This innovation avoided a detailed manual analysis of each photograph and the problem of trying to compare many photographs.

James and Wilson watched the analysis carefully for they had been unable to personally inspect the property during certain critical times associated with insect emergence and times that favored disease spread.

The sequences they had selected were to cover the timber holdings. As

. . . .

A Word to the Reader. This chapter concerns itself with a very advanced technology, whose realization is many years away. Nevertheless, various components of the concept are either under development or study. No technological breakthrough is required for implementing the equipment or techniques which are described here.

Information available to Wilson and James certainly will one day be available to anyone. The small farmer would scarcely need space imagery which on a single photograph can cover 10,000 square miles. On the other hand, many small farmers acting as a cooperative could make invaluable use of the kinds of information available to them about their agriculture.

. . . .

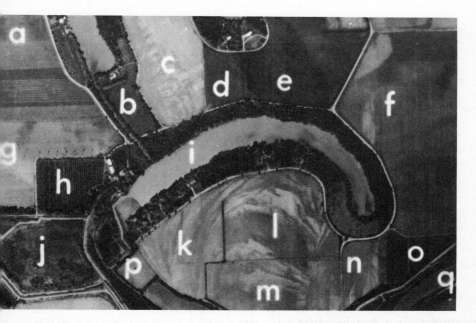

Present-day techniques using infrared images taken from airplane show soil moisture characteristics around Moon Lake in lower Rio Grande Valley, Tex. Letters on photo above taken with normal (panchromatic) film indicate fields of sorghum, a and f; vegetables, b, d, and e; and cotton, c, g, o, and p; bare fields, k to n; and citrus grove, h. Moon Lake, oxbow in Rio Grande River, is indicated by i, a marsh by j, and part of river by q. Three photos at right taken at different times of day show soil moisture contrasts in bare field labeled 1 below lake that can be detected with heat-sensitive infrared. Note temperature difference at 6 a.m. From this imagery scientists can tell farmers when to irrigate.

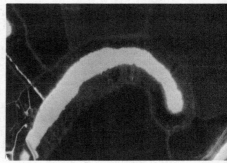

6 A.M.

2 P.M.

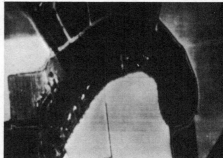

7 P.M.

expected, they immediately noted the change in some of the trees from no leaves to full leaf imagery. All the evergreen (coniferous) trees were omitted from the picture since these were the only trees exhibiting no change. One could now map the boundaries of timber stands. Then in a later comparison, a drought condition caused a sufficient change in the reflectance pattern which is referred to as the spectral signature, so that all the vegetation on the higher ground appeared, and only the more moist lowland areas were not displayed.

On the last comparison, the drought condition was the same. Because of the present fire hazard and the lack of rain in the 14-day forecast, James decided to close the area to campers— and to have fire detection aircraft fly the entire area following each lightning storm.

Next, the range area was displayed. Here, too, the change from early spring to lush growth was evident. As the sequence progressed, it was apparent that a few areas were overgrazed and should be fenced and the cattle moved. In one particular area a decided change was shown.

James switched to voice override and asked the center to hold this sequence for comparison with the spectral signature memory bank in the poisonous weed section. His concern at this point was the cattle and not the pasture condition. In a matter of moments, a digital printout of the affected area and an identification appeared on the display. It was as he suspected, locoweed, a serious poisonous plant, now spread over several acres on an isolated corner of the range. He took a quick photograph of the display tube for a base map for the fencing and herbicide application crews.

The sequence proceeded to the dryland holdings largely planted to wheat. Since it was nearing harvesttime, Wilson was interested in a yield prediction. He had made his own evaluation, but was anxious to check it against the computer. The inputs to the computer involved the change of vegetation density over a fixed time period, moisture content of the vegetation, a careful evaluation of the rate of change of color over time, and no deviations from the rate of change during the period. Computer analysis for this application was quite involved, and James and Wilson waited what seemed a long time, even though only a few minutes had gone by.

Forty bushels per acre was the average yield. Wilson immediately used the voice override. He notified the center that he had calculated 50 bushels per acre on his sample. Would they display the change detection sequence? The spring image came on, and then the screen went black for at

least two sequences, but on the fourth a large area of wheat appeared. Quickly locking on this image, Wilson commanded the display to run a spectral band sequence.

Because the sensors had the capability to look in many parts of the electromagnetic spectrum simultaneously, it was possible to display the individual colors. They could, for instance, look at a field and separately assess the amount of blue or green or yellow or red reflectivity. In addition, because the instruments were sensitive beyond the visible spectrum, it was also possible to quantitatively assess the infrared reflectivity.

In a different part of the electromagnetic spectrum, they could see the thermal or temperature characteristics of the vegetation. These images could be displayed sequentially so that deviations from the normal could be assessed.

In this case, the green band showed a negligible change; however, the infrared band showed a definite loss of reflectivity. In addition, there was a rise in the thermal infrared response, which often is an indicator of stress conditions in plants.

While the sequence was displayed, Wilson photographed the areas affected. It was obvious to him now that his sample had been too small, and that he had in fact not sampled this particular area. He made a note of the time to harvest and was relieved to realize that even if his survey party should find stem rust, there was still time to spray and preserve at least the computer-predicted yield.

Finally, the irrigated acreage was reviewed. This would be the most detailed part of the study since the crops varied all the way from citrus to market vegetables.

Because of the detail required, the only space data that Wilson asked for was the thermal imagery.

In voice contact, he now requested day and night orbital coverage data. He asked that hard copies of the original images be sent to the laboratory, but for the present he would photograph the TV image.

16

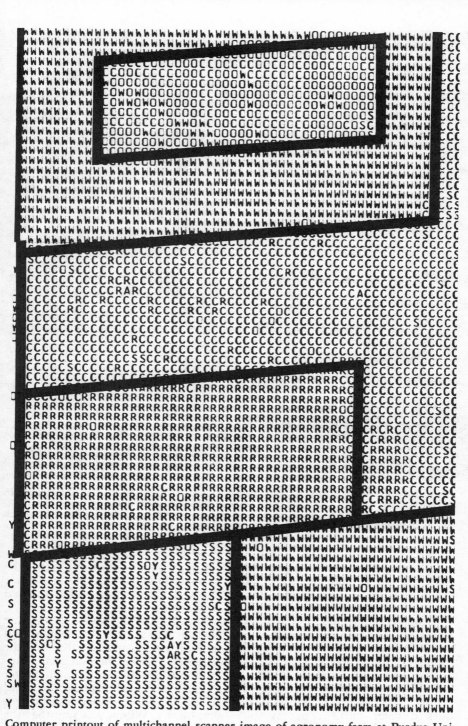

Computer printout of multichannel scanner image of agronomy farm at Purdue University, Lafayette, Ind. Printout shows wheat, W; oats, O; corn, C; rye, R; soybeans, S, and alfalfa, A, as recorded by scanner from aircraft. Y's are inadvertent errors in system. Lines have been added to printout to outline areas of different crops.

Photo on infrared film taken from airplane detects brown soft scale infestation in irrigated citrus grove. Healthy trees appear light colored, infested trees are dark. This means of detection permits quick control measures against infestation, which causes damaging sooty mold on tree leaves.

As the sequence was displayed, they were relieved to note that of the 18 possible images, only five were cloud covered, three day and two night. This was certainly much better than predicted cloud-free coverage. Because of this, Wilson decided to use the audio command which would hold the sequence and go directly to the computer for a change in program. He pressed the command bar and requested color infrared photography on two of the orbital passes to be displayed following the thermal data run and, switching to voice communication with the center, asked the operator to follow this on the monitor and switch in the appropriate thermal images for a rerun.

The reason for this last minute change in plan was that Wilson had noticed about midway through the sequence some rather unusual "hotspots." Although the thermal imager did not have high spatial resolution, it was possible to orient oneself geographically. Wilson was sure that the hot-spots were in the soybeans and he was likewise sure that they should not have been there.

As the two men evaluated the rest of the thermal and color infrared imagery of the irrigated area, they kept in mind an 80-acre cropped field that had deep cuts and fills from land leveling the year before. They knew the cut areas required special applications of nitrogen and phosphorous fertilizer as the growing season progressed. The color infrared display of the field showed suspicious signs indicating the possible need for another fertilizer application.

On command, Wilson then produced a multispectral display of the cut areas. Two near-infrared wavelength bands revealed that an application of nitrogen fertilizer would be necessary in about 2 weeks—adequate time to have the fertilizer and the application equipment on hand. A third band of the multispectral imagery indicated no phosphorus deficiency existed.

It appeared that their irrigation water impoundment decision, based on preliminary aircraft coverage with side-looking radar, was correct. Because of the particular wavelength of this radar, there were two returns in the early spring snowpack imagery. One return, a TV-like ghost image, was from the top of the snow and the other from the ground beneath.

In addition to being able to measure the depth of the snowpack from the distance between the ground return and the ghost image, the relative brightness of the ghost image was directly related to the amount of the water in the pack.

On the thermal imagery, it was quite apparent that their irrigation schedule had been correct, at least at the time of the orbital pass and for more than 10 days previously.

Any deviation from schedule resulting in inadequate moisture would have been quite apparent on the nighttime orbit imagery.

The two hotspots worried Wilson. He quickly located these areas on the TV display of the color infrared photographs. It was quite obvious that something was wrong. There was a drastic loss of reflectivity as well as the apparent rise in temperature. He reviewed the data again; although not so apparent, the temperature deviation in the area persisted. He had no reports of any malfunctions in the irrigation system. There was no logical reason for this condition to appear in two relatively isolated areas, at about the same time, with no subsequent change in the surrounding area.

He would certainly have to check up on this immediately.

James and Wilson were now finished with the Teleservice set and spent the rest of the day reviewing aircraft coverage. The low altitude large-scale data were essential for many operational decisions, but they were thankful they did not have to use them exclusively. Satellite coverage was certainly the method to use to look at the entire co-op holding and even better to select those areas where a closer look was obviously needed. Furthermore, a technique known as high resolution sampling permitted them to do a quite detailed analysis on a small-scale image.

A brief look at a single image which covered 2,500 square miles (50 by 50 miles on a 9- by 9-inch photograph) would allow them to select a few large-scale photographs which covered only a few square miles within the 2,500, but were representative of a condition which extended over many square miles in the small-scale image.

Concerning the "hotspot," Wilson found out that one of the spray crews had been spraying weeds along several miles of ditchbank and had gotten careless on a couple of occasions.

They had chosen not to report it, obviously hoping that on such a large farm no one would notice that a few soybeans were missing.

"Bill," said Wilson, "it never ceases to amaze me that two of us could do a professional job of managing a place this size."

"It's hard to believe," said James, "but with this new technology, we have the most powerful management tool to come out of research during the last 50 years."

Food From the Sea and Inland Waters

SIDNEY SHAPIRO

· ·

An oceangoing research vessel is heading for the lobster grounds off Boothbay Harbor, Maine. A team of diver-biologists is putting on the latest in scuba equipment.

When the vessel reaches the fishing grounds, the anchor is set and the team enters the water.

At 90 feet below surface, the divers find lobsters—some on sandy bottom and others peering from burrows. Experimental work begins. Through firsthand observations the divers record the way in which lobsters live—how they behave, feed, and move about.

You may ask: Of what importance is such research in providing food for people? One goal is to determine the number of lobsters that can be caught without overfishing, which would reduce the number that can be caught in future years. Another goal is to determine whether present fishing methods can be made more efficient. Forward-looking biologists are also dealing with the possibility of raising lobsters artificially. If this is to be done, the conditions under which lobsters can be cultivated must be determined. What better way is there to do this than to make scientific observations directly on the lobster and its environment?

Three thousand miles away, along the southern California coast, another team of diver-biologists is preparing to enter the compression chamber that will carry them below surface waters to a depth of 450 feet. There the chamber—which has been slowly pressurized to the water pressure prevailing at this depth—is opened, and the team swims a short distance to enter the already-anchored SEALAB III. This is the Navy's third Man-in-the-Sea venture, and biologists from the Bureau of Commercial Fisheries are participating.

The divers will live in this underwater dwelling for 2 weeks with their lungs filled with a mixture of helium and oxygen. Since the pressure in their bodies and living quarters is the same as that of the surrounding water, the divers will be able to leave and enter SEALAB III at will. In this way they will be able to conduct research that will tell more about marine life and how it can be used to the advantage of mankind.

Marine scientists have also been working with our space scientists. Two hundred miles up, astronauts have taken a series of photographs of designated coastal and oceanic areas around the globe. This is spacecraft oceanography. It tells us many things about the ocean below—how currents behave, where areas of abundance of fish and shellfish might be expected, and where the waters are sterile and would yield nothing to the fisherman. When these techniques are developed,

·:· ·:· ·:·

SIDNEY SHAPIRO *is Special Assistant, Resource Development, Bureau of Commercial Fisheries, U.S. Department of the Interior.*

telemetering devices may be stationed in space to relay information periodically to fishing fleets below.

These are but a few of the many exciting new techniques being explored and developed by fishery scientists to understand more fully the nature of the ocean and the living aquatic resources it contains.

As the human population increases, there will be a growing need for food. Even now half the world's population of more than 3 billion people suffers from malnutrition—mainly because diets lack sufficient animal protein. This is a major problem in developing areas. The world's population has been increasing at an annual rate of 1.8 percent; the food supply has been rising only slightly more than that.

The Food and Agriculture Organization of the United Nations has estimated that as early as 1970 the world's deficit of animal protein will be about 13.2 billion pounds. Agriculture may be sorely beset to provide adequate food for the expected 6 to 7 billion people that will probably inhabit the earth by the year 2000.

We may have to go more and more to the ocean and inland waters to help provide people with the animal protein which they so vitally need.

The world harvest of fish, shellfish, and aquatic plants was about 125.2 billion pounds in 1966, nearly double the harvest a decade ago. This increase was at an annual rate of over 6 percent. More than 85 percent of the 1966 harvest was taken from the sea. The rest was obtained from rivers, lakes, and other fresh waters or was cultivated in natural or artificial freshwater impoundments.

Fishermen are now utilizing only a small part of the potential productivity of the ocean and inland waters. These waters are truly a huge reservoir of food, and research is now beginning to move rapidly to show how living aquatic resources can be used more widely and more wisely.

Balloons are new approach to spotting schools of fish at ocean surface. At height of 500 feet, spotters can locate schools 30 miles away. Here balloon is inflated from deck of fishing vessel during tests off California.

Left, Bureau of Commercial Fisheries technician prepares to lower Niskin bottle, used to determine temperatures and salinities of ocean waters at various depths. *Below,* underwater TV camera being installed in trawl net. When net is dragged along ocean bottom, scientists on BCF research vessel *Delaware* can observe fish behavior and design more efficient nets.

A brief look at the abundance of marine plant and animal life—and how each kind relates to the others—shows that the sea is much more productive than one visualizes when a school of fish is taken by commercial fishermen.

Many parts of the ocean contain vast pastures of tiny drifting plantlife called phytoplankton. As in plantlife on land, chlorophyll in the phytoplankton has the ability to convert the sun's energy into organic substances (like proteins, fats, and carbohydrates) using simple dissolved nutrients in the surrounding water. In some places in the ocean, phytoplankton is so abundant that it changes the natural blue color of the water to shades of green, brown, or even red. Microscopic phytoplankton is the basic food that supports all aquatic life.

The next step-up in the food web consists of grazing animals, many also very tiny. These small creatures—known as zooplankton—range in size from simple one-celled microscopic animals to more complex and abundant forms, like fish larvae, copepods, and somewhat larger shrimplike euphausids, but still tiny. Free-swimming copepods, perhaps more than any other animal, eat tiny phytoplankton and convert an otherwise inaccessible food supply into a form readily available to larger animals. To indicate how abundant zooplankton is, baleen whales—the largest animals in the world—also feed on small animals, and their stomachs may often contain tons of euphausids (or krill).

Feeding on zooplankton and also on microscopic plants are the filter-feeding fishes. The gill arches of these fishes have comblike filaments that strain plankton from the water. Good examples of the filter feeders are the sardine and anchovy, which are among the smaller fishes of the sea and also the most plentiful.

Feeding on the smaller abundant fishes are larger fishes—carnivores, 1 or 2 feet long as adults. A mackerel illustrates this level in the food web.

Finally, we come to the top layer in the food web, large carnivorous predators, like tunas, swordfish, and sharks.

The food web, as presented here, is an oversimplification of much more complicated processes and interactions. It serves, however, to illustrate that, at each higher level of the web, a smaller and smaller quantity of fish or shellfish is present in the ocean.

A commonly accepted average value for the conversion of food to flesh and other tissues is 10 percent. When, for example, a mackerel feeds on herring, only 10 percent of the herring is converted into mackerel; the rest of the herring provides energy for swimming, breathing, and other body functions. If an assemblage of marine plants and animals existed in a simple, theoretically balanced community, 100,000 tons of phytoplankton might yield only 10,000 tons of zooplankton—10,000 tons of zooplankton, 1,000 tons of small plankton-eating fishes—100 tons of small fishes, 10 tons of small carnivores—and 10 tons of small carnivores, 1 ton of large carnivores.

If commercial marine fisheries were to concentrate on the more abundant fishes in the food web, more animal protein would be available for human food. Large-scale conversion of plankton into nutritious animal protein—using artificial methods of cultivation—also is not too farfetched a concept in this present age of rapidly moving technology.

Fishery experts believe that the marine harvest can be increased at least five times to give the world a catch of 550 billion pounds. Some believe that this catch can go as high as 1.1 trillion pounds or even higher. This may be achieved if we change our fishing and processing methods and our fish-eating habits to use effectively the vast numbers of marine animals not now being caught. The amount of each herbivore and each carnivore that can be cropped without diminishing the ocean's sustained productivity must be known, however. This is a principal goal of fishery scientists.

Fishery research is infinitely complicated, especially in the ocean. Until the advent of underwater television, scuba diving equipment, sea sleds, submersible vehicles, and other devices that allow direct observation, marine scientists have been handicapped. They have had to work blindly, depending on indirect methods to study aquatic animals and plants.

Traditionally, the fishery scientist has conducted research from a vessel that is essentially a floating platform. Instruments could be towed or sent down from this platform to record information on the environment—for example, salinities, water temperatures, strength and direction of water currents, and the amounts and types of plankton. Nets or other fishing gear could be used on the surface or at various depths down to the ocean bottom. From the fish and shellfish caught, life history studies could be made. Using various indirect techniques, like tagging, the size of a population of fish and shellfish could be estimated.

In the laboratory, many things could be done. The age of fish could be determined from rings on scales or from ear stones known as otoliths. Blood serum analysis could be made to sort out the different races that often make up what we call a species.

Using knowledge of the age and size of fish—as well as the catch records of fishing vessels and statistical records of the annual catch of a species over a period of time—signs of overfishing could be detected.

Many of these traditional research techniques have been refined, and much valuable biological information has been gathered. Fishery research, however, is still in its infancy. As more and more attention is given to the ocean as a storehouse of food, newer and better tools—submarines, surface and subsurface telemetering buoys, underwater laboratories—are being developed for fishery research.

An important aim of fishery biological and oceanographic research is to determine the point at which commercial or sport fishermen can catch fish or shellfish, year after year, without destroying the ability of a species to reproduce and sustain itself.

Individuals of a species will die, but before they die, fishermen can and should catch the surplus which may safely be removed.

Biologists have coined a phrase—*maximum sustainable yield*—to denote this equilibrium or balance that needs to be achieved if successful fisheries are to be conducted in perpetuity. When fishermen take more than the permissible surplus, the numbers or weight of fish available to fishermen will decline. This is known as *overfishing*, and eventually the number of individuals in a resource is reduced to a level where fishermen find it unprofitable to fish.

All this is not as simple as it appears. An ideal equilibrium is never maintained for very long—as every farmer, fish culturist, or horticulturist knows. Only when an animal or plant is raised under completely controlled condi-

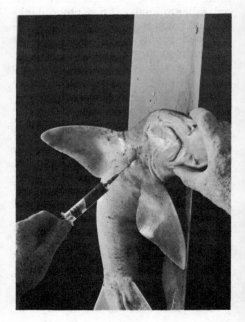

Blood is drawn from shark. Analysis of blood serum enables scientists to sort out various races that make up a species.

24

Submarine built by Reynolds Aluminum for oceanographic research has been used in exploratory fishing. In October 1967, scientists aboard studied density and distribution of scallops off New Smyrna Beach, Fla. Commercial fishing has since been started in the area.

tions can a balance between favorable and unfavorable environmental conditions be maintained.

Variation in nature is as enduring a phenomenon as is the rising and setting of the sun. This variation is one of the most difficult problems facing fishery biologists and oceanographers. If the major factors that cause variation are sorted out and understood, a fishery can be managed to produce the maximum sustainable yield. The ideal is reached if variation is controlled. In the ocean, this is most difficult with present-day research tools and technology. In inland waters—like small lakes and other enclosed bodies of water—food, spawning, predation, and other conditions that affect the size of a population of fish or shellfish can be controlled more easily.

A striking example of uncontrollable variation is the change in the stocks of Pacific sardine available to fishermen. In 1936, U.S. fishermen landed three quarters of a million tons of sardines. In 1967, fishermen were able to take a mere fraction of the peak catch—

only about 50 tons. Overfishing was partly, but not entirely, responsible. Scientists believe that the changing environment, which affected the capability of the sardine to reproduce and survive, was an important reason for the almost complete disappearance of the species from its former locale.

In the marine fisheries, many fish or shellfish are not caught—or are caught in small amounts—simply because markets do not exist for them or fishing methods are inadequate and too costly or the fishing grounds are not known. Other species are vulnerable to overfishing because the consumer prefers them, and the fish can be caught easily with today's equipment. Fishermen concentrate their effort on these more valuable species. Outstanding examples of this are the fisheries for salmon, halibut, yellowfin tuna, haddock, shrimp, crabs, oysters, lobster, and fur seals. In some instances—salmon, halibut, yellowfin tuna, northern fur seal, and oysters— the fisheries were so intense in the past that production declined seriously.

25

Top, fishing in central Pacific for tuna from Bureau of Commercial Fisheries research vessel. *Right,* landing yellowfin tuna aboard U.S. research vessel in Indian Ocean. Commercially valuable tunas sometimes migrate from one ocean to another. To study them, scientists must follow these fish to distant parts of world. *Below,* skipjack tuna behavior is studied from underwater observation chamber of research vessel.

Fishery research has been successful in restoring some of these overfished species, but only because they have been studied and managed under international agreement.

The halibut fishery in the northeastern Pacific Ocean is a classic example of overfishing, then decreasing catches, and finally restoration of the stocks through research and management. Total catches of Pacific halibut by U.S. and Canadian fishermen declined from 91.5 million pounds in 1915 to 56.5 million pounds in 1922.

The International Halibut Commission, established by treaty between the two countries, has conducted research on the different races or stocks of this giant flounder, the areas in which each race is found, conditions under which the species can spawn favorably, and other details of the way in which the fish grows and lives. Every year the Commission, acting on the recommendations of scientists, establishes quotas for the different halibut fishing areas. Fishing is discontinued in an area when its catch quota is reached.

The U.S. and Canadian halibut fishery has now been restored, and a catch of 83 million pounds was made in 1966. It is believed that with continuing research and management the catch can be raised even higher.

The fishery for fur seals is an even more exciting and accurate demonstration of what can be accomplished through research coupled with effective management. The story of the fur seal is all the more dramatic, for by 1910 the fur seal herd on the Pribilof Islands, off Alaska, had declined to about 200,000 animals. Since 1911, the Pribilof fur seal has been protected by treaty. This animal breeds on land, and reliable estimates can be made of the total number of individuals that have existed at different times during this century.

Thus, we can follow the decline in the population and correlate its rehabilitation with research and management. Furthermore, accurate determinations can be made of the number of males and females that can be harvested each year. The Pribilof herd has now been fully restored to about 1,250,000 seals. During the period of restoration (from 1911 to 1966), over 2.8 million sealskins were harvested.

With the five species of Pacific salmon, we move from a truly oceanic fishery to one in which the fish inhabit marine and fresh waters at different stages in their lifespan. Pacific salmon breed in fresh-water streams, then the young migrate into the ocean where they feed and grow. Finally, the adults return precisely to their home streams to spawn, after which they die.

Research and management of salmon becomes even more difficult because—apart from the overfishing that can and has occurred—the fish are extremely vulnerable to manmade obstacles in rivers. Dams in river systems of our Pacific Northwest block passage of salmon to their upstream spawning grounds. Though much still needs to be done, especially to prevent loss of young salmon migrating downstream, some of the valuable salmon runs have been restored. Fish ladders, which allow salmon to pass by high dams, have been built. Spawning beds have been built to replace others that have been destroyed by industrial development or pollution. Artificial propagation in hatcheries adds to the number of young that migrate to the sea.

Research by itself cannot restore a species to full production. Social, economic, industrial, and political forces often combine to prevent research knowledge from being applied. Production of east coast oysters in the United States has drastically declined. In one area—New England—the oyster catch in 1910 yielded nearly 27 million pounds of shucked meats; in 1966, the yield was 408,000 pounds. Similar sharp reductions have taken place in other Atlantic areas.

After many years of study, science knows how to restore oyster production. This has not been done because local laws, disputes between oystermen, domestic and industrial pollution, and political expediency override other considerations.

27

Left, studies are underway to grow oysters suspended from the surface and above their natural habitat—the bottom of estuaries—so as to decrease mortality and improve growth. This scene is at Oxford, Md., biological laboratory of Bureau of Commercial Fisheries. *Right,* salmon on way upstream to spawning grounds often must leap over natural barriers like Brooks Falls in Alaska.

Estuarine areas—bays, sounds, river outlets, marshlands, and other waters where rivers meet the sea—are the homes of oysters, clams, crabs, and many kinds of fish. Some fish, like salmon, shad, and alewives, have to pass through estuarine waters on their spawning migrations into fresh waters. Eels, which develop from the juvenile to the adult stage in fresh waters, migrate through brackish waters to spawn in the sea. Some coastal marine fishes enter estuarine waters seasonally.

Estuaries are subject to intense environmental fluctuations caused by such conditions as excessive freshwater runoff or lack of it, storms and hurricanes, and sharp temperature and salinity changes. Sometimes the effects of agricultural, industrial, and commercial development are more damaging and more enduring than these fluctuations. Development may bring with it many types of pollutants—pesticides used in agriculture and washed into estuaries, chemicals from industrial plants, intense warming of waters passing through atomic and electric powerplants, or domestic pollution resulting from too much sewage.

At the same time, large coastal areas—often marshlands—are being "reclaimed" and used for commercial development and housing.

Of vital importance to our fisheries is the fact that estuarine waters and salt marshes are nursery grounds for many valuable fish and shellfish. Shrimp and menhaden are probably the best examples of the need to maintain estuarine areas in their natural state.

Shrimp are the most valuable resource in the U.S. fisheries. Menhaden—used to make fish meal and oil—is the species caught in largest amounts. Adult shrimp and menhaden spawn in offshore waters of the Continental Shelf. By the time the fertilized eggs have become juveniles, the immature shrimp or menhaden have migrated into estuarine waters where they remain for several months. In truth, estuarine waters are nursery grounds for fish and shellfish that contribute over half the quantity and value of the U.S. fishery catch.

28

In inland waters, fishery science so far has been able to make the most progress. The growth of a fish and seasonal changes in water conditions can be followed and controlled much more readily in a lake or pond than they can in the ocean.

A population of fish can be managed to yield maximum poundage. A demonstration of this is the research done on stunted fish. Small lakes were selected that contained very large numbers of adult, undersized, and underweight yellow perch. Many of these small fish were removed from the lakes. The rest of the fish, freed from overcompetition for food and space, grew to a larger size, and the poundage caught was far in excess of that caught when overabundant and undersized fish dominated the lakes.

Methods of rearing fresh-water fishes in hatcheries and in artificial farm ponds have been brought to a stage of near perfection. Warm-water fishes, like largemouth bass, crappies, bluegills, and catfish, have been grown successfully in ponds. A well-managed fishpond can easily produce 1 ton of fish per acre annually. In hatcheries, cold-water species like salmon and trout have been raised from egg to juvenile stage and then released in rivers and lakes.

Most of the research on artificial cultivation has been done by biologists working on sport fish problems. The procedures that have been developed, however, have application to commercial fisheries.

Rice farmers of the central-south United States have been raising catfish in flooded ricefields. Catfish have also been cultivated commercially in large artificial ponds and in waters used for producing minnow bait. From small beginnings, about 15 million pounds of channel catfish—worth $6 million—were harvested in 1966.

The potential for raising fish in freshwater enclosures is enormous. Indonesian and Chinese fish culturists have attained annual yields of various carp as great as 8,000 pounds per acre.

Control of predators is vital to good management in inland waters. The story of the sea lamprey, the destruction that it caused, and the way in which science has been working to eradicate this predator is a unique chapter in fishery research.

The story began in the early 1930's, when the sea lamprey first entered Lake Erie through the Welland Canal, which had been built to allow vessels to bypass Niagara Falls. This destructive parasite—which attaches to fish and sucks their blood—severely reduced populations of the valuable lake trout in the Great Lakes. Within 20 years, the catch of lake trout by U.S. and Canadian fishermen dropped from 15 million pounds to less than half a million pounds annually.

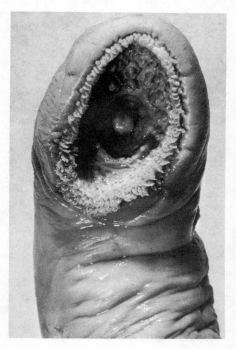

With their rasping teeth, lampreys can attach themselves to a fish and suck its blood—often causing death. The eellike lampreys have decimated lake trout in the Great Lakes. Scientists using electrical and chemical controls have reduced lamprey populations, and the lake trout are being restored.

In the mid-1950's, biologists, chemists, and engineers at the Bureau of Commercial Fisheries Biological Laboratory, Ann Arbor, Mich.—in collaboration with their Canadian counterparts—began waging a vigorous attack on the sea lamprey. First, electrical barriers proved effective in catching and destroying many adult lampreys as they migrated from the Great Lakes into tributary streams to spawn. Then, chemicals were discovered which killed young lampreys (but not other fish) in streams before they could enter the Great Lakes to do their damage as adults. Lamprey populations in the Great Lakes, particularly in Lake Superior, have declined sharply. The battle has not yet been fully won, but lake trout are now on the rise.

Harvesting fishery resources, once a hit-or-miss search, is rapidly becoming an exacting science. Sonar devices and depth recorders are now being used to locate schools of fish. An air-bubble curtain has been developed by scientists of the Bureau of Commercial Fisheries. Let us see how effective this curtain is in bringing fish to the fishermen. Off Maine, schools of small herring, used to prepare canned sardines, often stay out to sea where fishermen are unable to catch them. The curtain of air bubbles guides the schools into coves and small bays where they can be caught.

While not yet in commercial use, this curtain may—when the technique is fully developed—have wide application in fisheries.

Many species of fish do not school. How can these scattered fish be concentrated so that fishermen can catch them economically? Scientists at the Bureau's laboratory in Honolulu have been testing the reactions of tuna to different sensory stimuli. These experiments suggest that scattered tuna can be brought together by chemicals with odors that attract the fish.

Electrical devices for attracting and catching fish have been developed, and a few are commercially useful. At the Bureau's Pascagoula, Miss., gear research base, an electric device has been developed that allows shrimp trawlers to catch pink and brown shrimp by day, as well as by night. These shrimp burrow into the bottom during daytime and emerge from their burrows to feed at nighttime. Electrical impulses sent through the bottom or sweep line of the fishing gear cause burrowing shrimp to jump up into the path of the trawl. Fishermen are beginning to use this device.

Exploratory fishing, a scientific approach to the location of new fishery resources and how they can be caught efficiently, has its place in fishery development. Science has been able to predict with great accuracy the location of shrimp grounds. The main domestic fishery for shrimp has been conducted along the southern Atlantic and Gulf coasts of the United States. Through exploratory studies, minor shrimp grounds along our Pacific coast, from California to Alaska, have been extended to more productive grounds.

In the Atlantic Ocean, Bureau vessels, using knowledge of the life history of shrimp and the type of environment that they prefer, early in this decade located extremely valuable shrimp grounds off the Guianas of South America. A large fleet of U.S. shrimp trawlers is now fishing this area.

Once caught, how can fish and shellfish be best preserved and utilized? This is the work of fishery food science and technology, a branch of science as complex as the study of the ocean. Research has developed and is continuing to develop new techniques to bring the harvest of the sea and of fresh waters to the consumer in many new palatable forms. In another closely related area of work, scientists are unearthing information which shows that fish and shellfish are important in our diet from the standpoint of health, the growth of young people, and the repair of tissues in elderly people.

We have shown that many small marine animals, which are among the most abundant renewable resources in the ocean, are not utilized to full capacity or are not used at all. The very large and prolific group of herring and

Separated fish oil components are exposed to action of oxygen in special containers, in study of how fish oils oxidize. Bureau of Commercial Fisheries chemist withdraws sample for analysis.

herringlike fishes now provides about a third of the world's fishery catch. Increased catches of this group and other small schooling fishes are possible in many places.

Most of the herring and herringlike fishes are processed into fishmeal and oil. The meal is a high protein ingredient which is widely used in the feeding of poultry and livestock. The oil, which is a byproduct obtained during the preparation of the fishmeal,

goes principally into margarine and into paints.

Fishery scientists here and abroad are interested in using herring and other small fish more efficiently as direct food for humans. A high-protein edible meal, known as fish protein concentrate (FPC), has great potential for providing underfed and undernourished people with much-needed animal protein.

The staff of the Bureau of Commercial Fisheries Technological Laboratory at College Park, Md., has developed a chemical method for extracting oil and water from fish, leaving a dry, powdery protein-rich substance that can be produced for as little as 25 cents a pound. Only a fraction of a pound of this FPC is necessary daily to provide a person with the animal protein needed to balance a plant protein diet. A pilot plant is being planned on our Pacific coast to produce FPC commercially. The raw material for this protein food will be Pacific hake, which is abundant and virtually unutilized.

Probably the most important problem facing fishery food scientists is quality. Fish and shellfish are especially prone to bacterial decomposition. A major effort to reduce the bacteria in fresh fish is being made now by using irradiation. At the Bureau of Commercial Fisheries Technological Laboratory in Gloucester,

In the final step of the fish oil analysis, chart is examined to determine the chemical components of the oxidized material.

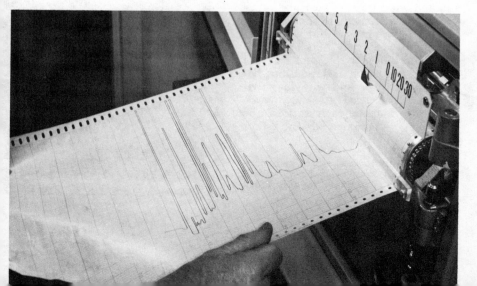

Mass., the Atomic Energy Commission has built an irradiator which is being used experimentally by Bureau scientists to reduce spoilage and increase the "shelf life" of fresh fish. Experiments have also been conducted with a shipboard irradiator on the Bureau's vessel, *Delaware*.

Low dosages of radiation can double or triple the storage life of fish and shellfish. Maintenance of flavor and palatability for several weeks will be a boon to the distribution of fishery products to consumers in all parts of the United States. At this writing, an application is before the U.S. Food and Drug Administration to permit commercial use of radiation.

Another example of product development is the preparation of freeze-dried products. This is a vacuum technique which extracts nearly all the water in a fish or shellfish. The animal is thus preserved in dry form and can be kept in plastic wrapping for a long time without spoilage. Adding water merely restores the product to its original wet state and it is ready for use. Freeze-dried products like shrimp are now on the market, but they are expensive. When further refinements are made in the processing technique, it is hoped that fishery products can be freeze-dried economically.

At this stage in our knowledge of fisheries, it is impossible to know whether the potential harvest from the ocean can be fully achieved. We need to know more about the most productive fishing areas, where they are, and what types of gear and other devices are needed to harvest the resources efficiently and at a profit to fishermen. We need to know more about the different stocks of fish and shellfish and their relationship between each other and with the environment. We need to know more about how much of each stock can be removed by commercial and sport fishermen without overfishing, and to know how each species can be managed on a State, national, or international basis.

And, finally, we need to know better methods of processing and preserving fishery products so that they can be brought to people with fresh, just-out-of-the-water taste.

This means not only better use of the fish, shellfish, and seaweed now being marketed, but use also of resources that are not being caught.

Many scientists think the important fisheries of the future may well take the form of artificial cultivation in brackish and shallow marine waters and especially in fresh waters—for then favorable growing conditions can be controlled precisely. Some believe artificial cultivation may even be practiced in deeper water on or over the ocean bed of the Continental Shelf. Assembly-line factories will harbor fish or shellfish—and spawning, growing, and even harvesting conditions will be controlled automatically.

A bag of haddock ready to come aboard research vessel *Silver Mink*. Scientists will analyze catch to determine size of haddock population off New England.

So far, few marine species have been brought under artificial cultivation. Successful large-scale commercial ventures have been the artificial cultivation of oysters, other mollusks, and seaweed in shallow coastal waters of Japan and some other countries. Fishery science is working toward this end with crabs, lobsters, and other species, and there is little doubt that the problems of artificially raising them will be solved. How long this will take depends on consumer demand and on the capital necessary to practice artificial cultivation with commercially economic large-scale ventures.

Reproduction Outside the Parent

THOMAS M. BYRD

. . . .

Smokey would have been a good name for the baby ram. His body was a soft gray; his face, ears, and legs almost black, typical of a Hampshire lamb. A vigorous appetite kept him from noticing the men clustered around his pen that warm March day in 1959.

"He's a healthy-looking little fellow," one of the men proclaimed.

"A real Easter lamb," another observed.

Smokey was also a scientific milestone at North Carolina State University (NCSU), for he was born of two mothers: the mother who conceived him and the mother who carried him from early embryo stage until birth. Or, as NCSU scientists described it, Smokey had a real mother and a host mother as well.

Smokey had remained in the body of his real mother for only a few days after conception.

Soon after the sperm from his father and the egg (ovum) from his mother united, the fertilized egg (embryo) was removed surgically and placed in the body of his host mother. Smokey was born 150 days later, handsome, healthy, and completely acceptable to his host mother.

Smokey was soon joined at NCSU by a host of mice, rabbits, and pigs of similar parentage.

Some of the animals, like Smokey, were conceived in one mother and born of another. Some were conceived in one mother, transferred to a host mother for a few days, and then returned to the real mother for birth.

Species of animals which normally produce multiple births made it possible for scientists to exchange all or part of the embryos recovered from two or more mothers. Thus, different mothers could give birth to animals which were genetically, at least, full brothers and sisters.

Transferring embryos from one mother to another is not an end in itself for NCSU scientists. Instead, it is their way of learning more about the causes of embryonic deaths in mammals.

Animal reproduction is the result of a series of biological events. Sperm deposited by the male unites with the egg ovulated by the female, thus causing the egg to become fertile. The fertilized egg or embryo begins cell division. One cell divides into two identical cells. Two cells become four cells; four cells become eight cells.

∴ ∴ ∴

THOMAS M. BYRD is News Editor, Department of Agricultural Information, North Carolina State University.

This lamb was conceived by Dorset ewe after being mated to Dorset ram. Resultant embryo was transferred to western ewe few days later by scientists at North Carolina State University. Although born to western ewe, lamb was accepted by Continental Dorset Club, Inc., as purebred Dorset.

Within a few days the embryo is a mass of cells, and these cells begin to differ from one another as the first outline of new life appears.

In the meantime, the embryo is slowly moving down the oviduct, to the uterus, where it attaches itself to the uterus lining and stays for the remainder of the pregnancy—if all goes well.

These biological events necessary for reproduction must occur with great precision and in precise order. A breakdown in any one of the events ends the whole process. Research at NCSU centers around those first few days of pregnancy; the time that appears to be the most crucial of all.

For example, from 30 to 40 percent of all mammalian embryos die before birth, and most of these die within the first week after conception. As many as 40 embryos have been found in the reproductive tract of a gilt a few days

after mating. Yet, few gilts give birth to more than 12 or 14 pigs.

Why? This is the question asked by scientists at NCSU and other locations around the United States.

"We want to know what causes one embryo to die and another to live," says Dr. L. C. Ulberg, professor of animal science at NCSU and leader of the university's research program on embryonic death.

Ulberg's fascination with the general subject of animal reproduction has existed since his graduate student days in his native Wisconsin. The subject was taboo in many circles. But this did not stop Ulberg. Independent, provocative, and innovative, he plunged into an area of research that was extremely fundamental yet full of possibilities for practical farm application. Ulberg's first research job took him to Mississippi State University, where he had an excellent opportunity to observe the reproductive performance of animals under a vastly different set of climatic conditions.

For decades scientists have noted that climate affects animal reproduction. Sheep, for example, will not breed during hot weather. Many wild animals have a seasonal mating pattern. One study even shows the human conception rate in Hong Kong falls 30 percent during the summer.

Climatic or environmental forces affect animal reproduction in many ways. They affect the production of sperm by the male and eggs by the female. They affect estrus or the heat cycle in the female. They cause embryonic deaths and cause newborn animals to be smaller than normal.

While the general relationship between environment and animal reproduction is fairly well established, scientists still lack a biological explanation for this relationship.

What precisely happens within the parents of an animal when they are subjected to environmental stresses? How do these stresses affect the ability of parents to produce offspring?

These are the questions Dr. Ulberg and his colleagues are attempting to answer. To find the answers, they turned their attention to the first few critical days in the creation of new life.

So far, the primary environmental or stress factor Ulberg and his colleagues have studied is temperature. Their primary research technique, as pointed out earlier, is the relatively simple surgical practice of embryo transfer. Embryos from females kept under various environmental conditions are transferred back and forth.

This permits the scientists to isolate those defects that may have been inherent in the embryo itself from those which may have been caused by stress put on the female.

A typical experiment may go something like this. Two female sheep at the same stage of the estrus cycle are bred. One ewe is immediately placed under heat stress; the second ewe is placed in optimum temperature surroundings.

When the embryos are judged to be in the eight-cell stage (about 3 days after mating), the two ewes are opened surgically and the reproductive tracts exposed. The embryos, both of which appear healthy, are transferred.

Experience shows that the embryo taken from the heat-stressed female and placed in the body of the normal female usually dies. The embryo transferred from the normal female to the heat-stressed female usually lives.

Basically, the same kind of experiment has been repeated in countless patterns. Thousands of embryos have been transferred in the Reproductive Physiology Laboratory which is maintained by NCSU.

Heat stress was put on female sheep, swine, rabbits, and mice at many stages of embryonic development. Heat stress also was put on the male sperm before mating occurred and on the unfertilized eggs of the female.

Embryos were transferred from one species of animal to another. For example, sheep embryos were placed in the reproductive tract of rabbits for several hours as another means of introducing stress.

Cattle were included in the experiments, but the NCSU scientists have not been able to get an embryo transferred from the real mother to live for long in a host mother. This, of course, raised many questions for the scientists.

A big boost for the research has been the ability of scientists in recent years to grow embryos in culture outside the body. Embryos from pigs, sheep, and rabbits can be kept growing in culture for several days without harm, and stress can be applied directly to the embryos at this stage if desired.

"We are just getting into embryo culture," Dr. Ulberg explained. "It's an interesting area of research; one that offers many possibilities for the study of animal reproduction."

The technique of embryo transfer itself was gradually refined and perfected. Ulberg and his colleagues can usually get 60 to 70 percent of the transferred embryos to survive. The embryos must be transferred while they still are floating free in the oviduct. After a few days, they will enter the uterus, attach themselves to the uterus wall, and start drawing nutrients directly from the mother. Transfer after this time is not successful.

Findings of the research at North Carolina State University show the damage to embryos as a result of stress usually occurs very early in their development, but the results are usually not apparent until later.

Most embryonic deaths occur after the embryos enter the uterus, and this is where many scientists have looked for the cause of death. Ulberg showed that what happens in the uterus is often determined by what happened to the embryo within the first few hours of its existence. Stress placed directly on sperm of the male and the unfertilized egg of the female also affects reproductive performance. But, again, the most noticeable effects do not appear until after the embryo enters the uterus.

This phenomenon of delayed embryonic death is illustrated by a typical study at NCSU. Involved were two groups of female sheep.

One group was kept at a comfortable (for sheep) temperature of 70°. The second group was kept at 90°, which was sufficient to raise the rectal temperature of the sheep about 2° and to cause "heat stress."

Both groups of sheep were mated, and the embryos recovered from their oviducts when the embryos were about to enter the uterus. Fertilization rate for the heat-stressed ewes was 29 percent less than the rate for the ewes kept at a comfortable temperature.

Surviving embryos were examined, and those judged sound transferred to two groups of "host" ewes.

At the end of 30 days, only 10 percent of the embryos transferred from "stressed donors" were still living. The survival rate for nonstressed embryos was 56 percent.

"This indicates to us," Dr. Ulberg explained, "that death was not the result of an abnormal physiological function at the time of death. Instead,

death resulted from something that happened to the embryos before they entered the uterus."

In another study, Ulberg and his colleagues took ova (unfertilized eggs) from a stressed and nonstressed group of females and transferred them to two groups of host females. The host females were then mated. Fertilization and embryo development were the same for the two groups of females.

"This study suggested to us that the stress did not alter the ovum prior to fertilization," Ulberg said. "Again, it looked as if the critical period for embryo development is between the time of fertilization and the time the embryo enters the uterus."

A similar study tested the response of sperm to stress. Highly fertile male rabbits were mated to heat-stressed females. Sperm were recovered 6 hours after mating from these females and transferred to normal females near the ovulation stage.

Sperm from the heat-stressed rabbits were as effective as sperm from nonstressed rabbits in causing pregnancy. But the embryo survival rate was 18 percent less for females receiving the heat-stressed sperm.

In variations of these studies, Ulberg and his associates applied stress to ova, sperm, and embryos growing in culture outside the body.

The ultimate survival rate was the same as if the stress had been applied to the ova, sperm, and embryos while still inside the parent.

All these studies confirm Ulberg's belief that embryonic death is usually due to stress applied early in the embryo's development even though death does not occur until later.

Findings of the NCSU research also suggest that a variety of factors can contribute to embryonic death, and that these factors seem to be additive. NCSU scientists further conclude that only minor variations in the environment, coming at a critical time, can cause embryonic death. A body temperature rise of only 2° is often sufficient, for example, to cause embryonic death if applied at the critical time.

Attention is now being turned to stress factors other than heat.

Scientists at NCSU are convinced a better understanding of reproductive physiology is essential to solving some of the world's most basic problems.

"Look at the world today," Ulberg commented.

"On the one hand, man must learn to control his own population. On the other hand, man must learn to feed the people who already exist."

The greatest food need of the world today is more protein. By delving into the beginnings of life, Ulberg and his NCSU coworkers hope to find ways to increase the supply of animal protein through making each breeding animal more productive.

How this research might relate to human population control is a subject that must be pursued by other scientists. There is no doubt, however, that greater animal reproductivity and reduced human reproductivity are but two sides of the same coin.

Chicken in Every Pot— the Broiler Bonanza

H. R. BIRD

. . . .

Suppose you went to your favorite market to get a ready-to-cook broiler and found that it was marked 62 cents per pound instead of the customary 33 or 35. What would your reaction be? Astonishment? Unbelief? Rage? Yet 62 cents is about the "normal" price one would expect if broilers had followed the general trend of consumer prices in the last 25 years.

Why didn't they follow the general trend? Research has changed the broiler's genes, diet, family life, physical environment, life expectancy, and even his personality.

The young chicken may well be the most researched animal in this much-researched world.

Research workers and growers have done great things to the broiler, but they have not always been very successful in predicting what the broiler would do next. In 1938, I first visited the Delmarva Peninsula and became acquainted with broilers and broilermen. Every conversation eventually got around to "overproduction" and "low prices." Where would they find the people to eat all the broilers that they were producing?

Well, the total number produced in the United States in 1938 was 82 million. In 1966 it was 2.5 billion. The average price of live broilers was 17 cents per pound in 1938. It was 15 cents per pound in 1966.

In 1953, I served with a committee appointed by the American Feed Manufacturers' Association to estimate livestock numbers and feed use for the next year. The statistics indicated that broiler numbers in 1954 should be about 987 million. One member of the committee suggested we could get some publicity by being the first to predict a one-billion-broiler

∴   ∴   ∴

H. R. BIRD *is Chairman of the Department of Poultry Science, University of Wisconsin. He was formerly in charge of Poultry Investigations, Agricultural Research Service.*

Brooder cover is lifted from chicks, *left*, in a Bethlehem, N.C., family farm operation involving several 10,000-bird broiler houses. *Above*, closeup of chicks.

year. We squelched our colleague. We were interested only in an accurate prediction, not in publicity. But he had the last laugh. There were 1,048 million broilers in 1954.

In 1938, there was one major broiler area, the Delmarva Peninsula of Delaware, Maryland, and Virginia. In 1964, the 10 leading States in order of importance were Georgia, Arkansas, Alabama, North Carolina, Mississippi, Texas, Maryland, Delaware, Maine, and California.

In Delaware I was told that a major factor in the beginning of the industry in the 1930's was the success of Mrs. Wilmer Steele in growing broilers for the New York market. Wilmer Steele retired from the Coast Guard to join his wife in the broiler business and went on to become a leader in feed manufacturing, poultry processing, and banking in his area.

The low cost of modern broilers is

not the sole reason for the great increase in consumption. There have also been major improvements in quality. About 1940, one writer stated: "A broiler is a scrawny, blue-looking object that tastes good in spite of its unfortunate appearance."

Why were they blue looking? Partly because they had no fat and therefore no yellow pigment in the skin. It was considered impossible to put fat on a young chicken. The other reason for the blue look was dark pigment in the skin of the dark-feathered broilers.

All the early broilers were Barred Plymouth Rocks, with black-and-white barred feathers. Then the general-purpose red-feathered New Hampshire breed was developed by Andrew Christie and other New England poultrymen. These birds excelled in growth rate and efficiency, but the industry still clung to barred feathers. They crossed Barred Rock males with

38

New Hampshire females to produce fast-growing barred-cross birds. But the New Hampshires were big boned and angular, and even well-fleshed birds sometimes looked scrawny when they were dressed.

The big increase in consumption of broilers during World War II convinced industry leaders that there were still greater opportunities for expansion if better quality birds could be produced. Under the leadership of Howard Pierce of the Great Atlantic & Pacific Tea Co., Inc., a series of Chicken-of-Tomorrow Contests was held, with the financial support of the A. & P. Co. Breeders submitted samples of eggs which were hatched at a central point. The chicks were reared to broiler weight, slaughtered, dressed, and scored for growth rate, efficiency, viability, fertility, hatchability, and dressed grade, including a grade for conformation (shape or build).

The New Hampshire could provide everything except conformation. The Chicken of Tomorrow had to have a broad breast and thick drumsticks. One needed only to look in the Standard of Perfection to find the model with the right conformation. It was the Cornish. But for years the Cornish were reputed, more or less accurately, to grow slowly and inefficiently, to feather slowly, to lay poorly, and to have low fertility and hatchability. A combination of the good qualities of New Hampshire and Cornish seemed like a good approach to the Chicken of Tomorrow.

However, some breeders concentrated on improving the White Plymouth Rock from the standpoint of growth rate and conformation.

National contests were held in 1948 at the University of Delaware and in 1951 at the University of Arkansas. For the award ceremony in 1951, the principal address was given by Vice President Alben W. Barkley. Dr. Lewis Webster Jones, president of the University of Arkansas, presided, and Governor Sid McMath welcomed the visitors—including a congressional delegation. But the man of the hour was Charles Vantress of Live Oak, Calif. His Cornish-New Hampshire crosses had won the first national contest in Delaware, and they repeated their victory in the second. In 1940, the Vantress Poultry Breeding Farm was almost unknown beyond the boundaries of its own community. With the impetus of the two victories, it quickly grew into one of the largest international poultry breeding operations.

Today's broilers are produced with maximum efficiency by crossing two strains having different characteristics. The strain furnishing the female parents must lay well and hatch well to produce broiler chicks efficiently. Of course, its growth rate and conformation are important, too. In the strain furnishing the male parents, the breeder puts primary emphasis on growth and conformation, letting egg production and hatchability be secondary.

Male broiler lines derive mostly from Cornish and New Hampshires.

Cut-up broiler fryers in Takoma Park, Md., supermarket.

39

The female lines are derived mostly from White Rocks.

But even a modern broiler, with his genes all properly arranged, doesn't grow very well on an old-fashioned diet. We tried this at the University of Wisconsin in 1957, feeding male broiler chicks a diet that was recommended in 1907, one that was recommended in 1932, and one that was recommended in 1957. At 9 weeks of age, the average weights of the three lots of chickens were 0.6, 2.0, and 3.2 pounds, respectively. The pounds of feed required per pound of gain for the three groups were 5.2, 3.0, and 2.0. In the 1930's, broilers reached 3 pounds in 14 weeks on 4½ pounds of feed for each pound of gain. Now 3-pound broilers are grown in 8 weeks with 2.25 pounds of feed per pound of gain.

Research on vitamin D by Hart, Halpin, and Steenbock at the University of Wisconsin in the 1920's made production of poultry independent of sunshine and permitted it to move indoors. The Wisconsin investigators developed feeds containing corn, wheat byproducts, meat meal, milk byproducts, alfalfa meal, minerals, and cod liver oil. Early broiler feeds were of this type, and most of the time they were satisfactory. But knowledge of the chick's requirements was sketchy, and nobody knew much about the normal variation in vitamin content of feedstuffs. Vitamin deficiencies were rather commonplace.

Information on nutritive requirements accumulated rapidly, and in 1947 Scott, Singsen, and Matterson developed the Connecticut Broiler Formula, based largely on research on the requirements published by the Universities of California, Cornell, Texas A. & M., and Wisconsin and the U.S. Department of Agriculture. By using synthetic vitamins, the Connecticut investigators were able to reduce the levels of wheat byproducts and increase the corn, thus raising the energy content of the feed. Higher energy levels made it possible to put some fat and yellow color into the skin.

Broilers need protein, too, but we never had enough protein to feed our livestock properly until 1957. We achieved sufficiency by an enormous increase in production of soybeans and soybean meal. Formerly, soybean meal was considered unsuitable for chickens, but research revealed how to supplement it with vitamins and minerals, and it is currently our major source of protein.

The last big step in supplementing soybean meal was taken in the USDA laboratories at Beltsville in 1946 when we showed that soybean meal plus an unidentified vitamin from cow manure was as effective as animal proteins. The unknown vitamin was shown to be formed in manure by fermentation. In 1948, vitamin B_{12}, isolated in the laboratories of Merck and Co., proved to be identical with the "cow manure

Left, lazy susan rotary table with 24 bins for ingredients helps assure accurate mixing of vitamins and other microcomponents in commercial feed company "microroom" facility. *Right,* control panel at another feed mixing installation.

vitamin." Soon it was being produced in large quantities by more esthetic fermentations.

In 1950, Stokstad and Jukes of American Cyanamid Co. were experimenting with a fermentation residue from the production of the antibiotic, chlortetracycline, to determine its effectiveness as a B_{12} supplement. They found B_{12}, but they also found another growth-promoting substance which turned out to be the residual antibiotic which had not been completely removed in processing. Low levels of antibiotics in feeds improve growth and conversion of feed to broiler. Use of antibiotics since 1950 has saved an estimated 3 million tons of broiler feed. Even with use of the most sensitive methods available, no antibiotic can be found in the meat of broilers fed low levels of antibiotics.

Before World War II, broilermen tried to keep the death loss below 10 percent. Today a grower can't stay in business unless he can keep death loss below 5 percent. Lloyd and D'Armi of the University of Delaware showed that average mortality in commercial flocks in Delmarva in 1952 was 7.2 percent. In 1962, it was 3.67 percent. Formerly, the biggest killer was the group of diseases called coccidiosis, caused by several species of microscopic parasites that attack the chicken's intestinal tract. These diseases are still a problem, but they are quite effectively controlled by drugs called coccidiostats. Other important developments in disease control were vaccines against fowl pox, Newcastle disease, and laryngo-tracheitis.

Since 1950, antibiotics have been used to control Mycoplasma infections. Progress is being made in eliminating these diseases by testing breeding stock and slaughtering reactors.

Through a similar testing program, carried on by the National Poultry Improvement Plan, pullorum disease was largely eliminated from chickens even before the broiler industry began its rapid growth.

In 1938, in order to minimize infections, most broilers were grown in houses that were 20 by 20 feet. Such a house accommodated about 500 broilers. As methods of disease control improved, producers began to experiment with larger houses. Now most broiler houses are 40 or 50 feet wide. Ventilation is more difficult if they are wider. Length seems to be limited only by the amount of money the builder has or can borrow. Some new houses are windowless with "controlled environment," including heating and cooling systems.

So today's broilers have different genes, different diets, different family life, different life expectancy, and different environment than their predecessors. I mentioned earlier that the broiler's personality also has changed. Growers used to explain the 20 by 20 house partly as a disease-control measure and partly as a means of preventing piling up and minimizing cannibalism. An unaccustomed noise might cause a whole population of broilers to pile up in a corner with many deaths resulting, or an epidemic of cannibalism might occur; and the greater the number of birds per unit, the greater would be the losses.

Today's large broiler houses may have a few partitions or they may not. I have seen at least 40,000 broilers in one pen. Neither the 40,000 broilers nor their owners seemed concerned about piling up or cannibalism.

Perhaps the geneticists, besides getting rid of the scrawny blue look, have also eliminated some of the broiler's antisocial tendencies.

Or perhaps the better diet and better physical environment have reduced tension and frustration.

Broilermen worry about prices, about the number of chicks the competitors are starting, about viruses, about feed supplies, and about the merits of different coccidiostats, and ventilation systems.

The broilers just keep rolling along, increasing in numbers, and producing tastier drumsticks and white meat faster and more efficiently.

Grow a Forest in 3 Years

A. M. HERRICK

. . . .

Harvesting trees for pulpwood every 2 to 3 years—compared to the present 20 to 40 years—is a revolutionary new concept being explored by forestry scientists in Georgia.

It holds promise of helping the United States and other nations meet growing needs for timber, pulp, and other wood-based products. And costs would be greatly reduced.

The new system, called "silage sycamore," consists of planting sycamore trees at a very close spacing and then harvesting crops of sprouts with a silage cutter every 2 to 3 years. Time and space savings result compared to conventional wide-spaced tree plantations for pulpwood or other wood products. And higher yields of wood fiber per acre of land are expected. At present, trees are harvested for pulpwood every 20 to 40 years.

Regeneration of forests by sprouts is not new. Willow shoots have been grown for basket weaving since the dawn of civilization. But bulk production of fiber or cellulose, by harvesting young sprout growth of trees, would be a real innovation. What we need for our 2- or 3-year forest is a tree that sprouts vigorously and that has the fiber properties sought by industry to make reconstituted products like particleboard and paper.

Ten years of sycamore studies by the U.S. Forest Service at Athens, Ga., proved the great versatility of that species. It occurs naturally in all States east of the Great Plains except Minnesota and grows on a wide range of soils and sites. Under reasonably good sunlight, soil, and moisture conditions,

sycamore grows fast. It sprouts prolifically from a low stump and responds well to fertilization. Then too, it has relatively few insect and disease enemies in the South.

We are not overlooking other species like sweetgum, yellow-poplar, and cottonwood. Even boxelder is a possibility because of its rapid early growth, light wood color, seeding characteristics, and possibilities for direct seeding. For reasons mentioned hereafter, though, we favor sycamore.

Besides, "silage sycamore" is a nice alliteration to describe the mechanized culture and harvest of a versatile crop every 2 or 3 years.

In the beginning, the new forest is to be planted on a well-prepared site by using seed, seedlings, or cuttings. Use of cuttings is particularly attractive since genetic gains are realized quickly; superior stock can be selected in 1 or 2 years and reproduced vegetatively. Mechanical weed control and cultivation improve survival, and growth. Repeated cropping will require fertilizer applications, and intensive management may call for irrigation. Possibly both irrigation and fertilization can be accomplished by applying discharges from sewage treatment plants to the forest crop.

Fertilizers, and pesticides if necessary, can be applied from aircraft. Likewise, when the product to be manufactured will not tolerate leaves, an aerial spray can be used for defoliation

∴ ∴ ∴

A. M. HERRICK is Dean of the School of Forest Resources, University of Georgia, Athens.

luring the growing season. It would
)e nice to do all the harvesting in the
lormant season when the leaves have
allen, but mills need supplies of chips
he year around. The 2- or 3-year
orest will replace itself by sprouting
fter each harvest cutting.

Sprout stands differ from annual
crops which must be harvested when
ipe and then stored. Our tree silage
rop can be stored on the stump for 1
r more years when harvesting needs
o be delayed for any reason. We may
ven gain a little volume by growth.

Experimentation so far suggests that
nitial growing space should equal the
quare of as many feet as there are
ears in the harvest interval. For ex-
mple, in a planting designed for a 3-
ear cutting cycle, the trees would be
iven 9 square feet initially. The close
pacings make full use of the site almost
mmediately. In conventional plantings
t 8- by 8-foot or wider spacings, the
ree crowns do not fully shade the
round for several years.

Two-year-old rootstocks in a nursery
lanting of sycamore placed 1 foot
part in 4-foot rows produced an aver-
ge of more than 17 tons of 1-year-old
prouts per acre. When a similar
lanting was harvested after 6 years,
nly a few of the trees had died, but
rowth was drastically reduced during
he last 4 years. At the end of 6 years,
2 tons of green material were pro-
uced per acre. This equals 7 tons or
 respectable 2.3 cords per acre per
ear. However, if the sprouts had been
arvested each year for 6 years, the
otal yield probably would have ex-
eeded 100 tons per acre or about 2½
imes the total of the single cutting.

A rig like a forage harvester is used
o convert the forest of sprouts to
hips. In one pass, the machine severs
he stems 3 or 4 inches above the
round, chips up the entire miniature
ree, and blows the "silage" into a
ailer towed behind. When full, the
ailer is replaced with an empty one
nd hauled to a loading dock or trans-
ort terminal for dumping.

Chips are either stored or sent to
he mill for processing.

Foresters are not the only ones pleas-
antly surprised with sycamore as a
short-term wood producer. Pulp and
paper technologists have been amazed
to discover that this "upstart" of the
timber world has excellent characteristics for making certain types of
products. Its very thin bark permits
use of the whole tree and eliminates
the cost of debarking before chemical
conversion.

Fresh samples of paper made from
unbeaten pulp show green flecks from
the chlorophyll in the leaves that were
cooked with wood and bark just as the
sprouts came out of the silage chopper.
Yet, the strength properties, bleaching
qualities, and printability of whole-
tree young sycamore sprouts command
the respectful attention of the paper
industry.

A vast variety of paper products,
fiberboards and hardboards or molded
articles for building and other purposes, can be manufactured from
seedling-sprout silage, as is now being
done from wood grown the conventional way. Soon, entire wall units as
well as floor and deck units for homes
and other small buildings may be
molded in pairs, with a dead-air space
in between to serve as insulation. These
units would be light in weight and
structurally very strong. The wall units
would be ready to receive completed
door and window units. Such buildings
could be erected quickly at low cost.

With the silage sycamore concept,
we expect some tremendous cost savings in wood production. Gains are accomplished by cashing in on both bio-
logic and economic principles. Every
square foot of growing space is used.
Yields are near capacity. Production
is mechanized, and rotations (number
of years between crops) are minimized.
Consequently, both time and space are
conserved.

Our sprout forest continually renews
itself and yields heavy crops, thanks to
close spacings and rapid growth. Rootstocks not only replace the newly
harvested stems by sprouting, but also
stimulate new growth by giving the
sprouts carbohydrates stored in root

43

tissues. Yields per acre are tremendous; the young stems are easy to harvest and chip with fairly simple and light equipment. The young wood is relatively uniform in its characteristics. Bark and leaves are not considered trash in some products.

Maybe our young forest of sprouts will mass-produce raw material for mass-produced housing to help shelter our exploding population. What about the other two necessities of life—clothing and food? Rayon, along with other chemical converts, may also be an end product of the new forest, helping to clothe our people in generations to come. Sugar, molasses, and yeasts can also be derived from wood. They could help considerably to provide the world with vital and urgently needed energy foods and proteins at low cost. Thus, the silage connotation in the designation "silage sycamore" may not be so weird after all.

The Brain and the Egg

RAYMOND D. SCHAR

Mother Nature originally intended the egg of a bird to be used exclusively to perpetuate the species. To accomplish this parental instinct, the bird was endowed with internal organs and glands that responded to certain external stimulations that occurred in nature. However, man has altered many of these external stimulants in order to force the domesticated fowl to better serve him.

The domesticated chicken is thought to have originated from the jungle fowl. This ancestor laid her eggs in the spring and early summer months as the length of the days increased. She would lay 10 to 12 eggs, incubate them, and brood the chicks, and then repeat this process once and occasionally twice. When man discovered the egg was a good food, he started to domesticate chickens. By taking the eggs from the hen's nest as she laid them, man disrupted her normal reproduction cycle. Since she no longer had to incubate her eggs and brood the chicks, her body underwent physiological adjustments that permitted her to lay more eggs.

Through selection, man developed groups of chickens that gradually became more and more proficient in their ability to produce eggs. As the birds were kept confined to smaller areas, they could no longer forage for their feed. Man became the provider. Through trial and error, he learned that a chicken would lay more eggs when fed one kind of feed than another. By observing that a hen began to produce more eggs in the spring of the year as the days became longer, man reasoned correctly that if he provided artificial light to lengthen the day, she would lay more eggs. Protection against the elements and diseases permitted additional production.

All these efforts down through the centuries have increased yearly egg production from 20 to 30 eggs per hen to 250 and above in the better producing strains. But modern man is not content. He is intensifying his effort to produce an even more prolific chicken. Refined selection principles crossing and incrossing of families and

∴   ∴   ∴

RAYMOND D. SCHAR is Coordinator, National Poultry Improvement Plans, Animal Husbandry Research Division, Agricultural Research Service,

Chicken egg seems minute compared with egg from biggest bird ever known, Madagascar's elephant bird, extinct for centuries. National Geographic Society, which found giant fossil egg, estimates that when fresh it weighed about 20 pounds, equal to 160 hen eggs.

rains, fortified diets, and improved nvironmental conditions are but a ew of the practices under constant udy and improvement. In addition, uring the last several decades, this ever ending search for perfection has rawn a new group of scientists into he picture. These are the physiologists.

The physiologists are studying the unctions and activities of the organs nd glands to find their relationship o each other and to determine the fects of natural and artificially in-uced internal and external stimuli. Dr. Richard M. Fraps, while a hysiologist at the University of Chi-ago, investigated the effect of hor-ones on feather development in hickens. In time, he expanded his aterest in hormones to include the art they played in ovulation. Since he ovaries of birds produce eggs that aature singly, chickens provided an xcellent opportunity for this study.

A domestic hen will complete ore than 200 ovulations a year in ather definitely established cycles. his allows a reasonably accurate stimate to be made of the time of atural ovulation, thus permitting the time of artificially stimulated ovulations to be reliably measured.

Some of the earliest studies of ovulation led to the conclusion that light is probably the main external stimulus to egg production. Since the hen's eye picks up the light and sends signals to the brain, it was reasoned that the brain must be the initial biological clock involved in ovulation. It was also discovered that the anterior pituitary gland, located directly beneath the brain, is the organ responsible for secretion of the hormones which are necessary for ovulation.

The portion of the brain known as the hypothalamus apparently is directly responsible for the initial internal stimulation. This was verified when ovulation was consistently induced by the infusion of extracts from the hypothalamus into the pituitary gland. Conversely, intentional injury to the hypothalamus stopped ovulation for an extended period. Also, when certain drugs known to affect the nervous system were injected into the hen, the ovulation cycle was disrupted. However, if extracts from the hypothalamus were injected into birds from which the

45

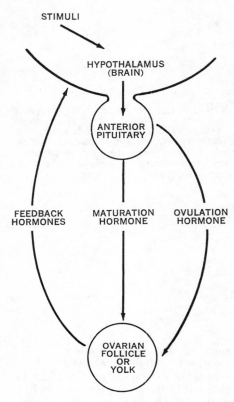

STIMULI

HYPOTHALAMUS
(BRAIN)

ANTERIOR
PITUITARY

FEEDBACK
HORMONES

MATURATION
HORMONE

OVULATION
HORMONE

OVARIAN
FOLLICLE
OR
YOLK

Hormone secretion and flow in hen's ovulation process. When brain is stimulated by light, it signals anterior pituitary gland to release maturation and ovulation hormones. After maturation and release of an ova, the ovary secretes feedback hormones which tell brain it is time for pituitary to reduce its hormone production, thus completing ovulation cycle.

pituitary gland had been removed, no ovulation took place. This made it appear that hormone secretion from the pituitary was necessary for ovulation.

There is considerable evidence that upon receipt of a light-controlled signal, nerve terminals of the hypothalamus discharge a substance called releasing factor into the bloodstream. This is carried to the pituitary where it stimulates that gland into secreting the maturation and ovulation hormones. These hormones travel to the ovary where the ovulation, or luteinizing, hormone (LH) causes rupture of the

saclike membrane which surrounds the single, fully developed yolk. This permits the yolk to be released from the ovary. The infundibulum, or upper end of the oviduct, then engulfs this free yolk and starts it on its journey down the hen's reproductive tract.

Besides causing maturation and ovulation of a yolk, the pituitary-secreted hormones cause the ovary to secrete hormones of its own. These are thought to be estrogens and progestagens and are called feedback hormones. When they reach the hypothalamus, they cause a signal to go to the pituitary which inhibits its hormone production, completing the cycle.

After Dr. Fraps came to work for the U.S. Department of Agriculture at Beltsville, Md., he and his coworkers studied time patterns involved in the intricacies of ovulation. After repeated experiments and observations, they determined that release of LH closely relates to the onset of darkness in the light/dark cycle of the day (or other light/dark cycle from 22 to 34 hours in length). In most instances, the membrane or follicle surrounding the yolk ruptures about 8 hours after the LH release. After ovulation, or rupture of the follicle, the yolk spends approximately 26 to 28 hours in the oviduct where various glands secrete the albumen, membranes, and shell that go to make up the complete egg.

It was known that under a normal period of daylight a hen will lay an egg on each of two or more consecutive days, skip a day, and then repeat the cycle. So when a hen has produced an egg on each of 2 consecutive days, she is said to have a two-egg sequence production on 3 consecutive days gives her a three-egg sequence, etc.

The hen usually lays the first egg in a sequence during the first part of the lighted or daylight period. Within 1 to 45 minutes after she lays this first egg, ovulation of the second egg takes place. The time lapse between laying an egg and the succeeding ovulation becomes less as the number of eggs in a sequence increases. Thus, if a hen has a two-egg sequence, the time be-

46

ween eggs is about 28½ hours. If she s on a four-egg sequence, the time etween eggs is about 26½ hours, and or a six-egg sequence, about 25½.

In longer sequences, the lag time for ggs in the middle of the sequence was ss than for the first or last eggs. One esearcher, who observed a group of irds for a complete year, recorded lag mes for various hens that laid two- hrough 13-egg sequences. He noted hat when the sequence was above 10 ggs in length, some of the consecutive ggs were produced in less than 24- our intervals.

Observations of the time required for hases of the reproductive cycle were ade on chickens not subjected to any nnatural domestic environments. ow the scientists set out to find which nvironmental factors affect the ovula- on process. They soon had enough vidence to strongly suspect that hanges in the amount of light had a irect bearing on hormone secretion y the pituitary gland. For example, hanging "night into day"—exposing he birds to light from 6 p.m. to 6 a.m., ith the rest of the 24 hours in dark- ess—brought about a corresponding hift in time of ovulation.

One team of researchers found that hen hens were exposed to constant ght, they laid eggs at any time during he day or night. However, Dr. Fraps nd his coworkers found that under his same system of constant light, the ens assumed practically the same pat- rn of ovulation and subsequent egg ying as they did under the normal 4-hour light period. Even though ghts in this experiment were on at l times, the caretaker started his ores at a regular time each morning, nd the activity of the birds seemed to ary with that of the caretaker. By late ternoon, when he was ready to quit ork, the hens started to settle down, they would do at the end of a nor- ally lighted day. This suggests that the H release mechanism may respond to her environmental rhythms beside ght. However, light is still believed e main factor which contributes to e time of ovulation.

Exposure to very high intensity light for a short period of time has produced inconclusive results for different re- searchers. Additional studies of light intensity, as well as types of light, are needed.

Other physical environmental fac- tors thought to affect ovulation include temperature, moisture, and diet. More research has been done on the effect of these factors upon mammals and other birds than with chickens. This is true also of external psychological factors such as group interaction or the pres- ence of the opposite sex. Ovulation cannot be accomplished in some species without some form of stimulation from the mate. However, that is not the case with the domestic hen.

Much of the work on ovulation has been basic research. Anything as in- volved as this biological process must be thoroughly understood before ap- plied research projects can be planned. However, from results obtained in some of these experiments, one might suggest how commercial poultrymen of the future could benefit.

For example, one scientist removed the pituitary gland from a group of chickens so they would not produce LH. He then injected each hen with LH, varying the amount given as well as the time of the injection. Multiple ovulations were produced. The ovi- duct, which normally contains one egg yolk at a time, now had two, and in one bird, three eggs in various stages of development. The oviducts appar- ently had no trouble secreting the necessary albumen (egg white) and membranes. However, the uterus, where the shell is added, did not seem to function properly after the first egg passed through, thus the subsequent eggs were soft shelled.

If the specific hormones produced by the ovary could be identified, it might be possible to make them synthetically. This compound could be put in a capsule that would be implanted in the bird's body, designed so as to make the hormones available to the brain at a given rate. They could thus stimulate the brain into signaling the pituitary

47

gland to produce its hormones in the necessary amounts for ovulation for several months. The number of ovulations could possibly be correlated with the maximum ability of the hen to produce a complete egg.

Determining the complete effects that various environmental conditions have on the biological clock in the brain may make it possible to get all ovulations to take place at the same time each day. This should increase the number of eggs in each sequence and lessen the number of "vacations" a hen takes each year.

Under a project in progress at Beltsville since 1962, hens are exposed to light for 12 hours and to darkness for 6, creating an 18-hour "day." This is equivalent to 486 light/dark days a year. The scientists are attempting to discover if this short day will speed up the ovulation cycle, and whether a strain of chickens can be developed which will genetically pass this trai to their offspring.

As scientists continue to find addi tional keys to unlock the many my teries of the hen's brain, and geneticist nutritionists, and pathologists continu to make advances in the poultry fiel the people of the world hopefully wi be assured enough eggs for future need

For further reading:

Fraps, Richard M., "Effects of Extern Factors on the Activity of the Ovary." In t Ovary II, Sir Solly Zackerman, edito Academic Press, New York, 1962.

——— "Photoregulation in the Ovulatic Cycle of the Domestic Hen." Presented the International Colloquium on Photoreg lation of Reproduction in Birds and Man mals, Centre National De La Recherc Scientifique, Montpellier, France, 1967.

Nalbandov, A. V., "Mechanisms Contro ling Ovulation of Avian and Mammalia Follicles." Control of Ovulation, C. A. Ville editor, Pergamon Press, New York, 1961.

Opel, H. and Nalbandov, A. V., "Ovul bility of Ovarian Follicles in the Hypoph sectomized Hen." Endocrinology. Vol. 69. 196

Faster Growing Trees Are Boon to the South

KEITH W. DORMAN

. . . .

Did you ever wonder who grew the pine trees used for the paper in those brown bags stacked at supermarket checkout counters? Chances are they grew on a farm somewhere in the southern United States. The important question is, will those bags keep coming when the supermarkets go on increasing at a rapid rate and the number of people using them increases even faster?

Tree breeders at many locations in the South are crossbreeding lots of trees to make certain we do have plenty of paper for those brown bags and brown paper boxes. So far, the are ahead in the race to create ne types of trees and get seed produce before the squeeze of more people an pulpmills and less land pinches off th supply of paper.

Tree breeders are working not onl to make a faster growing tree, but or that can be harvested easily, perhap by machine, and has little waste branches and bark. Trees grow fast

∴   ∴   ∴

KEITH W. DORMAN is a Research Project Lead at the Southeastern Forest Experiment Station, U. Forest Service, Asheville, N.C.

48

the South because of the long hot summers and the abundant rainfall, and the scientists are taking advantage of this fact.

Instead of closely grown trees carefully tended for many years to make them tall, straight, and clear of branches, the new forests are widely spaced with fast-growing trees that are inherently small crowned and small branched. The stands are untouched for 25 to 30 years, then cut, and the area replanted. Trees of sawlog size take longer to grow.

Tree breeders have created pine trees which in test stands produce twice the normal volume by crossing wild trees carefully selected for a dozen or more traits. These traits are the ones affecting growth rate and general desirability or quality of the tree for either pulpwood or lumber.

State forestry agencies and many of the large forestry industrial companies have started using the first seed produced from a few thousand acres of grafted seed orchards of forest trees.

The grafts were taken from trees that were genetically selected for many exceptionally good traits.

Pollinating slash pine in Olustee Experimental Forest, Fla. Bagged flowers are pollinated with puff or two of pollen from syringe which punctures bag. Tape is used to reseal bag. After flower scales have closed and conelet is no longer receptive to pollen, bag is removed.

Key factor in the fascinating game of picking the "winner" trees for parent stock is being able to tell if the visible traits are true inherent traits or are merely the result of some favorable environmental factor. The breeder of annual crop plants compares his selections in cultivated fields with uniform soils—the tree breeder, in wild woods with perhaps 30 years of growth behind them. Hindsight is important, but not easy.

The angry snarl of the chain saw is bringing a good income to southern tree farmers, and tree farmers are increasing their production. Tree nurseries of the Forestry Commission in Georgia, a pivotal State in the South, sell nearly 50 million trees each year. For the whole South, the figure is nearly 400 million. Landowners received $661,224,000 from pulp and paper companies for pulpwood purchased in 12 Southern States in 1966.

Most of us are familiar with the seared and ravaged fields after annual crops are harvested, but our concept of the forest is one of enduring greenness. It is a shock to learn that, if con-

centrated in one area, all the trees fro 15 square miles have to be cut ea week to keep the papermills suppli in Georgia alone, and nearly this mu is required for lumber and other pro ucts in addition. The average Americ uses 250 board feet of wood and 5 pounds of paper a year. We have plant, grow, and harvest the trees produce these products. In spite of huge annual harvest, volume grow still exceeds wood cut.

Growth of the pulp and paper i dustry in the South has been astoun ing. The total number of mills h passed the 100 mark and more a under construction. Mills operating 1946 could stew up only about 16,0 tons of pulp a day, but in 1967 th spewed out over 60,000 tons—close two-thirds of the Nation's total.

In 1940, Georgia's treegrowers c about 700,000 cords of pulpwood; 1966, the cut was over 6 million cor A lot of tree seedlings have to go in the ground each year to keep up th production. In 1966, the entire Sou produced enough pulpwood to bui a fence 4 feet wide and 4 feet high th

Made from southern pine pulpwood, paper bags pour out of a final assembly line the millions. These bags have long been a necessity for merchants and housewive

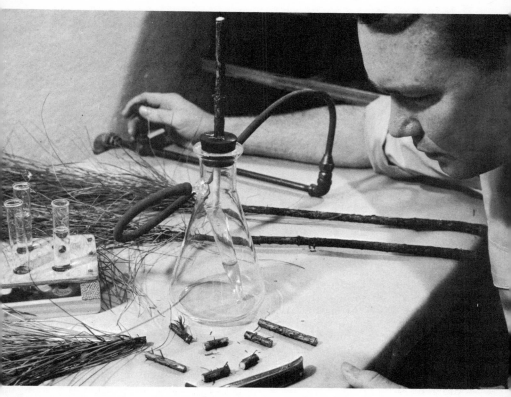

Vacuum extraction of sap from stems of slash pine seedlings. In this study, solution was then analyzed to determine forms in which mineral nutrients and organic compounds are moved within tree tissue.

could have wrapped itself around the world at the equator nearly two times.

Much of the South's production is kraft paper or the familiar brown stuff for bags and cardboard boxes. But some woodpulp goes into tissue paper and newsprint, too.

Some counties in the South are 90 percent forested. Holdings of over a million acres are not unusual for pulp and paper companies. Tree farming is on a grand scale in this region. Two-thirds of the land in timber is a good round phrase used to describe the forest land area from the Potomac to the Pedernales.

Tree breeding is not for the impatient. After pollen is sifted among the scales of tiny new conelets high in tree crowns, nearly 2 years pass before seed ripens. Seedling offspring

are grown a year in a tree nursery and 5 or more in the field test plots before first estimates are made of good or bad traits. Accurate facts about traits come years later.

To keep forging ahead, tree breeders carry many studies so that as some mature others are being started. It's more efficient to follow several lines of attack at once than string out jobs one after the other.

The South has four major species of pines: Slash, loblolly, longleaf, and shortleaf. About half the total wood volume is in one species, loblolly. Shortleaf pine is present over the largest geographical area, Pennsylvania to Texas. Loblolly doesn't cover quite so broad an area, longleaf still less, and slash pine covers the smallest area.

Races of these pines have developed

that seem adapted to the various climates and soils. Seed from one location cannot be planted in other States without chance of loss because of slow growth or cold damage. It is risky to move seed very far north or south, but a little less so east and west.

Racial differences in pines mean strains must be bred for various locations. A strain which performs well in one State may not do so in others, or it may even be poorer than the local types of trees.

Unlike annual crop plants, trees must be able to withstand bad weather in all four seasons and, in addition, the extremes of weather cycles over many years. Thus, a test period for new strains is pretty long.

After tree breeders have produced the best trees possible from crossbreeding within each species, the next step is to cross different species. It takes much skill to set up a good crossing plan. The goal is to pick the best single trees of the best geographic race of the right species to create a truly new tree. This must be done for many different locations.

Southern pine species all have certain traits that differ. Some are good and some are bad, like susceptibility to certain insect or disease pests.

The tree breeder hopes to produce trees with a good combination of desirable traits, but he may produce some with combinations of the bad traits of both species. He needs a special sort of insight to know which trees have the traits he wants and will transmit them to offspring. That's why tree breeding is an art.

U.S. Forest Service tree breeders have been working on southern pines for about 25 years, and many problems have been solved. Today, the main challenge is how to apply what the tree breeders have learned on a scale large enough to increase production throughout the South.

Southern tree breeders are growing in number, and they are well trained. Drs. John C. Barber and Charles D. Webb, who have bred strains of trees in Georgia with doubled volume growth combined with many other good traits, are southern born, professionally trained foresters. In addition, they studied for doctorates under renowned plant breeders at the University of Minnesota and North Carolina State University.

Drs. Bruce Zobel and Raymond Goddard, who teach forest genetics at North Carolina State University and the University of Florida, received their training at the University of California and Texas A&M College. They advise State forestry agencies and forest industries about tree breeding and seed improvement programs covering most of the South. Other Federal, State, and university research scientists are equally well trained.

Southern pines have not been influenced by years of selection and breeding like cultivated plants. The wild trees are a huge mixture of growth and form types and various degrees of resistance to insects and diseases. The good traits are all mixed up with bad ones, and the secret of selection is to pick out those rare ones with the best combination of a dozen traits.

The main traits affecting volume growth in the forest area are vigorous constitutions to withstand the rigors of transplanting in forest stands, good growth rate to put on the wood volume after planting, and resistance to diseases to keep trees healthy and occupying all the space on each acre.

More trees, each with faster growth, in other words.

But the new trees have to be "good" trees, also. We want straight stems so there is no bad fiber or crooked boards; small diameter branches growing straight out from the tree trunk so there are small knots and little wood lost in branches; unforked trunks so there is no waste wood in crotches or small tree trunks; fairly rapid natural pruning so that tree trunks are clear and machine harvesting is easy; resistance to insect attacks that kill the tree or cause it to break in the wind; and good seed production at an early age so that seed for tree nurseries is produced quickly.

52

And we want wood that is about normal for the species, to fit mill equipment and processing procedures—unless especially heavy or light wood is required for a certain product—so as to keep up the quality of the finished product. Last, but far from least, we want trees with the ability to transmit all the good traits to offspring.

In certain parts of the South, trees are "worked" for turpentine and rosin production before they are cut for pulpwood or saw logs so that yield of the sticky pitch becomes an important trait, also.

One important disease of southern pines is a rust canker of stem and branches. Spores from infected oak leaves settle on new growth of pine seedlings and small trees and cause disfiguring cankers. If the infection is on the trunk, the tree may die; if it is on branches near the trunk, it may grow into the trunk. Spores from infected pine reinfect new oak leaves.

In tree nurseries, the seedling can be sprayed and protected from infection. No controls are available for planted stands. Eradication of oaks near pine stands is hardly feasible with 20 or more species and wide distribution of each. Sprays can't cover all susceptible tissue and, besides, they are very costly.

Genetic control of rust seems the only feasible method. Fortunately, resistant trees occur within slash and loblolly pine species. This means hybrids between species aren't necessary to create resistant types.

In some forest stands, certain individual trees will grow 20 years or more without becoming infected. Other trees nearby may be heavily infected or killed.

Cross-pollination of trees that seemed to be resistant has resulted in offspring relatively free of rust while other families of trees in the same test area are 95 percent infected.

The tree breeder searches out the seemingly resistant trees, but he would like them to have fast growth rate and good form also. This requirement complicates his work, but it is worth it. Newly created strains of trees survive transplanting better, grow faster, and are more disease resistant. Thus, the cumulative effect of these good traits nearly doubles production per acre.

Furthermore, there is no loss in quality—often there may be an increase. Fast growth does not mean poor quality.

Breeding for disease resistance has the most effect on volume growth in areas where losses are greatest. This area stretches across the South from South Carolina to Louisiana, the heart of the southern pine region. Losses are lighter north of the band—northern Georgia, Alabama, and Mississippi—and south of it, southern Georgia, Alabama, and Mississippi.

Breeding for resistance seems to be promising for other diseases, such as root rots and bark beetles. Tree insect and disease specialists are working with foresters and tree breeders to control these enemies.

If our scientists keep on guessing right, we will always have plenty of those brown bags for your supermarket groceries.

The Insect Destroyer—
Portrait of a Scientist

MARSHALL GALL

. . . .

Back in the 1930's, when flies had little to fear except flypaper, a young entomologist in the U.S. Department of Agriculture began working out a new theory of insect control—a theory that was to earn him first ridicule, then worldwide acclaim.

At the time, Edward F. Knipling did not consider himself a theorist, really. He was just looking for a better way to destroy insects.

His job at USDA called for controlling screw-worms and other livestock pests on the Nation's cattle ranges.

This was a frustrating assignment. Arsenic, mercury, phenolic dips, and other poisons were available at the time, but these sometimes killed animals as well as insects. Furthermore, insects had on their side the advantage of tremendous reproductive capacity. Consider the ordinary house fly, for example: One pair can produce nearly 200 billion *billion* offspring during the course of a summer.

This capacity for reproduction, it seemed to Knipling, lies at the heart of many major insect control problems. Killing every insect within reach doesn't solve the problem—not if a few insects remain out of reach and continue to multiply. If an insect's reproductive capacity could be sabotaged—if an entire population of insects could be made infertile—the problem of controlling that insect would be solved once and for all.

These musings led to development of the sterility principle of insect con-

trol, one of the most original scientific ideas of this century.

Briefly, the sterile-insect principle involves raising insects in captivity, sterilizing them, and releasing them into the environment in overwhelming numbers. Some of the sterilized males mate with wild females. The resulting eggs are infertile, and the insect's population dwindles.

Knipling's early efforts to win support for his scheme were largely unsuccessful. The thought of introducing birth control to the insect world was too farfetched for most scientists to accept. Still, a few loyal colleagues thought he had something—among them, R. C. Bushland, another USDA entomologist, whose contributions to the sterility principle Knipling is very quick to credit.

The first thing the scientists had to do was figure out a way to sterilize insects. Other scientists had sterilized certain insects with X-rays. Could the feat be duplicated on a large scale? An Army hospital made its X-ray facilities available for the project; Knipling's men spent weekends and holidays at the hospital, exposing insects to the rays and noting the effects. Later, an obsolete cobalt-60 gamma ray source was acquired from the Atomic Energy Commission. This helped, but the work still progressed slowly.

∴   ∴   ∴

MARSHALL GALL *is a Writer in the Division of Information, Agricultural Research Service.*

54

Meanwhile, Knipling's reputation was advancing on the basis of other efforts. In 1938, he demonstrated that treating an animal internally could destroy external parasites. During World War II, he directed a USDA entomology laboratory at Orlando, Fla., where work was being done to furnish the Armed Forces with insect and disease control measures.

From this laboratory came louse powders used by grateful GI's all over the world, as well as insect and disease preventatives that were to be adopted by health agencies throughout the world.

Knipling could have put aside his "crackpot" scheme and settled back to enjoy the fruits of his other successes. But this son of an immigrant Texas farmer was not accustomed to taking the easy way. As a child, he worked in his father's fields, sometimes picking insects off from plants by hand in order to save a crop. In college, he mowed lawns, waited on tables, and studied.

To go with talent and willingness to work, he exhibited a wide stubborn streak; it was this quality that kept the sterile-insect principle alive. As his scientific reputation spread and his authority as a research administrator grew, he was able to channel more and more research effort toward perfecting the sterility technique. In 1953, he was named director of all USDA entomology research. Now he was in a position to put his pet theory to the test.

Screw-worms were to be the first victims of the sterility eradication technique. The screw-worm is the larva of a large fly. The fly lays its eggs in barbed wire cuts or other small wounds of livestock. When the larvae hatch, they burrow into the flesh of the animal. If undeterred, screw-worms can kill a full-grown steer in 10 days.

Screw-worm flies were raised in captivity and sterilized. The first field test took place on Sanibel, a small island off the coast of Florida, in 1953. It was successful, but proof of eradication could not be demonstrated because the island quickly became reinfested by flies from the nearby Florida coast.

In 1954, the technique was tried again, this time on the 170-square mile island of Curaçao, which is located far enough out in the Caribbean so that no outside screw-worm flies could possibly reach it. The screw-worm was eradicated from Curaçao within less than 6 weeks.

The next step was a large-scale program in 1957–58 to eradicate the screw-worm from the Southeastern United States, sponsored by USDA, the Florida Livestock Board, and other organizations. During the program, more than $2\frac{3}{4}$ billion sterile flies were released from airplanes. These flies completed the race-suicide scheme over an 80,000-square mile area within 18 months.

A few years later, similar results were achieved in a screw-worm eradication program in the Southwest.

Knipling's project, 20 years in the making, was a success.

Now in his fifties, the soft-spoken research director has amassed a closetful of scientific awards and citations, including the $10,000 Rockefeller Public Service Award, one of the highest honors accorded Government employees, and the $10,000 Hoblitzelle Award for achievement in agricultural science, shared with collaborator Bushland. In 1966, he was elected to the National Academy of Sciences, a limited-membership group consisting of the top scientists in the country.

But Knipling continues to sprout new ideas upon the subject of insect control.

One of the shortcomings of the sterile-insect technique right now is that insects must be raised in captivity, he points out. And this creates nursery problems.

The screw-worm fly, for instance, normally lays her eggs in open wounds. To get her to lay eggs in captivity, researchers had to duplicate an open wound on a mammoth scale. They did this by heating up a ground meat mixture to the body temperature of livestock.

But the principle of sterility can probably be used against insects in

Trail-blazing Entomologist Edward F. Knipling with jar of moths used in research.

ways other than by releasing sterile males, Knipling believes. For example, a sterilizing agent might be mixed with an insect attractant and broadcast throughout an infested area. Insects would be drawn by the attractant and would be sterilized upon eating or touching the sterilizing agent. Selective attractants that appeal to specific insects would have to be used in order to avoid sterilizing nontarget species.

But why all this bother? If you are going to spread poison, why not spread something that will kill rather than sterilize?

"Look at it this way," Knipling says. "If 90 percent of a population of 1,000 pests in a given area are killed, 100 will remain to reproduce. If 90 percent are sterilized, the 900 which are sterilized cannot reproduce. So far, it's a draw. But remember, the sterilized insects are as sexually active as ever

and are competing with the unsterilized individuals for the attentions of the opposite sex. Under such circumstances, we would expect only 10 individuals to reproduce. This brings our efficiency up to 99 percent for the sterility technique."

Another promising variation of the sterility technique may be to use it in combination with pesticides, Knipling says. To illustrate, he cites a fruit fly eradication program carried out by his researchers on the island of Guam. In 1963, the island was struck by a devastating typhoon. Breadfruit trees and other fruit fly breeding places were destroyed, and the fly population fell sharply. Knipling's men immediately began releasing sterile flies. In a short time, and at modest cost, the fruit fly was eradicated from the island.

"We can do the same thing with pesticides," Knipling contends: "Use them to get the population down to a minimum, then release sterile insects to eradicate." Pesticides achieve peak efficiency when they are used against large insect populations, because the same amount of pesticide must be applied to an area whether it contains a thousand insects or a million. The sterility technique, on the other hand, is most efficient against small populations because fewer sterile insects are needed. Thus, by reducing an insect population with pesticides, then releasing sterile insects to eradicate the remaining individuals, entomologists would be making the most efficient use of both techniques.

Whatever the innovations, it appears certain that Knipling's sterility technique is here to stay. Besides making insect eradication or suppression possible, it has other advantages over conventional methods of insect control. It is selective, it leaves no harmful residues to accumulate in the environment, and it solves the problem of immunity—the tendency of insects to build up resistance to pesticides.

Some insects are probably more vulnerable than others, but research thus far indicates that the sterility technique will have broad application. Boll weevils, codling moths, and various fruit flies seem likely candidates for sterility treatment.

The technique has one important limitation, however: Some insects, particularly biting ones, should not be released into the environment because they could do considerable harm themselves before their sterility brought about eradication. In Burma, entomologists used the sterility technique to eradicate a disease-carrying mosquito from one village—but they released only sterile males, and the male of the species does not bite. In contrast, plans to use the sterility technique against tsetse flies in Africa are proceeding with caution; both sexes of this species bite. Scientists will try to lower the population by some other means, then use sterile flies just long enough to finish the eradication job.

Theoretically at least, anything that breeds can be sterilized—and wiped out. Biologists are exploring the sterility principle as a means of eradicating unwanted animals—rats, for example. Furthermore, the principle could be used to manage as well as to eradicate animal populations. Sometimes deer and other desirable wildlife produce more offspring than the available food supply can support. In such cases, induced sterility would be one way of balancing population and food supply.

To many, perpetuation of life is something not to be tampered with, yet population control on this crowded planet seems destined to become commonplace among humans as well as animals if we are to avoid widespread starvation. In the animal world, Knipling asserts, sterilization is infinitely more humane than poisoning, and it is more efficient.

Knipling is a tall, slim man with a craggy face and intent blue-grey eyes. He is well known internationally among scientists and has served on national and international committees, but he looks more like a cowboy than the popular conception of an egghead scientist. He does spend a good deal of his time out of doors, usually hunting or fishing.

He doesn't do anything by halves. A couple of years ago, an associate got him interested in bowling as a wintertime substitute for fishing. Knipling didn't just bowl—he analyzed his game, came up with his own ideas on improving it, and studied the techniques of bowling exhaustively. Within a short time, he was bowling like a professional.

The same Knipling thoroughness goes into hunting, which he does with bow and arrow. Several years ago, he got a wild turkey—a wily creature most hunters can't hit with a shotgun.

Knipling and his wife Phoebe enjoy vacations at their mountain cabin in Virginia—when they get time. Phoebe, who like her husband has a Ph. D. degree from Iowa State, is a supervisor of science teaching in the Arlington, Va., public school system. They have five grown children.

Tailoring Vegetable Crops to Order

THOMAS W. WHITAKER, RAYMON E. WEBB, *and*
WILLIAM J. ZAUMEYER

. . . .

Vegetable crops have been and continue to be enormous users of hand labor. Until recently, these crops have resisted the trend toward mechanization. Although some of the cultural, postharvest, and marketing practices of vegetable growers are among the most modern in present-day agriculture, vegetable thinning and harvesting operations do not differ essentially from those used in the 1920's and 1930's.

This picture is now commencing to change, and change rapidly. The scarcity and cost of hand labor are creating pressures that have accelerated the trend toward mechanization in vegetable production. There seems little doubt that those vegetable crops produced in large volume will soon be fully mechanized. The processing tomato in California is a good example of a crop where the harvest has been almost completely mechanized within a period of less than 10 years. Rapid progress in mechanical harvesting of this crop must be credited to the close cooperation of plant breeder and mechanical engineer.

Designing plants for complete mechanization has presented the plant breeder with a challenging array of new and exciting problems. The problems of each crop demand somewhat different solutions.

In lettuce, for example, it may not be necessary to alter present-day varieties drastically to make them suitable for mechanization, although varieties with an upright frame and with the lower leaves a half inch to an inch above the soil are likely to be preferred to those having leaves flush with the soil. Lettuce is self-pollinated, and usually the percentage of outcrossing is low. Therefore, we should expect great genetic uniformity in this crop, and generally this is found.

If we assume that the commonly used varieties of lettuce are genetically uniform, further uniformity in growth and development must come from improved cultural practices.

In other words, the grower must create a more favorable environment for planting, germination, and development of the plant.

Proper bed design and precision planting of high-quality seed are essential for mechanization. Usually in conventional planting, an excess of seed is used, and the plants are hand thinned to the desired spacing. This procedure is wasteful of seed and uses costly hand labor.

But an even more serious defect of overplanting is that it favors uneven

.·.   .·.   .·.

THOMAS W. WHITAKER *is Research Geneticist with the Vegetables and Ornamentals Research Branch, Agricultural Research Service, at La Jolla, Calif.*

RAYMON E. WEBB *and* WILLIAM J. ZAUMEYER *are Research Plant Pathologists, also with the Vegetables and Ornamentals Research Branch, at Beltsville, Md.*

58

Lettuce harvesters developed by University of Arizona *top* and University of California *below*. California harvester, shown mounted on trailer, picks at rate of 1½ heads of lettuce a second. Paddle wheel under harvester feels individual heads to determine if they're firm enough to harvest. Paddle "fingers" grasp firm heads, and knife automatically cuts them. Then fingers lift head to conveyor for packing.

plant growth, because of crowding, competition, and mechanical injury to the young seedlings from which they never completely recover.

The ideal is to plant to a stand, that is, one seed, one mature lettuce plant at the desired spacing.

Some recent research has pointed out avenues for achieving this goal. The first step is to plant high-density seed, fractionated by air and treated with chemicals to promote germination. Kinetin is the chemical commonly used to treat the seed. Next the seed is dried and prepared for precision planting by embedding a single seed in a cone or disk with a material which prevents the soil from crusting such as vermiculite. As an alternative, a single seed can be pasted at regular intervals to a water-soluble tape, and when planted, covered with an anticrustant material.

After the seed is planted, sprinkler irrigation to provide a uniform source of soil moisture promotes even germination. Besides, sprinkler irrigation provides better aeration, tends to reduce soil temperature, and—vitally important in the arid Southwest— leaches salt from near the soil surface where the seed is planted.

Planting the exact amount of seed for a perfect stand has not yet been perfected. Planting slightly more seed than is necessary for a perfect stand permits the use of a mechanical thinner to establish the desired stand of plants. Either the fixed-space type blocker or those machines with a selective device could be used. At harvest, uniform development of the plant should permit use of a simple combined harvester employing the "once over" harvest principle or the more elaborate machine with a selective device for harvesting the firm heads in a planting.

At this stage of mechanization, skills of the plant breeder are needed. Varieties that are highly uniform under sharply dissimilar environments will be in demand or will be rapidly developed through plant breeding methods. Breeders have available material to quickly produce varieties which are more adaptable to mechanical harvesting. Such varieties, in addition to being exceedingly uniform in growth rate, size, and shape, will have an upright erect growth with the oldest or "frame" leaves slightly above the soil level.

Beans have a new and different set of problems. Production of snap beans and lima beans is an operation that has been successfully mechanized for years. Hence, retailoring the plant is not nearly so critical as the development of modern varieties with disease resistance and specific horticultural characters such as long, slender, dark, tender, green or wax pods. As an example, thousands of acres of rich farmland in the Columbia River Basin of Washington could be profitably used for snap bean production except for the ravages of curly top, a virus disease spread by the beet leafhopper. Because of an ideal environment such as hot, dry conditions, the leafhoppers thrive and are continuously present in the region.

Until recently, the efforts of plant breeders and plant pathologists to control the disease in varieties acceptable to the processor have been futile. Suddenly a breakthrough occurred; breeders were able to combine resistance with pod color and quality desired by processors. As a result, we can confidently predict that within a short period, varieties of snap beans resistant to curly top and attractive to the processor will be available. This chain of events could produce a new and important processing and canning industry for the region's economy.

Again in the Columbia River Basin, fusarium root rot of beans, a fungus disease, is prevalent in the soil and frequently responsible for severe crop losses, especially when beans are grown continuously on the same land. Prolonged search for a source of resistance culminated in discovery of a wild bean from Mexico resistant to the disease. Discovery of this bean by one of the U.S. Department of Agriculture's plant explorers has opened the way for plant breeders to make rapid progress in producing varieties with good-quality characters, resistant not only to fusarium root rot, but to other diseases as well.

A completely different approach is needed to cope with white mold, a fungus disease of beans. This disease is chronic in the Northeastern United States and thrives under high moisture conditions. An extended search over the past 20 years has failed to turn up a source of resistance to white mold.

Confronted with this problem, the plant breeder has turned to developing plants that avoid the disease as the most practical means of control. To reach this objective, the breeder must modify the plant structure by developing plants with fewer leaves and branches which still retain high productivity. Fewer leaves permit better aeration of the plant, creating conditions unfavorable for fungus growth.

Plants with a minimum of foliage and intertwining branches are more easily harvested by machines than those with moderate or excessive foliage. Thus, varieties with less foliage have the added bonus of being better suited to mechanical harvesting than present-day varieties.

Problems of the lima bean breeder are not radically different from those found in snap beans. At present, there are lima varieties with excellent quality, resistant to several important diseases, and well adapted to mechanical harvesting. But they lack other characteristics that would make them ideally adapted to efficient mechanization.

For instance, seed of newly developed varieties should germinate rapidly and evenly in cool, wet soils and should be resistant to various root-rotting organisms. The plants must have a vigorous, deep-penetrating root system, with a sturdy frame, bearing short, erect, pod-bearing branches, that develop below the leaves. Plants designed to these specifications provide cool, moist conditions favorable for the best pod development during hot, dry weather. Other refinements need to be added, such as even pod maturity, pods easily opened when harvested, and seeds with bright, dark green color.

Another vegetable crop, spinach, has been specifically redesigned for complete mechanization within the span of a few years. Just 12 years ago, the best that could be offered growers were disease-susceptible, relatively small-leafed, hand-harvested varieties with semierect stature. Furthermore, spinach production in all areas of the country was extremely hazardous because of downy mildew, a fungus disease. Yields of susceptible varieties, even in the absence of disease, rarely exceeded 4 tons per acre. Harvesting by hand was slow, backbreaking work. The best workers could harvest only a maximum of a ton of spinach in a 10-hour day.

Today, due to the successes of plant breeders, growers can choose from an array of highly uniform, vigorous, upright-growing, large-leafed, mildew-resistant, high-quality spinach hybrids and varieties that can be harvested by machine. Also, hybrids and varieties of different maturity groups have been developed that are adapted to fall, winter, spring, and summer production areas. Smooth, semisavoy, or full-savoy leaf types have been designed for specific uses as canning, freezing (including prepared foods), and the fresh market.

In most areas a consistently high rate of crop production is assured if the grower uses the newer hybrids and modern varieties, because they are resistant to downy mildew. Yields over 8 tons per acre of high-quality spinach are normally anticipated. One man on a machine can harvest an average of 8 tons an hour from fields planted with modern erect-growing, highly uniform hybrids and varieties. As a result, about 98 percent of the spinach acreage in the United States is planted to newer hybrids and varieties, and approximately 95 percent of all spinach is harvested by machine.

The new spinach hybrids and varieties were developed by design. The first step was taken by P. G. Smith of the University of California at Davis. After a long search, he found resistance to downy mildew in a wild spinach

A spinach harvester.

from Iran, designated P.I. 140467. In 1949, H. A. Jones of USDA at Beltsville, Md., obtained seed of progenies segregating for resistance to downy mildew from Smith. From this source, Jones commenced the development of mildew-resistant spinach of both smooth- and savoy-leaf types, primarily for southern production areas. He selected upright-growing, large-leaf, high-quality types with a small stem-to-leaf ratio from among mildew-resistant progenies. The seeds of these improved types were increased for growers to use as new varieties.

During the course of these investigations, Jones recognized the potential of hybrids as well as improved varieties. He was impressed with the erect, highly uniform, vigorous growth of the hybrids compared to their parents. In a final step, Jones developed a method for producing hybrid spinach seed.

The method of hybrid seed production is wonderfully simple. Spinach is a dioecious species, that is, about 50 percent of the plants in a population bear male flowers and the other 50 percent, female (seed) flowers. It is wind pollinated and cross pollinated. The male and female parents are chosen; the female (seed) parent is planted at double the normal seeding

rate in blocks of four to eight rows. The male parent is planted at the normal seeding rate in one or two rows adjacent to the seed parent block.

When male plants in the seed parent block commence to bolt (develop flower stalks), they are removed from the field. Roughly 50 percent of the plants in the seed block are removed. Thus, the male parent rows produce the pollen for fertilization of the females in the seed parent block. Seed is harvested from the female plants in the seed block, and this seed when planted produces the hybrid plants.

Making use of mildew resistance and selection for improved quality characters, Jones introduced Early Hybrid No. 7, a semisavoy type. At present, this is the most widely grown variety in the Eastern United States and in the winter-producing areas of Texas. He also produced Early Hybrid Nos. 424 and 425—flat-leaf types, widely grown in the Western States. As this program progressed, such excellent varieties as Dixie Market, Dixie Savoy, and Savoy Hybrid 612 were made available to growers. These varieties are savoy-leafed, erect-growing, fresh-market types, capable of being harvested by machines, and designed for specific uses.

Planned Parenthood for Livestock

MAX B. HEPPNER

. . . .

Planned parenthood for livestock is an ancient and widespread practice—if you're willing to include poultry as livestock.

Records from the beginning of history point out that Chinese farmers saved fertilized chicken eggs, and they brooded them out simultaneously when convenient. Poultry farmers have done this ever since then, in order to have a whole group of baby chicks on hand when labor, space, and prices are most favorable.

If man and large animals also laid large eggs, there would be no need for contraceptive pills. Women would get babies only when they were ready to hatch people eggs. Sheep producers would have "spring lamb" available throughout the year by periodically hatching sheep eggs. And cattle producers could regulate and standardize calf raising much the same way.

However, the one-celled eggs that people, cattle, and sheep do produce remain inside the mother's body for development. To apply planned parenthood, a way had to be found to reach inside the mother to regulate egg production.

About 1935, scientists were first starting to clarify which of the numerous hormones that control reproduction determines when eggs are produced. Evidence pointed to progesterone, the hormone secreted by the corpus luteum, a small temporary gland growing on the ovary.

The corpus luteum is formed after an egg is ovulated (sent into the reproductive tract). If no pregnancy results, the gland shrivels, progesterone production stops, and the next egg is released. If pregnancy does result, the corpus luteum stays alive in most species and keeps new eggs from forming until it finally disappears after the young are born.

Dr. Hans Selye of McGill University, working with laboratory rats, was the first to show that injected doses of progesterone can keep an egg from being ovulated after the corpus luteum quits. This was the first step toward a practical program of planned parenthood.

Further progress, however, was slow. At the time of Selye's discovery, the first contraceptive pills were still 24 years away, and William Hansel, who eventually worked on applying their use to livestock, was still a teenager in high school.

The next major step forward came only in 1948, when Dr. Lester E. Casida and Dr. Ray H. Dutt, livestock researchers at the University of Wisconsin, adapted the findings on laboratory animals to sheep.

They found a whole flock of ewes would ovulate more or less simultaneously when injected with 10 milligrams of progesterone during the first 14

∴ ∴ ∴

MAX B. HEPPNER *is a Public Information Officer in the Information Division, Agricultural Research Service, assigned to reporting current progress in Federal livestock research programs.*

days of the normal sexual cycle. And, as the two explained to a group of farmers shortly after their discovery, ewes so treated would deliver their lambs fairly close together, thereby simplifying flock management problems.

Farmers, however, shrugged their shoulders when they heard the details. To inject ewes on the ranch, they would have to round up their flock every day for 2 weeks. Worse yet, the crops produced would number only about 70 lambs per hundred ewes, compared to the normal lambing rate of about 90 lambs per hundred ewes.

These objections were hard to overcome. Livestock researchers did find ways to make the effect of a single progesterone injection last longer, so that a herd to be synchronized had to be treated only twice. But the work of injecting hormones remained tedious, and the conception rate of treated animals stayed low.

Researchers in human medicine, however, continued to look for a practical application of progesterone to prevent ovulation. They set their sights on a pill to do the job, because women would be even less anxious than farmers to make daily injections, since they—not some animal—would have to be jabbed with the needle.

Progesterone pills, however, were failures. They were no harder to make than aspirin, but when tested on animals, enzymes in the liver attacked and inactivated the progesterone. A synthetic variation of the progesterone molecule was needed to give it "handles" with which to fend off liver enzymes.

Because the problem was complex, many researchers came into the field. They included such various experts as medical and veterinary doctors, chemists, biochemists, nutritionists, immunologists, radiologists, psychologists, physiologists of all kinds, hormone specialists, and scientists studying the effect of weather on the body.

Principals in this massive research effort met in 1959 to discuss fast-breaking discoveries, under sponsorship of the Worcester Foundation, a leader in the field. The drug repeatedly mentioned as a likely solution to the problem was a compound already in use to treat pregnancy disorders in women. This drug is called MAP, an acronym derived from the chemical name medroxy-progesterone acetate, with the order of the initials changed to the way that the drug's components appear in a more precise chemical description.

When Dr. Gregory Pincus, director of the Worcester Foundation, summed up the promising findings on MAP, few animal physiologists in the audience saw much in it for them. Although MAP might work in humans, livestock specialists thought it wouldn't be likely to work in cattle and sheep because large colonies of microbes housed in their gigantic first stomach denature drugs of this type on contact.

One scientist in the audience, however, disagreed with the pessimism about applying the contraceptive pill to livestock. He was William Hansel, who by then had finished high school, helped liberate Europe in World War II, and completed his doctorate in reproductive physiology of livestock at Cornell University.

Immediately after hearing Pincus' praise for MAP, Dr. Hansel made arrangements to feed this drug to 32 Hereford cattle and watch for response in their mating behavior. Females of most animals, including cattle, resist mating while progesterone is secreted. But when the progesterone level in the blood falls off, this inhibiting effect is removed. The ensuing mating period, which lasts only a day or two, is called estrus. Since the same hormone, progesterone, inhibits both ovulation and estrus, absence of mating behavior by cows indicates to the researcher that a synthetic progesterone treatment is working.

Hansel found that none of the cows on trial showed any signs of estrus while MAP treatment continued; but within 5 days after MAP was withdrawn, 28 of his 32 cows had ovulated. So, in 1960, Hansel was able to announce that MAP not only kept cows from ovulating while it was applied in the feed, it also effectively synchronized ovulation after withdrawal—all this apparently unimpeded by the activity of microbes in cattle stomachs.

This advance wasn't all roses. Hansel relates wryly that on the days when groups of cows came into estrus, it almost invariably rained.

Therefore, he got thoroughly soaked whenever he artificially inseminated the cows, a job which can't be delayed after estrus starts.

Hansel had bigger problems than discomfort, however. Only a quarter of the cows he inseminated after MAP treatment became pregnant in his first trial. He suspected that the dosage and length of treatment, which he had determined only by shrewd guesswork, needed to be refined. With help from the Upjohn Co., manufacturer of MAP, Hansel arrived at a more nearly perfect prescription, which allowed cows to get pregnant more readily than injections with natural progesterone. Although results varied from herd to herd, Hansel estimates that by 1966 the calf crop, in experiments throughout the country, was only 10 to 15 percent lower in synchronized than in nonsynchronized herds.

At that point, the Upjohn Co. felt the time had come to put planned parenthood for livestock to its most crucial test—a trial on the market. In December 1965, the company obtained the necessary Government clearances to sell Repromix, a feed additive containing MAP, to be mixed at the rate of 0.006 ounce per day into the grain ration of cows.

When asked how a western rancher can afford to provide this treatment even though the conception rate of cows might drop as a result, Hansel refers the question to another noted specialist in the field, Upjohn scientist Dr. Robert G. Zimbelman, who knows the rancher's viewpoint since he himself was raised on a Colorado farm.

"Well," Zimbelman replies, "the problem doesn't look as bad in practice as it does in the lab. Let us apply our experimental results with MAP in 1960 and 1961 to two imaginary beef herds, one with 100 cows receiving treated feed and the other with 100 cows fed normally."

Zimbelman explains that after one attempt at breeding, 47 of the treated cows would be pregnant, compared with 69 of the untreated ones. But since most ranchers using artificial insemination don't stop at one breeding, there would be a second opportunity for both herds. Nonpregnant treated cows would go through one complete sexual cycle together and be ready for rebreeding 18 to 26 days after MAP treatment had originally stopped.

As a result of the second insemination, 41 additional treated cows would conceive, compared to 20 additional untreated cows, so that the cumulative conception score of treated to untreated cows would be almost equal: 88 to 89. Apparently, interference with normal conception due to MAP treatment wears off during the period between inseminations, even though the cows remain fairly well synchronized.

After 9 months of gestation, the first group of MAP-treated cows to be inseminated successfully would deliver 47 calves spaced close together, and the second group of cows would deliver 41 calves close together. By contrast, the untreated cows would have their calves by ones or twos throughout a lengthy calving season.

Returns from raising the calf of a synchronized mother are considerably higher than the $4, or so, that it costs to treat a cow for a season, Zimbelman says. Principally, these returns come from lower labor requirements at breeding and the opportunity to offer two uniform groups of calves for sale early in the marketing season.

Beyond that, planned parenthood helps the small rancher find good bulls. Ordinarily the rancher has to breed his cows to his own bulls, which are often of mediocre genetic background because top-rated bulls are expensive to own.

Generally, he can't take advantage of semen from top bulls available through artificial breeding organizations because it is downright impossible to watch for estrus in 60 to 100 cows running about on 500 to 1,000 sparsely fenced acres. Breeding without regard to estrus would result in a conception rate close to zero.

But if the rancher feeds MAP, the entire cowherd will come into estrus within 3 or 4 days. When the MAP treatment is over, the rancher can round up his herd, breed it artificially in short order, and release it back to the range. With a second roundup and breeding 2 to 3 weeks later, he can count on mating most of his cows to first-class bulls.

The sheep breeder using planned parenthood for his livestock stands to benefit even more than the cattleman.

At present, sheep breeding is severely restricted because ewes generally mate only during late summer and autumn, so that practically all lambs come in late winter and spring. Since a ewe remains pregnant less than 5 months before she delivers, however, she could theoretically produce two lamb crops per year—if a way could be found around her restricted mating behavior.

In 1945, Dr. Harold H. Cole, reproductive physiologist with the University of California at Davis, showed that gonadotrophic hormones (a group that stimulates growth of reproductive tissues) could bring on estrus in ewes outside the normal breeding season. In early trials, however, researchers faced a familiar problem: Only about 5 or 10 percent of the treated ewes became pregnant after being bred.

Additional research helped improve ewe fertility. Leaders in this work, such as Dr. Clarence V. Hulet of USDA's Agricultural Research Service, achieved 50 to 60 percent pregnancy in 1966.

But the procedure, as yet, is complex. Ewes get progesterone in the feed for 14 days to condition their reproductive systems, with an injection of estrogen (a female hormone) at the start of the feeding period. Then, before breeding, they receive an injection of an ovulating hormone—which must be repeated at the start of the next sexual cycle for the large number that do not get pregnant at the first insemination.

One way around this complex ad-

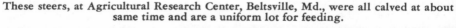

These steers, at Agricultural Research Center, Beltsville, Md., were all calved at about same time and are a uniform lot for feeding.

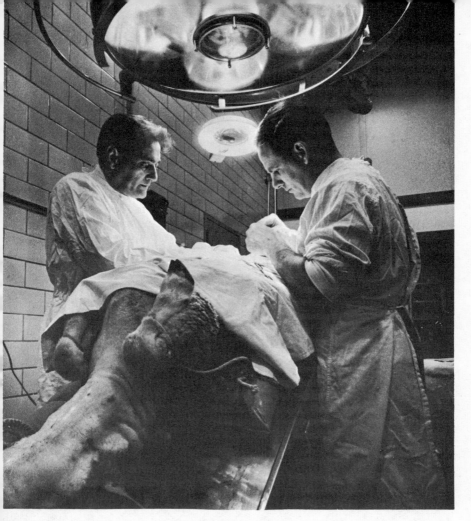

Physiologist William Hansel *left* of Cornell University surgically prepares sheep for sampling blood as it leaves ovary. Analyses for hormones in these blood samples provide information leading to better ways for regulating estrous cycle.

ministration of hormones is to genetically select a breed of sheep that will mate out of season. Such a breed, called Morlam, is under development by Dr. Clair E. Terrill at the research center of the Agricultural Research Service in Beltsville, Md. The breed is derived from mavericks in several existing breeds of sheep that have been showing the ability to mate out of season naturally.

In the end, sheep breeders hope to get two lamb crops per year from their ewes by a combination of breeding and hormone treatments. At present, however, they are shooting for an intermediate goal of three pregnancies every 2 years—a system permitting more time for rebreeding a ewe after a previous pregnancy. Dr. Hulet knows of farms getting 200 lambs per hundred ewes per year, compared to the current national average of 92.

In the near future, he expects to hear of flocks having 250 to 300 lambs per hundred ewes.

Asked to evaluate current progress with planned parenthood for livestock, Hansel of Cornell—who helped bring the idea to reality—points with some satisfaction to the progress made in expanded lamb crops and the advances toward better planning and practical use of artificial insemination in both cattle and sheep.

"However," Hansel cautions, "practical use of hormones to regulate egg production is still limited to a few herds of cows and ewes, and that is not surprising. Drug costs have to come down, pregnancy rate of treated animals has to come up, and problems in herd management must be overcome before we can expect really widespread use of estrus-control drugs."

To bring down costs, researchers are now testing compounds up to 100 times more potent than MAP that can be administered in lower doses. They are also screening drugs for minimal interference with pregnancy rate. One, called MATCH for short, shows excellent promise for swine—which cannot be effectively treated with MAP—but unfortunately, MATCH is not effective for cattle and sheep.

To simplify management problems,

scientists have devised a soft sponge that can be impregnated with a hormone and inserted into the vagina of animals to be treated. Already perfected for sheep, the sponge releases the drug slowly and steadily, holding back estrus and ovulation long enough to synchronize a flock. To stop the treatment and bring on estrus, the sponge is pulled out by a drawstring attached to it. Although this method requires two roundups on the range, it assures correct dosing and doesn't require changes in the feeding program.

Hansel believes that despite development of improved synthetic hormones, the best control over ovulation and pregnancy will eventually be achieved by natural progesterone.

He expects that future treatments will extend the normal life of the corpus luteum, so that it will continue secreting progesterone long enough to achieve planned parenthood without the lowered conception rates that accompany treatments with progesterone substitutes.

Ewes that were part of foundation stock for new USDA-developed Morlam sheep strain which approaches year-round fertility.

Lasers and Moles Make
a Pipe Dream Come True

JAMES L. FOUSS *and* RONALD C. REEVE

. . . .

The laser and a mole have teamed up with flexible plastic pipe to cut food costs. This unusual combination works largely underground, but it's very much on the level.

A down-to-earth problem was involved—how to reduce the expense of draining farmland and thus cut food production costs. Agricultural research came up with the answer.

That discovery of the space age, the laser, was put to work down on the farm. This was accomplished by Agricultural Research Service engineers working cooperatively with Ohio State University.

Here's how the system goes—laser, mole, and flexible pipe tubing:

A laser beam is projected to automatically control the digging depth of a mole plow, which is pulled by a large crawler tractor. A torpedo-shaped object—the "mole"—attached to a narrow vertical shank, forms an underground channel (without digging a trench) as it is drawn through the soil. An attachment on the mole plow feeds a continuous length of flexible plastic drain tubing into the ground at a consistent level controlled by the laser beam. As the tubing goes down, so too do farm drainage costs and food costs as well.

Before this intriguing development, tile drainage installation and materials had changed little from the middle 1800's. Laying short segments of drain-tile end-to-end in a trench is still the common method of field drainage.

Mechanical trenching machines have been used since the early 1900's to replace hand excavation. Trenching machines are slow and have been changed little, but laborsaving methods have been developed for handling and placing the tile. Despite these improvements, installation costs remain relatively high.

Introduction of coilable, corrugated-wall plastic drain tubing during the mid-1960's permitted a greater reduction in labor requirements. The tonnage of drainage materials that needs to be handled has also been drastically cut. A 300-foot coil of 4-inch diameter corrugated plastic drainpipe weighs about 80 pounds and can be handled by one man. By comparison, 300 feet of clay or concrete draintile weighs slightly more than a ton.

Corrugations in the wall of the plastic drain give the pipe its needed strength and provide longitudinal flexibility, making it coilable and easy to handle. Compared to smooth-walled plastic pipe, the corrugated tube is much lighter and lower in cost.

Corrugated plastic pipe can be rapidly installed with newly developed

∴ ∴ ∴

JAMES L. FOUSS *is Agricultural Engineer, Soil and Water Conservation Research Division, Agricultural Research Service.*

RONALD C. REEVE *is Investigations Leader in the Soil and Water Conservation Research Division.*

They work cooperatively with Ohio State University at Columbus.

69

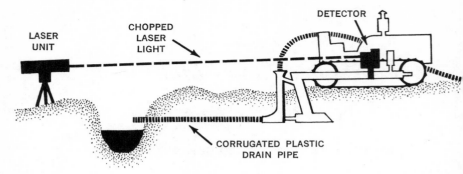

Basic elements of laser-controlled system for laying drainpipe. Laser projector is set up on tripod directly in front or behind mole plow.

mole plow drainage equipment pulled by a tractor. A tube-feeding attachment to the plow eliminates the time-consuming task of ditch excavation and backfilling required in conventional tile drainage. The plastic drainpipe can be installed at speeds up to 125 feet a minute with this machine. Under many field conditions, at least 2,000 feet of corrugated plastic drain can be put in per hour. This compares with about 4 hours needed to install the same amount of draintile with a conventional trenching machine.

To function properly, subsurface drains must be laid on a uniform slope or grade. The high-speed equipment for installing plastic drainpipe requires more accurate and responsive grade control devices than those presently used on trenching machines. Conventional line-of-sight grade control methods require continual resetting of many sight-bar stakes or the stretching of gradeline reference wires—time-consuming operations which involve high labor costs.

With the laser system, aiming the laser beam is all that's needed to establish the grading guideline reference. An electronic sensor on the machine receives the laser light and automatically controls the hydraulic mechanism which regulates the installation depth. Although the automatic system was developed especially for high-speed equipment, it can be used equally well on low-speed machinery.

The new system uses a low-power

gas laser that emits a small nondivergent beam of light. The beam projection unit is tripod mounted, lightweight, and portable. It is battery-powered for field use. The laser beam is projected from a remote location in the field, toward the drainage machine, on a line parallel to the slope desired for laying the drainpipe.

The machine-mounted electronic sensor includes phototubes for receiving the laser beam.

During the machine's forward motion, the automatic system continuously keeps the electronic sensor unit at an elevation so that the laser beam is centered on the phototubes. When the machine's digging depth varies from that established by the laser beam reference, the phototubes put out a signal. This causes the digging depth to be automatically adjusted by a hydraulic cylinder mechanism, thereby compensating for ground surface irregularities. Thus, the drainpipe is laid at both the desired depth and grade.

The automatic system typically corrects the digging depth within three-eighths of an inch or less over distances up to 1,500 feet. All the machine operator has to do is see that the plastic pipe feeds properly into the installation implement and steer the tractor in a fairly straight line toward the laser beam unit. Operator fatigue and carelessness that now cause gross inaccuracies in draintile installation are eliminated by the laser system.

The laser system can be adapted for

70

Laser beam detector is in rectangular box above tractor treads on drainage machine, *top*. Detector picks up laser signals and automatically controls digging depth. Photo at lower left shows how flexible plastic drain tubing enters mole plow at top and is fed out at bottom. *Lower right*, Agricultural Engineer James L. Fouss aims laser beam projection unit.

automatic grade control on other types of drainage or earth-moving machines. Automatic control of the cutting depth might be used on scrapers, graders, bulldozers, shovels, draglines, and other machines used in land leveling, dredging, and construction of open ditches and terraces.

This would greatly reduce labor requirements, increase operating efficiency, and reduce costs.

Savings can also result from its use in constructing roads, highways, airports, dams, sewers, and in many surveying operations.

While the original laser projected a small straight-line beam, a laser projection unit has now been devised that emits a "fan"-type light beam optically spread into a horizontal plane. This permits construction machines to operate in any direction in the field. It also enables several machines to operate simultaneously in the same area from one laser beam reference unit.

The role of the laser beam elevation and guidance control system is still in its infancy. Through research, new uses in many fields are sure to follow. Farming will become more efficient as this system is put to use both for drainage and for solving other farm operational problems. As this occurs, we may rightly expect to see the "pipe dream" of lower food production costs come true.

The Tricky Chemistry of a Blade of Grass

MAX B. HEPPNER

....

Grass is to the farmer as clothing fiber is to the shirtmaker. The shirtmaker must know the strength of rayon compared to cotton to make sure your shirt doesn't rip when he changes fiber. The farmer must know the feeding value of bromegrass compared to alfalfa to make sure a cow's production doesn't slip when he changes feed.

In this respect, the shirtmaker has it all over the farmer. The factory supplies the chemical specifications of rayon, whereas Mother Nature has been extremely guarded about revealing the feeding value of alfalfa.

For more than 100 years, animal nutritionists have been on the track of a blade of grass without complete success. They split the feed value of grass into basic fractions: Energy, protein, and minerals. Then, in the 1930's and early 1940's, they started discovering one vitamin after another.

By 1945, when they had worked through the alphabet from vitamins A through K, nutritionists came up with yet another unidentified feed factor. They noted that cows invariably responded with an increase in milk production of up to 9 or 10 percent after part of their alfalfa ration had been replaced by a portion of corn with equal energy value.

At that time, Dr. Lane A. Moore, a nutritionist with extensive research experience at Michigan State University and the University of Maryland, was just setting up shop at the U.S. Department of Agriculture's research center in Beltsville, Md. He had been working on the effect of vitamin A deficiency in dairy cattle. And—like his colleagues—he believed that nu-

72

tritionists doing the corn-for-alfalfa replacements were on the track of another vitamin, which was lacking in alfalfa, but present in corn.

Evidence for this "corn vitamin" was clear, yet the cause was elusive. Scientists could turn milk production up or down almost like turning the faucet on a water tap by changing part of the feed energy given a single cow from alfalfa to corn and back to alfalfa. But Dr. Moore completed more than 60 of these trials without finding a clue as to what the corn vitamin really was.

Undaunted, he decided to build a big extractor at Beltsville to extract the new vitamin from corn the way vitamin A is extracted from fish liver. Perhaps, again like vitamin A, the new vitamin could then be synthesized and added to alfalfa to overcome the drop in milk production when corn is taken out of the cattle ration.

One day, while Dr. Moore was impatiently waiting for congressional appropriations to build his giant extractor, he discussed his ideas with a young post-doctoral student from Finland, Dr. Pellervo Saarinen. The visitor scribbled some figures on a pad of paper and then interrupted Dr. Moore's discourse.

"Forget the giant extractor, Lane," he said. "There isn't any such thing as a corn vitamin. Your cows just haven't been getting as much feed energy on the all-alfalfa feed as they did on the corn-alfalfa mix."

Gently and kindly—as is his manner—Dr. Moore showed Dr. Saarinen the calculations that proved that the two rations, on the contrary, were exactly in balance from an energy standpoint. As Dr. Saarinen studied Dr. Moore's mathematics, however, an idea struck him.

"Lane," he said, "your reasoning is fine, your figures are right, but your

∴ ∴ ∴

MAX B. HEPPNER *is a Public Information Officer in the Information Division, Agricultural Research Service, assigned to reporting current progress in Federal livestock research programs.*

measuring system is wrong." Dr. Saarinen referred to the American system for expressing feed energy called *total digestible nutrients* or TDN. This system accounts only for wastes passed out of the body, whereas the European system, called *net energy* or NE, also accounts for energy lost by the animals generating stomach gases and body heat.

Dr. Saarinen showed that the TDN system rated alfalfa 9 percent higher than the NE system, whereas the value accorded corn was the same no matter which system was used. In the view of a person using the NE system, Dr. Moore and his colleagues mistakenly took alfalfa to be more of a tiger—from an energy standpoint—than it really was. When they replaced the weak tiger (alfalfa) with a fully potent one (corn), the result was bound to be noticeable.

Dr. Moore decided to check out this idea, no matter how farfetched it seemed. He delved into every published article with data that permitted direct comparison of NE and TDN.

He found NE and TDN values for just 25 feeds, but each upheld Dr. Saarinen's idea that the TDN system overrated the energy of grasses with respect to corn. The lower the TDN energy rating of a grass, Dr. Moore discovered, the greater is the error. To take an extreme example, the NE rating of wheat straw is only 25 percent of its TDN rating.

"Therefore," said Dr. Moore in a scientific article, "The Relationship Between TDN and Net Energy Values of Feed," published in 1953, "in (all) practical feeding experiments, the experimenter should not change the proportions of grain and forage on a TDN basis in evaluation of one in terms of the other."

Despite its quiet technical wording, the article produced a howl in response. To animal nutritionists it implied that thousands of experiments contained flaws. And to feed manufacturers it meant that they had goofed—although inadvertently—in making up many a feed formula.

Dr. Moore listened to arguments against his article with his usual unperturbed interest and admitted that perhaps his case supporting NE was weak because it was backed by only 25 proven examples. More complete tables of "estimated net energy" ratings were available, but in the words of the compiler himself, they were based on "the application of some intelligent judgment," or in plain English, "guesstimates."

If the evidence seems incomplete, Dr. Moore said, let's add to it. That, however, was much more easily said than done.

Since net energy takes into account energy losses inside animals, getting hard information on the net energy of a feed means "looking inside a cow" while she is eating. By contrast, a direct check on the total digestible nutrients involves tests only outside the cow—determining the difference in energy of the feed passing into the cow and the body wastes passing out.

Processes inside a cow, which obviously can't be observed directly, must be found by deduction. Scientists determine energy expended on stomach gases by monitoring changes in the volume, composition, temperature, pressure, and humidity of the air around a cow penned in an airtight chamber. And they calculate energy used for body heat from rectal temperature of the cow and her body movements. The buildings and equipment needed for these measurements are called an energy metabolism laboratory.

A quick survey around the country showed Dr. Moore that most of the energy metabolism laboratories on record had been abandoned. One of the last nutritionists to use such a laboratory extensively was Dr. Ernest B. Forbes, who had recently retired from Pennsylvania State University. So Dr. Moore went to his home to get some counsel.

"Running the lab," Dr. Forbes said, "was an unhealthy mixture of boredom and grief. Sometimes all components would work right, and we got some worthwhile basic information. But we were working with a few cows using a single test feed. You are proposing nothing less than testing all grasses and feed combinations—that's impossible. Suppose for a minute you had the equipment and manpower to do the job. Inside 96 hours you'd have enough data to fill a pile of notebooks stacked clear to the ceiling. How would you tabulate this mountain—much less analyze it?"

"Let me ask one more question," Dr. Moore replied. "If you had the opportunity to buy feed for a herd of cows either on a TDN or a true NE basis, which would you choose?"

Without a moment's hesitation, Dr. Forbes said: "I'd choose NE."

That settled the matter for Dr. Moore, and again he petitioned Congress to parlay the money intended for the giant "corn vitamin" extractor into the larger sum needed to start an energy metabolism laboratory.

Building a laboratory, in Dr. Moore's view, starts not with buying equipment or test tubes, but by finding a man to run it. During extensive interviewing, he met Dr. William P. Flatt, a post-doctoral student at Cornell University. This young man had been president of the Tennessee State Association of Future Farmers of America, an Eagle Scout, valedictorian of Trimble (Tenn.) High School, and recipient of the Borden Award for top grades (a 3.93 average out of a possible 4.00) at the University of Tennessee. His enthusiasm and determination obviously helped him come out on top of whatever he tackled—sufficient qualification, Dr. Moore believed, to help him lick the "impossible" job of taming the avalanche of data the new lab would produce.

Dr. Flatt decided his salvation would lie in borrowing an idea from progressive accountants who were starting to use computers to keep track of increasing files of figures. The idea was fine, but there was a hitch: No one at IBM had ever heard of an energy metabolism laboratory—much less ever bent a wire to connect one to a computer.

The problem of automating the dozens of devices comprising the energy metabolism laboratory is exemplified by the methane meter, which has to be read every half hour around the clock. (Methane is a gas produced in the first stomach of cows.) The operator has to fan air in each cow chamber toward a collection unit, pipe it to a meter, convert the methane reading to an electrical impulse, sensitize a computer to register the impulse, and program the computer to adjust the reading for changes in temperature and barometric pressure. To do the job, Dr. Flatt had to teach himself to be an electronics technician, a gas chemist—and a cow psychologist. The last specialty was needed because a cow is a confirmed social creature. She doesn't have any zest for life during a session inside a conventional solid-walled chamber— which amounts to doing time in solitary confinement. Dr. Flatt brightened the situation by substituting plexiglass walls for the conventional opaque ones, so that curious cows could still see each other and keep an eye on the men working in the laboratory.

Now, Lorna, who is the favorite subject of the lab's crew, is producing almost twice as much milk per day as the previous record producer in an energy metabolism lab.

The crew is also far more productive. One man in the new lab does the work of five in earlier models.

This productivity is the result of 6 years of designing, building, testing, rewiring, and retesting in the laboratory. Geared for high performance, six chambers working side by side collect twice as much data in a single year as was possible in the entire history of all previously operating energy metabolism laboratories combined. President Lyndon B. Johnson heard about this accomplishment and gave Dr. Flatt and his crew a citation and $1,480 in cash for saving the Government more than $400,000 in 1964 alone through efficient operation.

Since starting to operate in 1962, the energy metabolism laboratory has accumulated a list of net energy values for grasses that diverge from TDN ratings in precisely the direction that Dr. Moore had predicted. But besides giving information on the nutritional chemistry of grasses, the laboratory is updating farmers' knowledge about how a cow produces.

For instance, research at the laboratory showed that cows losing fat from their body do not always lose weight. Lorna, the star cow, for example, lost 330 pounds of fat in 3 months at her peak of production while keeping her weight about steady. Apparently she replaced body fat by putting extra water in her tissues. Farmers had previously assumed that the cow that grows thinnest is pushing herself hardest to give milk.

Even the speediest, computerized energy metabolism laboratory cannot run every feed and feed combination through cows to check feed energy directly. Dr. Moore knew that more modestly equipped and more rapidly working labs were needed to tell a farmer about possible differences in value between orchardgrass from his own pasture and hay shipped in from downstate.

Analytical laboratories providing such information to farmers traditionally have tried to rate grass samples by boiling them in alkali for part of the analysis. This was the best practical method to dissolve protein and starch from feeds. But unfortunately, this alkali process also dissolves some hemicellulose and lignin—rather indigestible fibrous components—along with the easily digestible protein and starch.

Chemists had been frustrated for decades in trying to determine the digestible portion of feeds with a simple but more accurate laboratory test. But Dr. Moore again felt that with the right talent and inquisitiveness, a man could solve the problem.

He found these requirements in Dr. Peter J. Van Soest, an honors graduate of the University of Wisconsin, who had just finished his military service.

After he had started to work on devising a better laboratory test for grass, Dr. Van Soest remembered his work as an Army medical technician using chelating dyes to detect traces of minerals in blood.

Chelating dyes are colored detergents, Dr. Van Soest explains to the inquiring visitor, with hesitancy in his voice—not because he isn't sure, but because he doesn't want to belittle the listener by flaunting his superior knowledge. Like other detergents, chelating dyes act by hunting out a desired particle like a retriever dog and bringing it to the "master."

Dr. Van Soest thought that perhaps the binding properties of detergents would change the way constituents could be dissolved from grass, and he was right. Held in the clutches of the detergents, protein and starch dissolved without the use of alkali, thereby avoiding contamination with hemicellulose and lignin. He built a whole new system of analysis around this discovery, so that today he can evaluate a sample of forage with existing laboratory equipment in about the same time needed for the traditional (but inaccurate) feed analysis.

In a way, we have come to the end of a story. The chemistry of a blade of grass has indeed become better known, and Dr. Moore says that he sees every indication that, within the next 4 or 5 years, nutritionists generally will have switched to the net energy concept for setting feed energy values. By that time, he thinks, feed laboratories will also have put to general use Dr. Van Soest's detergent method to analyze grass samples chemically. So Dr. Moore, who retired in 1967, has been granted the satisfaction of having his professional dreams become reality in his lifetime.

However, like most research stories, this one will have a sequel because new discoveries raise new questions. Dr. Flatt, studying the feeding value of grass from the cow's viewpoint, for example, found that a cow does not always convert grass into milk with the same efficiency. The outcome depends upon the extent that the cow uses feed energy to put on and take off body fat before she turns it into mil[k]

Dr. Van Soest, working with gra[ss] directly, also deals with a changeab[le] subject. For instance, chemical trea[t]ments he is investigating can remov[e] factors from grass that interfere with cow's digestion, thereby boosting t[he] natural feeding value.

Therefore, Dr. Flatt has called t[he] search for the chemistry of a blade [of] grass "a quest for the Holy Grail[."] But unlike that fruitless crusade, t[he] continuing search for grass chemist[ry] keeps providing dividends. As aut[o]mated analyzers click away in t[he] energy metabolism chambers and fo[r]age boilers steam in the chemist[ry] laboratory, the farmer is provid[ed] with new clues that show him how [to] squeeze extra drops of milk from ea[ch] blade in the pasture.

USDA Scientist Peter J. Van Soest maki[ng] chemical determinations on the nutrie[nts] in grass.

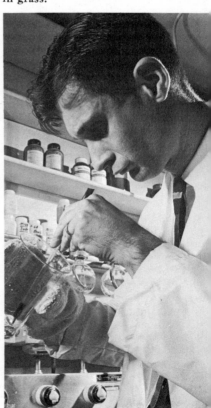

Wiles of Sex Attractants Used in War on Pests

STANLEY A. HALL

. . . .

What you and I smell is not what insects smell. Maybe that's one reason it took so long to find out that many of the insect species have sex attractants. These subtle attractant scents are emitted usually by the females—and less often by the males—in order to attract their mates.

Martin Jacobson and his coworkers at the U.S. Department of Agriculture laboratories in Beltsville, Md., have succeeded in isolating some of these powerful attractants after grinding up the bodies of millions of insects with a solvent.

And "millions" is no idle figure. For the amount of attractant carried by a single female insect is incredibly small. It takes only 1/10,000,000 of 1 microgram (1 microgram is 1/1,000,-000 of a gram) of the attractant released by virgin females of the gypsy moth to lure a large number of male moths flying upwind from a distance of a half mile or more.

The male is a strong flyer, but the female cannot fly and is dependent on her scent to attract males.

As a result of the Beltsville experiments, attractants have become the key to successful control of the tree-ravaging gypsy moth, the pink bollworm moth—a major cotton pest, the cabbage looper, and other destructive insects. The potential for control of our insect enemies through attractants, though not unlimited, is yet great enough to justify extensive research. Use of attractants alone or in inte-grated programs is expected to reduce the need for insecticides.

The gypsy moth, like many other injurious insects, was accidentally introduced into America. Trouvelot, a French mathematician and naturalist, brought it over in 1869, thinking he might cross the gypsy moth with the silkworm moth to breed a hardy strain of silk-producing insects.

In the course of his experiments in Massachusetts, some of the eggs or caterpillars were lost.

Trouvelot appreciated the danger and made public an announcement of the accident. But no one paid much heed. So, the moths multiplied and prospered in their new homeland, which was practically free of their parasites and natural enemies.

Twenty years later, the true seriousness of the accident was brought home to the public. Descendants of the gypsy moths that had escaped existed then in such vast numbers that they stripped the leaves from shade trees, fruit trees, and large areas of forest in New England.

The State of Massachusetts tackled the problem energetically, and between 1890 and 1900, the pest had been cut down by insecticide sprays so that its ravages were no longer apparent. The insecticide sprays were

∴　∴　∴

STANLEY A. HALL *is Chief of the Pesticide Chemicals Research Branch, Entomology Research Division, Agricultural Research Service.*

Caterpillars of gypsy moth feed on oak leaf.

discontinued, and this gave the gypsy moth its great chance.

By 1906, tree damage was so bad that Federal help was needed. Since that time, this ravaging pest has been brought under control and prevented from spreading over millions of acres of hardwood forest from northern Maine to the Ozark Mountains.

It was only possible to do this by using the sex attractant. The attractant was obtained by collecting female pupae in the field, allowing them to emerge from the cocoons, and then clipping the last two segments of the abdomen from each moth. The clippings were ground up with an organic solvent from which the attractant was concentrated.

This was used to bait thousands of traps which were hung on trees in New England and adjacent States. The faintest whiff of attractant in the trap would set the male moths flying irresistibly toward the odor's source.

The male gypsy moth is so sensitive to the odor that he can single it out from all the other odors in natur
Thus, it was possible to detect t
limits of infestation and prevent t
pest from spreading by applying i
secticide only to those areas where t
insect was found and as long as
continued to be present.

To collect several hundred thousa
female pupae each year, wait for t
adult insects to emerge, clip off t
abdominal tip of each moth, and th
extract them all with solvent was te
ous and expensive. It was a challen
to the chemist to isolate and puri
enough of this naturally occurri
attractant and obtain a picture of
chemical structure. The chemist th
was able to devise a way to duplica
nature's creation and finally, in 196
to synthesize it in quantity.

The gypsy moth lure was the fir
sex attractant to be synthesized. Late
it developed that a synthetic lu
closely related to the true attracta
and nearly as active could be ma
for about $10 per pound. If used
traps for the moth survey alone,

78

ngle pound of material would fur-
ish sufficient bait for 100,000 traps
er year for 300 years.

Now that this and other subtle sex
attractants can be produced in quan-
ty, the entomologist seeks ways to use
ese powerful substances that nature
rovided for reproduction and turn
em against the insects. Thus far,
ere seem to be two schemes for using
sex attractant to reduce the popu-
tion of an insect pest.

One way is to attract the male in-
cts into many thousands of adhesive-
ated paper traps, which are best
stributed by airplane. This method
known as *male annihilation*. Once the
ales are eliminated, the females can
o longer reproduce. A variation of
is method may employ a toxicant or
emosterilant in the traps to either
ll or sterilize the males. Sterilized
ales compete with the unsterilized
ales for the females in nature.

The other method is to spread the
sect attractant over an infested area
such a way as to confuse the males
d thus jam the mechanism that
ables the males to find mates.

Sex attractants are being discovered
many different insect species, espe-
ally in the order of insects known as
e Lepidoptera (moths and butter-
es). The sex attractant of the pink
ollworm moth, a major pest of cotton,
as been isolated and synthesized and
being used to contain this insect
d to prevent it from spreading into
alifornia.

Still another destructive moth is the
bbage looper. Its sex attractant has
en isolated, its structure determined,
d the synthetic—identical with the
tractant material in nature—made in
ound quantities. This sex attractant
as been tried with success in a male
nnihilation experiment using 400
aps and covering a 4-square-mile
ttuce-growing area in Arizona. The
ay may thus be opened to eventual
radication of the cabbage looper
hich has become resistant, like many
ther pests, to insecticides.

The fall armyworm sex attractant,
ery closely related to that of the
cabbage looper, has been synthesized.
The codling moth, the most serious
pest of apples, is yielding up the secret
of its sex attractant to the probings of
the chemists.

All of the Lepidoptera sex attractants
thus far identified resemble each other
in their chemical structure or architecture. Each is a long chain of 12 to
18 carbon atoms attached to what the
chemist calls an alcohol or an ester
group; each has one or more double
bonds linking the carbons together.
Each attractant is a variation of this
type of structure and is highly specific
in attracting moths of the species from
which it originates.

Structures of sex attractants from
beetles and weevils (insect order Cole-
optera) are similar to the moth attractants in having carbon chains
usually with double bonds, but there
may be present an organic acid group
as in the structure of acetic acid (from
vinegar). An example is the sex attractant of the black carpet beetle, a
household pest. Sex lures of click
beetles (adults of wireworms which
live in the soil) also turn out to be
organic acids of this type.

Chemists in Government laboratories, research institutes, and universities have joined in an exciting search
to isolate, identify, and synthesize
these rare and powerful substances.
Chemists today have such sophisticated instruments in their laboratories
that they can determine the chemical
structure of a new material, even if
there are only a few micrograms to
work on, as long as they can extract
and isolate the substance in pure form.
This was not possible even 15 years
ago. The new instrumentation has
greatly stimulated work in this field,
and new attractants are being isolated and synthesized every year.

The sex attractant of the American
cockroach is extraordinarily powerful.
The amount needed to elicit intense
excitement and characteristic wing
raising in males of this species is so
small as to be almost impossible to
measure except in terms of numbers
of molecules. An attractant is thus

79

How synthetic sex attractant is used in war against gypsy moth, a pest that rava[g] hardwood trees. Tuft of cotton moistened with the attractant, gyplure, is placed insi[de] gypsy moth trap, *above.* Traps are then loaded into airplane, *below,* and dropped i[n] infested areas through special chute. *Below, right,* trap rests on ground after airdr[op]

Above, closeup of head of male gypsy moth, showing feathery antennae used to detect female sex attractant. *Right,* trap loaded with gypsy moths lured into it by synthetic sex attractant. Once inside, moth becomes entangled in a sticky substance and is unable to leave.

in the category of the most potent biologically active material that we know about.

If a chemist makes an extract, with an organic solvent, of sexually mature virgin female cockroaches, the males fail to respond to the extract until it has been separated into several fractions. Only one of the fractions contains active material which elicits an immediate and strong response from the male roaches.

If the active fraction is now mixed with the combined inactive fractions, there is complete masking of this extraordinarily potent sex attractant.

A similar phenomenon has been demonstrated in the laboratory with the cynthia moth. Ricinoleyl alcohol, which is obtained from the castor bean, can completely cancel out the effect of the gypsy moth sex attractant to which it is related in chemical structure. When a virgin female insect has mated, her sex attractancy quickly disappears or is somehow nullified. Whether this may be due to a naturally secreted masking agent is not proved, but it is suspected.

It may be feasible to release a masking chemical in the field and suppress an insect population. But this is yet to be tried.

Marvin Bobb, of the Virginia Agricultural Experiment Station in Charlottesville, observed that Virginia pine sawfly populations can suddenly increase into serious infestations. But, after 2 or 3 years of heavy damage to tree leaves, they may just as suddenly decrease to a level that is no longer a problem. During a population explosion of this insect, Bobb found that the males were strongly attracted to the females. When the population declined, he found that the females were not attractive to the males and only 2.5 percent mated.

We don't know why the female sawfly suddenly loses her sex attractant powers or why at another season the powers are regained to cause a persisting population to suddenly explode into a bad infestation. It could be due to a natural masking agent or to something that triggers the formation of s attractant in this insect. Jacobson a coworkers found that the pink bo worm sex attractant requires an "ac vator," a chemical (or more likely tv different chemicals) obtained from t female moth to make the sex attracta "come alive."

There are at least 50 species, inclu ing the boll weevil—a ruinous pest cotton, in which males produce a su stance that attracts and excites the f males. But generally these substanc are not as strong or far reaching as t attractants in species where fema attract and excite the males. There a also about a dozen species in whi attractants are produced by one sex lure both sexes. These substances ha been called assembling scents.

Lynn Riddiford and Carroll W liams at Harvard University fou that an emanation from oak leaves necessary for the mating of the p yphemus moth. The emanation w identified later on as trans-2-hexen which is the same chemical found mulberry leaves to attract silkwor larvae. Curiously, this chemical h been found in a few species of bu and cockroaches which secrete it repel their enemies.

Oak leaves are the natural food f the polyphemus moth. The oak em nation acts on the female and caus her to release her sex attractant whi in turn is necessary for the sexu activation of the male.

Many such subtleties are associat with reproduction of insects, whi have evolved into more different su cessful species than any other anima in existence.

Another way of discovering inse attractants is by screening a rando assortment of chemical compounds (an insect species until a compound found that exerts a measurable a tractancy. The chemist modifies t chemical structure of the weakly a tractive compound until he finds o which exerts a strong effect. Th random screening and synthesis a proach has been especially successf in finding attractants for the Japane beetle, the European chafer, and some of the tropical fruit flies—the oriental fruit fly, the melon fly, the Queensland fruit fly, and the Mediterranean fruit fly. These attractants—which do not sexually excite the insects—are not true sex attractants, but the compounds usually attract only the males.

The most powerful attractant of this type is a chemical called methyl eugenol. Males of the oriental fruit fly are so avid for this chemical that they zoom into it like iron filings into a magnet. Loren Steiner and coworkers of the U.S. Department of Agriculture's Honolulu laboratories carried out a highly successful experiment on the 33-square mile island of Rota, which is situated 37 miles north of Guam. Small cane fiber squares (2 x 2 x ⅜ inch) impregnated with methyl eugenol plus 3 percent of a quick-acting toxicant were dropped from aircraft at the rate of 125 fiber squares per square mile. The time between drops averaged 2 weeks.

Males of the oriental fruit fly, heavily infesting this small island, were drawn by the attractant to the fiberboard squares where contact with the toxicant quickly killed them. Finally, only females were left and these, deprived of mates, laid their last eggs which could never hatch.

After around 3 months, the remaining unmated females died off, having completed their lifespan.

The island has been entirely free of oriental fruit flies for more than 5 years. Mangoes and breadfruit which grow on this island used to be heavily infested with larvae of the oriental fruit fly. They are no longer infested. Isolated islands are ideal for such eradication experiments, which dramatically illustrate the power of the male annihilation method.

The Mediterranean fruit fly (medfly) was found in Florida in 1956. This highly destructive insect had hitchhiked, probably from Central America on an airplane. It had to be eradicated before extensive damage was done, especially to the citrus fruit in Florida.

USDA Scientist Martin Jacobson testing a chemical fraction for its effect on the American cockroach.

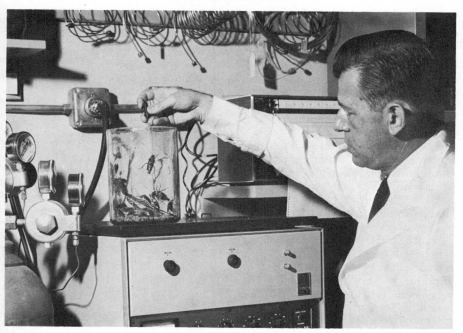

In 1956, the only attractant available for use in the many thousands of survey traps was angelica seed oil, which is obtained from a biennial plant grown in Belgium. Annual world production of this oil is only 600 pounds. Keeping about 50,000 survey traps supplied with attractant soon exhausted the stocks of angelica seed oil. The price rose from an original $56 per pound to $250 per pound.

Substitute concoctions were made up by the perfumery trade, which smelled to the human nose like angelica seed oil. But they did not fool the medfly—not attracting him in the least.

In the meantime, the chemists at Beltsville discovered a synthetic attractant and continually modified its structure to get more effective lures. There were about half a dozen of these synthetics, all more or less attractive to the medfly, and all of them of different odor to the human nose.

But the male medflies responded to something that must depend upon the similar structures of these compounds—and not to the smell that is perceptible to humans.

This brings us back to our starting point—what you and I smell is not what insects smell.

Tree Shaker Saves Our Cherry Pies

NORMAN E. ROBERTS

. . . .

One summer day in 1959, a strange-looking machine was wheeled into place under a cherry-laden tree in a Michigan orchard. A clamp at the end of a mechanical arm was secured to a branch of the tree. The machine's motor was started, and the tree shook violently, the cherries falling to a net spread beneath.

This was the first mechanical harvester for red tart cherries. Its introduction may have meant as much to 20th-century cherrygrowers as the gin and the reaper did to 19th-century cotton and grain farmers.

It may even have saved cherry pie, one of America's most popular desserts, from becoming a rare treat.

Picking cherries by hand is hard, slow work. An experienced picker would do well to gather 300 pounds in a day. The harvest season is short—a scant 3 weeks—and many thousands

of workers (45,000 in Michigan alone) have been needed to harvest a crop that usually runs around 190,000 tons.

In the past 10 or 15 years, the job of recruiting these armies of pickers has become well-nigh impossible. The last hope of maintaining the cherry industry with handpickers fled when the supply of foreign migrant workers was cut off at the end of 1964. How could an orchardist pay pickers fair wages by domestic standards to harvest only 300 pounds a day and still sell his fruit in today's competitive food market? And even if he could, where would the workers come from?

Some years before the clouds of economic disaster began gathering over the cherry orchards of Michigan, New York, Wisconsin, and Pennsylvania, Jordan H. Levin had an idea.

84

"Wouldn't it be great," he told his group of Agricultural Research Service engineers at Michigan State University, "if we had a machine that would just shake the cherries off the trees?"

Mechanical harvesters had already been tried for walnuts and some other crops. But most people thought Levin's idea was crazy—like a small boy's dream of getting his chores done effortlessly. How would you prevent bruising and maintain high quality if you allowed delicate cherries to fall on top of each other from heights as great as 20 feet? And wouldn't the tree be killed, or at least the bark ruined, by a mechanical monster which grabs the branches firmly enough to shake with such vigor?

Undaunted by this skepticism, Levin and his engineers began studying designs for mechanical harvesters, with the idea of developing an entirely new machine that would meet the special demands of red tart cherries.

In the meantime, Chemist R. T. Whittenberger was working with another group of ARS scientists at the eastern utilization laboratory in Philadelphia. They, too, were taking a critical look at traditional methods of harvesting and processing cherries. Yet, these scientists were not concerned with economics or labor, but solely with the quality of the processed product. They had established bruising as the number one cause of downgrading cherry quality. And they had proved that the human pickers themselves cause most of the bruising as they take the cherries off the tree and drop them into the pail.

Whittenberger's group began to experiment with other means of picking cherries that might cause less damage to the fruit. One such method was to suspend a minnow net beneath the tree and have the pickers loosen the cherries from the branches with their

∴   ∴   ∴

NORMAN E. ROBERTS is *Public Information Officer, Eastern Utilization Research and Development Division, Agricultural Research Service, Philadelphia.*

fingertips and allow the fruit to fall into the net. With the impact of their fall broken by the net, the cherries suffered much less bruising. "But what if a machine could be devised to do this shaking?" the experimenters mused.

It was not long before the two ARS groups were collaborating. The result of their collective labors was the crude machine that shook the cherries from about 300 trees in that Michigan orchard in 1959. There was no question that this first model did more damage to the cherries than careful handpicking. But with experience, Levin and Whittenberger were able to use it to gather cherries of reasonably good quality. They began to see possibilities for modifying the machine to make it a practical harvester.

Over the next few years, working with David Friday, an energetic and imaginative machinemaker, Levin and Whittenberger steadily improved and refined the harvester. Inertia shakers that shake only the tree—not the tractor they are mounted on or the operator—were developed to separate the cherries from the trees more easily. Self-propelling units were built that could be used on hillsides. Experiments were made with various cushioning materials to minimize bruising as the cherries fall onto the collecting frames. Special clamps were devised that virtually eliminated bark damage. Small models were built that could be operated by one or two men.

Growers became enthusiastic about the new machine with which they could harvest as many cherries in a day with a five-man crew as could be gathered by 100 handpickers.

But processors were skeptical. Despite their improved quality, machine-harvested cherries required a different kind of treatment than those picked by hand. Processors scorned them, except for making juice. In 1964, only about 3 percent of the cherry pack was machine harvested and the following year, only 8 percent.

Each season, Levin and Whittenberger worked together as a team, Levin with machine manufacturers to

85

Cherry harvester, *top*, is positioned beneath tree. It has two hydraulic shakers and a catching frame. Elevator takes fallen cherries to cold water tank. In processing plant, *below*, each of these eight electric sorters can handle up to 2,800 pounds of cherries an hour.

perfect the harvesting equipment and Whittenberger with processors and processing equipment manufacturers to help the canneries meet this new challenge.

Concurrent with the development of mechanical harvesters in the field, electric sorting machinery came into use in cherry-processing plants. First used commercially in 1963, the electric sorter does the work of three or four manual inspectors. It picks up each cherry individually, scans it photoelectrically, and accepts or rejects it on the basis of its reflectance.

The electric sorters can handle as much as 2,800 pounds an hour—that's over 5,000 cherries a minute. New sorters that work twice as fast are now in experimental operation. These scan the cherries as they fall freely past photoelectric cells, pneumatically removing rejects.

Electric sorters became a valuable complement to mechanical harvesters. Both have vastly improved the efficiency with which red tart cherries are being packed.

The destemmer is even more important than the electric sorter in enabling processors to handle machine-harvested cherries. When cherries are picked by hand, very few of the stems remain on them, and these are easily removed by inspectors at the plant. Shaking, however, allows many stems to remain on the cherries.

Until as late as 1966, processors were seriously slowed down in the handling of machine-harvested cherries by the tedious stem-removing operation. Whittenberger and Levin worked with equipment manufacturers to develop a device which would automatically remove the stems without damaging the cherries.

Several destemmers were under experimentation in 1965, when Russell and Vernon Smeltzer, two brothers who operate orchards near Frankfort, Mich., came up with the idea of installing a rotary blade above an oscillating tabletop. The cherries, in a single layer, are continuously kept in motion on the tabletop. As the stems turn up, they are knocked off by the dull edge of the blade rotating about one-eighth of an inch above the cherries.

Successful experiments with these destemmers were first made in 1965, and over 50 of them were in commercial use by 1967.

So a revolution has saved the cherry pie. Mechanization in the orchard has reduced the total cost of cherry harvesting to around one and a quarter cents per pound. Mechanization in the processing plant has speeded up operations to such an extent that even bumper crops can be processed within the brief harvesting period.

Mechanical harvesting is still a long way from completely replacing handpicking. In 1967, it was estimated that about 50 percent of the crop was harvested by machine; the year before that, only about 22 percent was.

It is significant that these 2 years, the first in which mechanical harvesting was done to any appreciable extent, both yielded unusually small crops. Experiences with mechanical harvesting in these seasons have proved its value in times when it might seem to be least needed. In poor crop years, many trees bear so few cherries that it is not worth the time and effort of handpickers to climb them. But a tree with few cherries can be shaken just as quickly and easily as one heavily laden, and the effort is economically rewarding, especially when shortages inflate the price.

It's estimated that the 1967 harvest of red tart cherries, 45 percent of normal, would have been only 40 percent of normal had orchardists been solely dependent upon handpicking. That's a difference of $2 million worth of cherries at 1967 prices.

It appears, then, that whether future crops of red tart cherries are large or small, mechanical harvesting and streamlined processing have saved our cherry pie from the near-oblivion to which it once seemed headed.

Bad Plants and Good Bugs

LLOYD A. ANDRES

. . . .

Bugs are bad, plants are good is an old myth that is rapidly dying out. Even the home gardener now recognizes the beneficial insects and watches for the first ladybug or green lacewing. He also realizes that gardening is another term for weeding out "bad" plants. Entomologists are further confounding the "bad bug-good plant" myth by importing "good" bugs to feed on weedy plants.

Klamath weed, once the scourge of the northwest range, was brought under control by bringing into this country and releasing two small beetles from Europe. This success sparked the formation of an investigations group within USDA's Entomology Research Division devoted exclusively to control of weeds with insects. Although their work offers little hope to the average suburbanite for controlling weeds in the quarter acre around his home, it does offer a new approach to control of over 250 weedy plants that have entered the United States from other countries.

Plant-feeding insects show a preference toward certain plants and are sometimes even restricted to a single species for food and shelter. This is also true for weed-feeding insects. Specialized feeding has been rigidly fixed through evolution, even to the extent that starvation occurs in the plant's absence. Entomologists are learning to search out and distinguish the specific weed-feeding insects in their native home and bringing them to the United States. If successful, the balance of nature is restored without the continuing need for pesticides.

A typical project is currently underway to control tansy ragwort, a poisonous range weed introduced from Europe. It occupies over 500,000 acres from California to British Columbia. Ragwort crowds out the useful forage plant species. Livestock forced to feed on it live poorly and often die. The rapid spread of ragwort to inaccessible areas made its control with chemicals uneconomical.

This prompted a survey of the weed in Europe where over 60 species of insects were recorded. Of these, the cinnabar moth, *Tyria jacobaea*, was thought most promising. It was studied and released at Fort Bragg, Calif., in 1959. From a release of 400 larvae, the number has increased to hundreds of thousands. These have already cleared the weed from many acres.

At the peak of the summer season, only bare stalks of the ragwort remain. In fact, there are often too many larvae on some plants, so that many wander off and starve to death. The fact that not a single larva has damaged other plants in the area confirms the host specificity testing conducted prior to introduction.

Although the cinnabar moth shows great potential for controlling the ragwort, it is too much to hope that a single insect can destroy ragwort over its entire range. Entomologists have also released a seedfly, *Hylemya seneciella*, whose larvae destroy the devel-

∴　　∴　　∴

LLOYD A. ANDRES *is Investigations Leader, Biological Control of Weeds Investigations, Entomology Research Division, Agricultural Research Service, at Albany, Calif.*

oping flower heads. They are continuing to study the root-feeding *Longitarsus* beetle.

The investigations group is headquartered at Albany, Calif., and is responsible for weed control with insects throughout the entire United States. Its variety of projects support laboratories in Rome, Italy, and Buenos Aires, Argentina. The weeds under study include Canada thistle (*Cirsium arvense*), puncture vine (*Tribulus terrestris*), alligatorweed (*Alternanthera phylloxeroides*), and many others.

The entomologists are enthusiastic about reducing the annual damage by weeds with nature's own weapons— "good" bugs.

More Beef
From Crossbreds

MAX B. HEPPNER

· ·

Dr. Keith E. Gregory, a tall, broad-shouldered cattle geneticist in the Agricultural Research Service, cuts an imposing figure with the broad-brimmed hat of the cattle rancher and the suit and tie of the college professor. This combination, which Gregory wears without overcoat even in near-zero weather, symbolizes perfectly his occupation for 11 years. From 1955 to 1966, he was coordinator of the State and Federal North Central Beef Cattle Breeding Project, a post he relinquished to direct the new U.S. Meat Animal Research Center in Nebraska.

As coordinator, he interpreted ranchers' problems to scientists and scientists' findings to ranchers. He took a broad look at research so that State and Federal scientists could pull together on beef cattle breeding projects in which both were involved. In his "spare" time, he personally directed experiments supporting the aims of projects he coordinated.

One line of inquiry dovetailed ideally with all these duties: The longstanding question whether crossbreeding could increase the efficiency of production on cattle ranches. Stated as simply as possible, crossbreeding is systematically mating females of one breed to males of another breed to produce offspring with hybrid vigor.

Hybrid vigor results from the contribution of good genetic traits from the two breeds used in the cross. A successful match can generate so much hybrid vigor that crossbred offspring are not only more productive than the average of the two parents, but more productive than the superior of the two parents.

Practical use of hybrid vigor was first made by corn breeders and then by chicken and swine breeders; all of them found that crossbreeding could cut production costs considerably. But cattlemen did not follow their lead immediately.

One good reason for this lag was that cattle breeding stock represents a high investment because much time passes before a new generation reaches breeding age. So, it is quite expensive

∴　　∴　　∴

MAX B. HEPPNER *is a Public Information Officer in the Information Division, Agricultural Research Service, assigned to reporting current progress in Federal livestock research programs.*

89

to experiment with new cattle breeding systems.

Experiments with crossbreeding—more than other attempts to make changes in breeding—required explanation to the cattle industry. Traditional color patterns of the various breeds are trademarks, and crossbreeding makes a hash of these patterns. Crosses between Herefords and Angus, for example, have neither the red bodies with white faces and ankle patches of Herefords nor the pitch-black bodies and sweet eyes of the Angus. Instead, their coloring is an odd mix of the looks of both parents: black bodies with white faces, but no ankle patches.

Without explanation, cattlemen easily could have jumped to the conclusion that Gregory and the research he coordinated were going to mix trademarks and mongrelize calves, so that millions invested in pure breeding would be wasted. This would especially upset professional breeders who supply ranchers with pedigreed bulls to upgrade their herds.

To avoid misunderstanding, Gregory visited officials of the major breed organizations and explained his objectives. "If crossbreeding worked as well for beef cattle as it has for hogs, only the meat-producing ranchers would need to change their breeding program," Gregory said. "These ranchers would still depend on outstanding breeding stock, including purebred bulls, as parents for crossbreeding—no less than for successful, conventional straight breeding."

Gregory said, in short, that crossbreeding did not threaten the pure breeders—but that, at best, it might do their customers some good. To help make this point, he presented a classic

USDA Cattle Geneticist Keith E. Gregory with Angus-Hereford crossbred.

statistical design for a crossbreeding experiment he had worked out as a graduate student at the University of Missouri. His professors had praised the paperwork, but it would prove nothing unless columns of formulas in tables were worked out into pounds of beef on the block.

Plans called for mating a bull to cows of his own breed plus cows of two other breeds each year. Calves born the same year would be half brothers and half sisters, with sires in common. A bull, therefore, would have the same effect on his crossbred offspring as on his straight bred calves. Each breeding season, cows of each breed would be assigned at random for mating, so that their genetic merit would affect crossbreds and straight bred calves to the same extent.

Altogether, the plan required 240 cows, 80 each of the Hereford, Angus, and Shorthorn breeds; and 48 bulls, with 16 each from the same three breeds. These numbers were large, but they allowed Gregory to be reasonably sure that, on the average, straight bred calves and crossbreds would have parents of equal genetic merit.

Under Gregory's leadership, Nebraska and Agricultural Research Service scientists started the breeding experiments in 1957, at Fort Robinson, Nebr., a former Indian pacification and trading post. Cows were bought from commercial herds in Nebraska, Montana, and Colorado. Bulls originated from an even greater variety of sources, making for a broad genetic representation.

Test results, which first became available in 1961, showed that 3 percent more crossbred calves lived to weaning age (about 7 months). And at weaning, the crossbreds weighed 5 percent more than straight breds. Prices for weaned calves change; but a weighted formula worked out by Gregory showed dramatically that cattle breeders who substitute crossbreeding for straight breeding have the equivalent of seven more calves to sell for every 100 cows bred.

After 1961, crossbreeding experiments continued at Fort Robinson and expanded to other Federal and State research stations. But the original figures on profitability of crossbred calves compiled at Fort Robinson still form much of the groundwork of explanations about crossbreeding.

These explanations are given mostly by agricultural extension workers in cattle-producing States. But when a rancher asks Gregory about crossbreeding research, he becomes an able salesman for his findings.

After showing the rancher tables and charts of figures, Gregory takes him to see the crossbred calves themselves. All the animals of an age are kept together, regardless of breeding, to avoid confusion from unlike feeding or management, and the visitor's typical reaction is one of utter surprise at the range and variety of color patterns.

"That shouldn't really bother you," Gregory replies. "On the surface, these calves lack uniformity, I grant you. But look under the skin at the muscling and fine proportions. Essentially, you're not selling color patterns. You're selling pounds of beef, and these calves have it."

"Well, maybe they do have a good size on them," the visitor answers. "But the cattle feeders who buy range-bred beef calves to finish for market will never go for calves that look like these."

Gregory has answers for the cattle feeders, too. Summaries on experimental calf crops raised at Fort Robinson from 1960 through 1964 show that average daily weight gains of crossbred steers were about 3 percent larger than those of their straight bred half brothers. And overall value of meat from crossbreds was $8.81 greater (based on 1964 prices) after taking into account feed costs from weaning to slaughter.

When the discussion is taken to the feeders, however, they also say that they themselves may not mind the variety of color patterns—but what can they tell the meatpackers who buy finished steers from them?

Tell them, Gregory says in answer,

that boneless, closely trimmed retail cuts from crossbred steers have the same composition and grade as meat from straight breds fed to the same market weight.

That's a mouthful, but it speaks the language which packers understand. And Gregory can back it up with a convincing series of color slides showing that cuts of meat from crossbred steers look fully as appetizing as meat from straight bred steers.

"Use some psychology and group the calves with similar color markings together before the buyer arrives," Gregory tells farmers and ranchers, to complete his argument. "Then you won't have much trouble selling crossbred calves, because each of their color patterns has its own attractiveness.

"I think the smoky-white Angus-Charolais cross and the deerlike offspring of the Hereford-Charolais cross are really nice looking. I also think the Hereford-Angus cross is positively striking with its contrast of white faces on black bodies. And always remember that when you have crossbred calves for sale, you are marketing the best available from not just one, but two breeds of cattle."

Gregory emphasizes, however, that he is not out to sell a bill of goods. "We have the data," he tells visitors. "We can interpret them for you and point out potential gains versus additional costs under various ranch conditions—but the decision to change is up to you. You have to decide for yourself whether your expected gain is worth the extra trouble. And you have to plan, not just for immediate changes, but also for several years into the future."

The most far-reaching changes affect the availability of stock for breeding.

"One day soon," Gregory tells visitors, "you'll have to replace a straight bred cow in your breeding herd, but all you'll have on hand will be crossbred heifers." He winks one of his sky-blue eyes. "What are you going to do then?"

There are alternative answers to this question. They are:

(1) Keep a stock of good parents in two breeds and sell all the offspring. When cows or bulls die, buy replacements. Gregory thinks this program is well suited to small herds unable to enter into complex breeding schemes.

(2) Use crossbred cows as mothers. The simplest way to do this is to buy crossbred females, breed them to bulls of a third breed, and market all the calves. Replace cows in the breeding herd with more crossbreds.

Crossbred mothers? Many ranchers who hear this idea raise their eyebrows. They have just been told that crossbreeding works principally because the parents are from unrelated purebred stock, and now they hear that crossbreds can be used instead of purebred parents.

Gregory then brings out records from followup breeding trials done in 1962 to 1967 and replies: "Yes, but you forget that hybrid vigor still works in the breeder's favor because the mother has hybrid vigor, and the performance of a calf depends to a large extent upon the health and milking ability of its mother."

Crossbred mothers have a headstart over straight bred mothers from birth. In research trials, crossbred female calves 1 day old had a 3-pound weight advantage over straight bred females. At 18 months, crossbred cows averaged 50 pounds heavier than their straight bred half sisters. Crossbred cows reached puberty 41 days earlier, and about 8 percent more of the crossbreds became pregnant at the first mating of the season. As a result, crossbred mothers are much more likely to have an early calf, which later brings more dollars from the feeder, because it is older and heavier at marketing.

In recent research, crossbred mothers were compared with their straight bred half sisters to evaluate maternal effect on the productivity of crossbred calves. All cows on trial, including crossbred mothers, were mated to an unrelated breed of bull; a Hereford-Angus cow, for example, was bred to a Shorthorn bull.

Calves from crossbred mothers were

Three-way cross steer in a California feedlot. Steer is product of a Shorthorn bull and an Angus-Hereford cow.

more numerous and more vigorous than calves of the same age produced by straight bred mothers. Crossbred cows weaned eight more calves per hundred cows bred than straight bred cows. And calves from crossbred mothers averaged 5 percent heavier when weaned at 7 months of age.

Gregory emphasizes that the calves in this comparison all were crossbreds. The question then arises—how do crossbred calves from crossbred mothers compare to straight bred calves from straight bred mothers? That is where the big payoff of crossbreeding becomes apparent.

It is statistically valid, Gregory says, to add the advantages of crossbreeding on the calves (discovered in early trials) to the advantages of crossbreeding on the mothers (discovered in more recent experiments). At weaning time, a rancher winds up with a total of 11 more calves per hundred cows bred and calves that are 10 percent heavier at 7 months of age, if he produces crossbred calves from crossbred mothers as contrasted with straight bred calves from straight bred mothers.

Although a rancher could conceivably buy crossbred replacements for his cow breeding herd, he would vastly prefer selecting replacements from his own calves—the method usually followed in a straight breeding program. Preliminary evidence shows that with extra care, this is possible through two breeding schemes.

The first is called a two-breed crisscross. A cow is always mated to a bull from a breed unlike that of her own sire, and fathers are switched from one of the two breeds to the other, generation after generation.

After the fourth generation of crossbred cows, their breeding stabilizes at two-thirds unlike that of the purebred bulls to which they are mated.

As a result, this mating system should theoretically maintain 67 percent as much hybrid vigor as a scheme in which two purebred lines of cows and bulls are crossed.

The second breeding system is called the three-breed crisscross. In this system, the original crossbred cow is mated to a bull of a third breed, and succeeding generations of females are then bred to a continuous rotation of sires from the three breeds involved.

After three generations, the breeding of the cows stabilizes at seven-eighths unlike that of the bulls to which they have been mated.

This mating system should give 87 percent as much hybrid vigor as a scheme of crossing two purebred lines, and therefore a three-breed crisscross should theoretically yield more hybrid vigor than a two-breed crisscross.

Trials intended to establish the relative merits of the two crisscrossing systems in practice are still underway, but systematic crossbreeding already has won over many practical beef producers. USDA estimates show that about 5 percent of the beef cattle which were marketed in 1967 were produced under a carefully planned program of crossbreeding.

Recent changes in the makeup of the cattle business have promoted the changeover. A significant proportion of the feeder calves sold today are bought by huge commercial feeding corporations directed by hardheaded businessmen who care little about color patterns on calves, but who look only at weighing scales and balance sheets.

The influence of these large firms on the market and the pressures of a tightening cost-price squeeze are helping win more converts to crossbreeding in 1968. Eventually, Agricultural Research Service estimates show, crossbreeding could cut production cost of the Nation's $8 billion beef industry up to one-fifth.

Today, Gregory himself is out of the mainstream of the crossbreeding research program. As director of the Meat Animal Research Center, he is concerned generally with experiments to improve production efficiency in beef, sheep, and swine and to increase consumer acceptability of products from these livestock. However, he will still direct some specific projects that develop and evaluate procedures for making optimum use of hybrid vigor in animal breeding.

Leaders in livestock research give Gregory great credit for his past work with crossbreeding, and in 1967, the American Society of Animal Science gave him its prestigious Animal Breeding and Genetics Award. Gregory's accomplishments have inspired colleagues to test crossbreeding further under a variety of conditions.

Research in the Southern States takes a special turn of interest because the breeds involved include Zebus and related Indian breeds that are noted for their ability to take hot climates. Crossbreeding experiments with Zebus and common, so-called British breeds of cattle showed that average daily gain of the crossbred offspring from birth to weaning is 10.8 percent greater than that of purebred calves from British breeds.

In the second generation of crossbreeding, calves with one-third Zebu blood exceed British purebreds by 15.4 percent in preweaning gains. Zebu crosses are widely used today, particularly in Florida, Louisiana, and Texas.

Potential Control of Insects With Juvenile Hormone

WILLIAM S. BOWERS

. . . .

Insects are man's greatest competitor for food and fiber and the transmitters of such ancient pestilences as malaria, sleeping sickness, yellow fever, and bubonic plague. These threats to our public health and agricultural abundance are held in check only through the energy and determination of the entomologist and the imagination and versatility of the organic chemist.

Discovery and application of the

insecticidal nature of DDT in 1939 was a major breakthrough in the development of organic pesticides. So effective was DDT in early studies that many predicted the eventual eradication of several insect species. However, they did not reckon with the ability of insects to develop resistance.

Heavy use of this insecticide resulted in the appearance of strains of insect pests resistant to DDT.

Undaunted, the organic chemists

proceeded to synthesize the chemical relatives of DDT and other chemicals, some of which were even more toxic to insects than DDT.

Toxicants such as the organophosphorus and carbamate insecticides were discovered which provided the farmer and the public health official with undreamed of weapons against the insect hordes. Inexorably, however, the insects retaliated with their extensive capacity to evolve strains resistant to most or all insecticides.

Recently, the development of more precise and sensitive methods of analysis for pesticide residues has revealed a remarkable and disturbing persistence of some of these chemicals in our environment.

Unhappily, most pesticides are not only toxic to insects, but to other animals and man as well. Concern about our environmental health and wildlife and the problem of increasing insecticide resistance requires a new approach to insect control. The agricultural and health demands of our society now will not permit a return to pre-DDT (1939) methods of control.

Thus, more fundamental approaches to insect control must be found. The biological, biochemical, and behavioral differences which set insects apart from other animals must be sought after, understood, and taken advantage of. A substantial investment in the study of insect life history, feeding, growth, development, and reproduction must be made in order to understand the fundamental differences between insects and other animals.

This will permit the development of selective tools for insect control uncomplicated by eventual insect resistance and the potential hazard to human populations.

One such approach to insect control is the application of our rapidly expanding knowledge of how insects rely upon hormones to regulate their

∴   ∴   ∴

WILLIAM S. BOWERS *is Senior Insect Physiologist, Entomology Research Division, Agricultural Research Service.*

growth, feeding, mating, reproduction, and diapause—a state akin to hibernation. Nearly everyone is aware of the complicated development of insects such as moths or butterflies marked by the growth of a tiny hatchling larva which goes through several stages, molts to a pupa, and finally to a winged adult. Each step of this involved scheme of development is carefully regulated by hormones. Experimental tampering with the hormone-producing machinery known as the endocrine glands can cause an immature insect to stop developing, grow too fast, or molt into monsters that are intermediate between larva and pupa or half pupa and half adult. Nearly all these effects result in the insect's premature death.

A hormone called the juvenile hormone is known to participate in the regulation of nearly all aspects of insect metabolism. This hormone was first discovered by insect physiologists who found that removal of a tiny pair of glands from an insect's head would cause it to molt to an adult long before it normally should.

The investigators reasoned that these glands, the corpora allata, must produce some substance which keeps the insect immature or juvenile. So, they implanted extra corpora allata into insects about to molt to adults and found their suspicions confirmed when the insects molted to larger but still immature forms. Thus, this substance which keeps an insect young through several immature stages was called the juvenile hormone.

Succeeding studies revealed that the juvenile hormone is produced within the insect at intervals during development of the immature stages and that it expresses its action at the time of molting.

An insect wears its skeleton or cuticle on the outside, and as it grows, it must periodically shed its old cuticle and build a new one in order to grow larger. When it reaches a certain size, it must molt to the adult form, which often bears little or no resemblance to the juvenile stage.

95

Giant monster nymph, *center,* of red linden bug was obtained by treating smaller last stage nymph, *left,* with a synthetic juvenile hormone. The small nymph would normally have molted to an adult, *right.*

At this stage of development (immature to adult molt), the corpora allata stop producing the juvenile hormone, and the molt results in assumption of the adult form. For some insects in which the change in body form is very radical, a pupal stage occurs between the larval and adult forms. This molt from the larval to pupal stage also must occur in the absence of the juvenile hormone.

The central theme of these discoveries is that the juvenile hormone must be present at certain periods of insect development and absent at others. If juvenile hormone or synthetic relatives of it are supplied to the insect at the larval-pupal or pupal-adult molt, the insect attempts to go in two directions at once, and the result is a monster intermediate in form which is unprepared to live in either world and thus quickly dies.

Since the main function of the immature insect is to grow and increase in size, any interruption of the normal sequence of development has disastrous consequences for it.

The adult insect, on the other hand, no longer grows in size, but serves out its life as the reproductive stage. It is

an axiom among entomologists that if the larval or nymphal stages are feeding machines, the adults are breeding machines.

One principal reason insects are so successful and competitive is their high reproductive capacity. Some method of reducing this staggering reproductive potential will have to be developed.

Adult insects are also dependent upon hormones for regulation of their behavior, development of the ovaries, and control of diapause. After the insect becomes an adult, the corpora allata again become active and produce a hormone identical with or very similar to the juvenile hormone. This hormone is necessary for sex attractant production and for egg development.

Many female insects produce a sex attractant which signals their maturity and willingness to mate with males of their species. Some sex attractants are so potent as to draw males for several miles to the "broadcasting" female. Removal of the endocrine glands which produce the sex attractant releasing hormone renders the female unattractive. Interference with the production of this hormone will produce unsexperfumed females condemned to unreproductive spinsterhood by their inability to attract a mate.

Sex attractant production and egg development are so closely tied together that any interference with the hormone which causes sex attractant production also spells doom for the eggs. In the absence of this hormone, the ovaries refuse to develop. Thus, if an unattractive female succeeds in mating, she remains unable to mature and to lay eggs.

Although it is possible to remove the endocrine glands surgically in the laboratory, it is clearly not possible to do so in order to control insects in the field. Consequently, it is necessary to develop antihormones which are sufficiently similar chemically to the insect's own hormone to enter the tissues and seek out the site of hormone action, but different enough so that they can jam the metabolic lock, so to speak, and prevent the tissues from responding to the hormone normally.

Insects are an ancient lot and have learned many tricks for survival during the eons of their life on earth. One trick is their ability to survive prolonged periods of drought, flood, and cold. Many insects are able to enter a condition of suspended animation during which there is little or no feeding, mating, or reproduction. This extended sleep is called diapause.

In many cases, diapause is induced by photoperiod. That is, short day length as in the fall signals to the insect the imminent approach of winter and induces it to prepare for this harsh period by entering diapause. In this condition, survival is assured. Agricultural Research Service investigators have found that a synthetic relative of the juvenile hormone will break diapause and wake the insect up. In a state to feed, mate, and reproduce, in the absence of a host plant, and exposed to the harsh environment of winter, the insect dies.

All animals take great pains to protect their eggs and young. Insects also

Synthetic hormone caused yellow mealworm, *left*, to develop adult head and thorax, but kept it from developing adult abdomen. Normally developed adult is at right.

take advantage of every device to insure survival of their species. Many produce special egg capsules, bury the eggs deep in the ground, or tuck them under the bark of trees or implant them into the stems of plants. Bees build apartment houses and gather food for the young they nurture to maturity. Often insects intent on laying their eggs demonstrate extraordinary sophistication in seeking out the specific host plants upon which their yet unborn young will survive.

Despite this protection, ARS investigators have discovered a way to reach them via the female parent. During their attempts to break diapause with synthetic relatives of juvenile hormone, the investigators found that a certain chemical not only terminated diapause in the insect *Pyrrhocoris apterus*, but also prevented the resulting eggs from hatching. Embryonic development was apparently deranged by this chemical, even though the ovaries matured normally, and the eggs were not contacted with it directly. The compound which produced this effect was isolated from the balsam fir tree, chemically identified by ARS scientists, and called juvabione.

Thus far, juvabione exerts its juvenilizing, diapause-breaking, and egg-destroying effects only on insect members of the family Pyrrhocoridae which includes serious pests such as the cotton stainers that wreak havoc in Africa, Asia, and South America. Its action on eggs may be the first example of an antihormone. And the fact that it acts on only one family of insects may foreshadow development of other hormone killers that can be tailored specifically to destroy harmful insects while not affecting innocuous or friendly species.

To be sure, other methods of attacking and destroying insects will be found and made use of. However, to be permanent and lasting, these methods must be of surpassing sophistication since the insect is no mean adversary.

Presently, the concept of turning the insect's own hormones against him offers great promise. As the known insect hormones are unlike any known hormones of man and other vertebrates, no serious residue problems are anticipated.

Whether the insect can develop resistance to its own hormones without perishing is a question for the future.

More Tempting Apples for Modern-Day Adams

MAX W. WILLIAMS

Apples have been grown by man since the dawn of history. They are often mentioned in early legends, poems, and religious books. The "fruit" which the Bible says Adam and Eve ate in the Garden of Eden is believed by many to have been an apple. The ancient Greeks had a legend that a golden apple caused quarreling among the gods and brought about the destruction of Troy. The Greek writer Theophrastus mentions a number of varieties grown in Greece in the fourth century B.C. Apple trees were grown and prized for their fruit by the people of ancient Rome.

The apple species *Malus pumila*, from which our modern varieties developed, had its origin in southwestern Asia in the area from the Caspian to the Black Sea. The stone age lake dwellers of central Europe used apples extensively. Remains found in their habitations show they stored apples fresh and also preserved them by cutting and drying in the sun. The apple was brought to America by early European settlers.

The apple is more widely grown than any other fruit and is considered the king of fruits. Apple trees of one variety or another grow all over the world. Only in the very hottest and coldest regions are they absent. Average commercial apple production for the United States is about 6 billion pounds a year. Total world production is approximately 26 billion pounds annually. Apple production in the United States and the world has been steadily increasing and will continue to do so in the future.

Man, with his ingenuity, has done much to improve the production of apples. Even though the culture of

∴   ∴   ∴

MAX W. WILLIAMS *is Head of the Fruit and Nut Crops Research Laboratory at Wenatchee, Wash.*

apples has been a specialty with man for centuries, greater improvements have been made in the last 50 years than in any other period of history.

The science of apple production has in recent times become rather exacting. In the past, research men were primarily concerned with varieties, propagation, pruning, and other cultural practices. Today, the scientist working with tree fruits must also be well trained in chemistry and plant physiology.

Chemicals now play a major role in apple production. They are used to protect fruits from disease and insect pests and also to regulate many physiological and biochemical plant processes associated with fruit development. Growth-regulating chemicals are used to thin or reduce the number of fruits on a tree, control preharvest fruit drop, promote flowering, overcome biennial bearing, control shoot growth and fruit size, alter fruit maturity, and improve fruit shape. When used according to the pure food and drug standards, the chemicals are not a hazard to human health.

Without chemicals, very poor fruits would be produced.

Application of chemical sprays during the bloom or early postbloom period to reduce fruit set and to partially or completely overcome the necessity of hand thinning has become practical in recent years. Thinning or removal of fruits from an apple tree is essential. Thinning avoids a tendency toward biennial bearing and helps increase fruit size, color, and quality. If left unthinned, many apple varieties will only bear a crop every other year. Too many apples on a tree prevent formation of fruit buds and the ultimate blossoms necessary for next year's crop.

Hand thinning of apples is one of the highest production costs. A single mature Golden Delicious tree often costs up to $10 or more to thin by hand. By using chemicals, the thinning is done earlier, and a tree can be thinned for about 50 cents. Chemicals in general use for this purpose include dinitro-orthocresol, naphthaleneacetic

Applying thinning chemicals to apple blossoms.

acid, naphthaleneacetamide, and 1-naphthyl N-methyl carbamate. A number of varieties cannot be thinned by hand early enough to prevent alternate bearing, so chemical thinning is necessary. Final fruit size at harvest is also directly related to the earliness and thoroughness of fruit thinning.

Thinning apple varieties with chemical sprays is a standard commercial practice in most apple-growing areas in the United States and throughout the world. The total benefits to apple-growers from chemical sprays for thinning runs into millions of dollars.

One risk involved in apple growing is loss of apples from the trees just prior to harvest. Losses result from wind or from extended harvest periods due to adverse weather or lack of sufficient harvest labor. Apples tend to drop from the tree when they reach matu-

rity because of the formation of an abscission or cell separation layer at the end of the apple stem where it attaches to the tree. Scientists have found that formation of this abscission layer or zone can be delayed by applying growth-regulating chemicals to the trees a week to 10 days prior to harvest.

Naphthaleneacetic acid and 2,4,5-trichlorophenoxy propionic acid in dilute solutions are used as stop-drop sprays. These chemicals are effective for 1 to 3 weeks after application. Use of chemicals has essentially eliminated the drop problem on most apple varieties.

A new chemical, N-dimethylaminosuccinamic acid, has been tested and found very effective in preventing preharvest apple drop. It can be applied in the spring or early summer and still prevent fruit drop at harvesttime. This

100

chemical alters cell structure of the abscission zone and also delays fruit maturity. Delay in maturity is beneficial to the grower since a firmer fruit at harvest means the apple will keep better in storage.

N-dimethylaminosuccinamic acid not only prevents apple drop, but also affects the fruit and trees in other beneficial ways. Several investigators have obtained a marked delay in the respiratory climacteric or maximum carbon dioxide output of treated apples, which means that the fruit will have a longer shelf life.

Delay in maturity not only reduces losses from drop, but also delays the appearance of water core, an internal physiological fruit disorder associated with overmaturity. Losses due to early development of water core in some apple-growing areas is often considerable. Main effect of the chemical is to reduce vegetative growth, which can be cut by about two-thirds. In general,

Sorting Golden Delicious apples, *left*. Red Delicious apples ready for harvest, *below*, have ideal shape.

growth reduction is roughly proportional to chemical concentration. The reduced growth results in an increase in flowering, which tends to help bring young trees into bearing and offset biennial bearing in older trees.

N-dimethylaminosuccinamic acid, used in combination with 2,3,5-triiodobenzoic acid, is especially effective in controlling biennial bearing of the Golden Delicious and other apple varieties. It is unusual that one compound can have so many beneficial effects with so few shortcomings. Results obtained with this chemical demonstrate that many of the natural physiological processes in plants can be chemically controlled.

Recently we have found that another group of compounds known as cytokinins produce some outstanding effects on apples. When applied to apple buds, they promote spur and lateral branch development. Application of certain cytokinins and gibberillins to flower clusters a few days after full bloom improves the shape of Red Delicious apples. The length to diameter ratio of the fruit is increased, the lobes on the calyx end become more pronounced, and overall appearance of the fruit is improved.

Use of cytokinins and gibberillins to improve apple shape could become economically feasible. Many of the Red Delicious apples grown in warm climates are round, flattened in shape, and do not compete well on the market with the better shaped fruit from cooler growing areas.

Chemicals are used on fruits prior to entering cold storage to extend their storage life. Fruits harvested at optimum maturity for maximum storage life often develop a skin disorder known as storage scald. Diphenylamine used as a dip treatment effectively prevents scald. Sodium orthophenylphenate is used to prevent fungal and bacterial growth and spoilage of stored fruits.

Losses due to storage disorders would be considerable without chemical treatments.

The kings of old with all their wisemen and dreams, never envisioned apples as we know them today. It is also impossible for us to know what the future holds. We are at the beginning of a new era for agricultural chemistry. The future looks bright, and already we have learned to benefit from the use of many synthetic chemicals. The day may come when we have complete control over most of the biochemical and physiological plant processes. More and better chemicals will be found to improve the quality of apples and make their production easier and less costly.

Redesigning the Tomato
for Mechanized Production

RAYMON E. WEBB *and* W. M. BRUCE

. . . .

A redesigned tomato plant and its fruit have played a highly significant part in streamlining the mechanization of tomato production, harvesting, and handling.

Development of tomato varieties suited to mechanized harvesting was concurrent with harvester design and development. G. C. Hanna and associates at the University of California, Davis, first conceived the idea that tomatoes would some day be harvested by machine. In 1947, Hanna began developing a variety able to withstand the rigors of machine harvesting and bulk handling.

Early efforts indicated no current variety possessed the relatively small-vine stature, concentrated fruit set and ripening period, and pliability of fruit needed to pass through a machine with little or no fruit breakage. Fruit of the large-vined variety, San Marzano, withstood simulated machine harvesting and was used as a parent in combination with early-maturing, soft-fruited, small-vined varieties. The small pear-type variety, V Red Top–9, was developed. Though of little commercial value, it was useful in performance trials of the machine.

By 1959, Hanna had developed for simulated harvest by machine numerous strains sufficiently uniform in vine type, concentrated profuse fruit set, maturity, resiliency of fruit, quality characteristics, and ability to "hold" for 30 days or more on the vine without deterioration. A large number of these were harvested by the prototype mechanical harvester in 1960.

From similar trials with the harvester in 1961, varieties, VF 145A and VF 145B, were released to seedsmen and growers. These two varieties, and subsequently selected varieties, are the foundation on which California tomato growers of about 180,000 acres have been able to almost entirely mechanize harvesting and handling of the crop.

Strains of the VF 145 group and the variety with elongated fruit, VF 13L, released in 1963, comprise almost 90 percent of the acreage planted to tomatoes in California in 1967.

A few years after Hanna started working on varieties that might be mechanically harvested, C. Lorenzen of the University of California initiated work on a tomato harvester. By 1962, both the machine and the plant were ready to go. Subsequently, the U.S. Government in 1964 refused to extend the provision of Public Law 78 by which foreign nationals were allowed to come into this country to help with crop production and harvesting.

∴   ∴   ∴

RAYMON E. WEBB *is Leader, Tomato and Cucurbit Investigations, Vegetables and Ornamentals Research Branch, Crops Research Division, Agricultural Research Service.*

W. M. BRUCE *is Chief, Harvesting and Farm Processing Research Branch, Agricultural Engineering Research Division, Agricultural Research Service.*

103

As a result, tomato harvesting machines became all important almost overnight. The harvested acres of tomatoes for processing, which had dropped more than 20 percent in 1963 due primarily to a labor shortage prediction, began to regain these losses and to show some increase. By 1966, the tomato harvester had eliminated about 3.5 million man-hours of labor annually.

There is considerably more to mechanizing tomato production than just the harvester. Like all crops that are successfully mechanized, the real success of the project must go back to the plant, and indeed, even back to the seed from which the plant comes and the soil in which it grows. Machines are not made to harvest crops; in reality, crops must be designed to be harvested by machines.

It is the plant breeder, working with the engineer and many other agricultural scientists, that makes for a completely mechanized crop production system. There are few instances of completely mechanized crops where breeding and cultural practices have not had a hand in the venture's success. And there are no instances where the system cannot be improved upon by a step-by-step analysis and evaluation of each variable in the system by all branches of agriculture that are concerned.

Generally, the pressure is almost wholly on the engineer at the start to design a machine to harvest a given crop. However, in the case of tomatoes, Hanna had foreseen the need for tomato varieties that would lend themselves to mechanical harvesting and handling several years prior to any design work on the harvester. He envisioned a small, tough-skinned tomato whose plant would "set" a majority of its fruit over a short period of time, but that would hold the fruit

Prof. G. C. Hanna of University of California, developer of tomato variety VF 145. This is first and still most popular machine-harvestable tomato variety.

Harvesting tomatoes and loading them into bulk bins on a tractor-drawn trailer.

while waiting for harvest. To a remarkable extent, these goals have been accomplished although, as with all crops, improvements will continue.

Nor has quality been forgotten during this period. Today there are many plant breeders crossing and recrossing lines to produce that one perfect product. Such a perfect product is a goal and is not envisioned in the immediate future. However, in the newer varieties, breeders have maintained at a high level such quality factors as flavor, color, acidity, and product properties. Improvements are anticipated in the overall quality of tomatoes and their products that will be measured with more sophisticated equipment and techniques. Thus, fruit from large numbers of breeding lines will be rapidly evaluated for the many traits that influence quality and consumer acceptance.

Breeders and horticulturists alike have had a hand in increasing yields. In 1940, the average yield of tomatoes for processing in California was between 6 and 7 tons per acre. More prolific strains and better fertilization and cultural practices have raised this average to over 20 tons per acre, and fields that yield over twice that much are not uncommon.

In commercial practice today, fields are largely planted with seed directly and generally thinned to the desired plant spacing. However, there are some cases when precision seeding has minimized the need for extensive thinning.

The seedbed must be carefully prepared to avoid clods, allow for irrigation, and present a level bed under the plant for best harvesting results.

Plant population is a major factor affecting yield. In some California studies, 30,000 to 50,000 plants per acre have given good results although many plantings are in single rows 4½ to 5 feet wide, spaced 6 to 9 inches in the row, resulting in populations of 12,000 to 20,000 plants per acre. Twin-row production, or the planting of two rows close together, requires more precision and closer management; however, the results of skips and blank areas are minimized, giving a better utilization of cropland. This method is usually recommended where soil and weather conditions account for smaller plants.

Fertilization and irrigation are important for successful mechanization of the harvest. Both materially affect the "machinability" of the crop, bulk handling capability of the fruit, and

105

the quality of the product for processing. Growers have learned the need of a fertilization program based on an extensive soil-testing program.

All the phosphorus and potash where needed are either spread uniformly on the soil surface and worked in as the soil is prepared for planting or placed in the early active root zone at planting time. Nitrogen is either applied at seeding time or a portion applied then and the remainder in a band below the soil surface and between the rows just prior to plant thinning. This program of fertilization insures an optimum supply of nutrients for early seedling vigor and continuous growth through the fruit setting and subsequent development period. An oversupply of nutrients, particularly of nitrogen, will cause excessive vine growth, cyclic setting and ripening periods, lower fruit quality, and will increase certain fruit disorders.

Irrigation practices have been developed that insure continuous growth of the tomato seedlings through the fruit-setting stage. Once the crop potential has been established, irrigation is used only to size the fruit and maintain plants in a healthy condition until 3 to 5 weeks before harvest.

Through this general procedure, growers have been able to maximize the percentage of ripe fruit in a harvestable condition at the time the field is scheduled for picking.

Handling tomatoes from the harvester and transfer to over-the-road trucks still constitutes a production bottleneck. Lugs that held approximately 30 pounds each and served as picking containers, as well as containers for over-the-road transportation, are no longer economically feasible. Even pallet boxes holding approximately 25 lugs that are transferred from field conveyances to over-

Machine harvestable tomatoes developed by USDA.

>mato planting operations done simultaneously—planting beds are formed, fertilizer applied, seed precision-planted, and a weed control chemical applied.

e-road transportation are being placed by over-the-road trucks that e field going also. There is less undling of the individual tomato by is method, and transfer stations are • longer needed. The firm, tough-inned tomatoes, a product of ad-nced breeding developments, take ch treatment with little damage so ng as the proper depth allowances in e container are not violated and uling distances are not too great. And yet tomato harvesting machines d techniques are still in their in-ncy. Improved machines are coming ` the assembly line each year. In 66, some 800 machines picked al-ost 70 percent of the California crop. ith four major manufacturers now oducing machines, and others enter-g the field so fast it is hard to keep • with them, it is expected that more an 80 percent of tomatoes grown in e United States for processing will harvested by machine in 1968.
Still, the job is far from finished. hen tomatoes start coming off these achines in such profusion, bottle-cks occur which were never dreamed when the bracero (imported field-orker) was spending long backbreak-

ing hours at this dirty, menial, and seasonal task. Moving the tomatoes from the harvester, transporting them to the processing plant, and handling the increased volume at the plant over a shorter period of time are examples of problems that have yet to be solved. Add to this machinery breakdowns and newly introduced cultural prac-tices which are parts of the same problem and you get a picture of a new concept in farm production re-quiring laborers with higher skills, entirely new lines of machinery, and growers who are not just agriculturists, but farm managers in every sense.
So, with the momentous start that has been made toward streamlining tomato production and harvesting through the foresight of two investiga-tors at the University of California in the late forties and early fifties, im-measurably helped by a labor shortage and a demand for increased produc-tion, necessity has again become the mother of invention.
With these developments have come problems as well as benefits that will employ the best minds of plant breeders, horticulturists, and engineers for many years to come.

107

Wasp Livens Up Beef Production

REECE I. SAILER *and* BERNARD A. APP

. . . .

That wasps can liven up the action—be it that of man or beast—is scarcely news. But how can a wasp liven up beef production? The story starts in 1902 when the first seed of a superior grass arrived in the United States. It came from South Africa where it had attracted the attention of empire builder Cecil Rhodes.

Known as rhodesgrass in the New World, it soon became the base of a new empire. Tolerant of heat and drought, the new grass—combined with the heat-tolerant Santa Gertrudis cattle developed at the King Ranch—supported the prosperous cattle baronies of the Texas coastal plains.

Between 1940 and 1942, ranchers began to complain that drought and termites were destroying the previously lush rhodesgrass pastures. Where new pastures had remained productive for 6 to 8 years, they now had to be replanted after 3. Beef production declined and costs increased.

Then in 1942, the cause was discovered. Nico Dias, an agronomist with the Soil Conservation Service, found that plantings of rhodesgrass and perennial sudan growing near Kingsville, Tex., were badly infested with a scale insect.

Scale insects are small, almost minute, insects covered by a protective shell or scale of wax. The newly hatched scale insect, known as a crawler, seeks out a favorable site on its plant host and inserts its sucking mouth parts. Unless it is a male, it remains there for the rest of its l[ife] reasonably secure under its protecti[ve] cover. The males are gadabouts. On[ce] mature, they leave their shelter [to] seek and mate the females. The pr[o]tective cover of rhodesgrass scale co[n]sists of a white mass of wax filamen[ts]. The scales attach around the nodes [at] the base of the grass blades and for[m] small masses of cottony fluff.

The scale insect near Kingsville w[as] soon identified by Harold Morrison [of] the USDA insect identification unit [as] *Antonina graminis* (Maskell). This i[n]sect had been found in China a[nd] described in 1897. How it got to sou[th] Texas is undetermined. In 1960, t[he] scale had been recorded from Florid[a] along the gulf coast to Texas, and we[st] to southern California.

Most members of the grass fam[ily] were found to be susceptible to t[he] scale. But rhodesgrass, johnsongra[ss,] bermudagrass, and St. Augustine gra[ss] were the scale insect's preferred ho[sts] of economic importance.

Actual losses, though never ful[ly] assessed, were great. The King Ran[ch] alone reported loss of 100,000 acres

∴   ∴   ∴

REECE I. SAILER *is Chief of the Insect Identific[a]tion and Parasite Introduction Research Bran[ch,] Entomology Research Division, Agricultural [Re]search Service. From 1960–66 he was in charge [of] USDA's European Parasite Laboratory n[ear] Paris, France.*

BERNARD A. APP *is Assistant Chief of the Gra[in] and Forage Insects Research Branch, Entomolo[gy] Research Division, Agricultural Research Servi[ce.]*

plains. It did succeed in controlling the scale on paragrass in Florida.

However, in 1956 a USDA parasite explorer, George Angalet, working near New Delhi, India, discovered a small wasp that appeared to control rhodesgrass scale. This wasp was later named *Neodusmetia sangwani* (Subba Rao) and was imported from India in 1959. Entomologists at the Texas Agricultural Experiment Station quickly established that the tiny wasp was highly effective against scale.

hodesgrass, *above;* johnsongrass, *right.*

rodesgrass pasture between 1945 and 949. However, reliable interpretation damage is difficult because of inter-lated effects of a scale infestation, rought, overgrazing, and close mow-ıg, often in operation at the same me. It was obvious that while the cale insect alone seldom killed pas-ıres, the infested grass would quickly ie if it was either grazed or mowed.

At the request of the affected cattle-ıen, State and Federal authorities en-eavored to restore the productivity of 1e scale-infested land. Progress was isheartening. Three varieties of blue-em, together with Angleton grass, ere found to be resistant or tolerant o scale attack. Unfortunately, none as as productive as rhodesgrass be-ore arrival of the scale. High cost and roblems with residues eliminated use f insecticides except for valuable turf reas, such as lawns and golf greens.

Biological control was also disap-ointing. One promising parasite *Ana-rus antoninae* Timberlake was im-orted in 1950 from Hawaii. This tiny rasplike insect could not stand the hot ry summer weather of the Texas

109

The tiny female wasp would crawl from scale to scale stopping only long enough to insert its stingerlike ovipositor and leave a number of eggs in the host's body. The eggs soon hatched and produced small larvae which quickly killed the host. As many as 10 young wasps might issue from a single dead scale insect. The parasite produces a new generation in as little as 27 days. The rhodesgrass scale requires 60 to 70 days to complete a life cycle. At this rate, the parasite could quickly overtake and suppress its host.

During this period in the 1950's, a new variety of grass called Bell rhodesgrass was developed and released which tolerated large numbers of scale insects. When used in conjunction with the parasite *N. sangwani*, the scale population was reduced so low that no loss of yield occurred. Presence of the parasite was shown to increase yield by 30 to 40 percent.

Unfortunately, the female parasite are wingless and thus disperse very slowly. To obtain the maximum benefits in the shortest time, Micha Schuster, Texas A. & M. entomologist, seeded 900,000 acres with gra sprigs infested with parasitized scal

These sprigs were placed in froze food cartons and dispersed from lo flying aircraft at a cost of 34 cents pe square mile.

Thus, more than 25 years after th rhodesgrass scale was recognized as pest, the solution was achieve Thanks to the persistence, perception and ingenuity of agricultural scien tists and a tiny wasp from a foreig land, cattlemen of the gulf coast ca again produce more beef for the Ame ican consumer at a lower cost.

Tailormade Bees
Do Honey of a Job

S. E. MCGREGOR *and* OTTO MACKENSEN

. . . .

Bill Nye watched a truck loaded with hives of bees turn off the Utah highway and into a field of flowering alfalfa. As it moved across the field, it stopped every tenth of a mile, and the driver manipulated a hoist that gently set off a dozen hives. They had been picked up with the same hoist the previous evening in California and had been hauled all night. Within minutes after their arrival in the field, the bees eagerly began visiting the alfalfa flowers. In doing so, they accidentally carried pollen from one flower to another.

This cross-pollination results in a bountiful seed crop for the farmer—a

benefit that also extends to the bee keeper in pollination fees for the bee the hay producer who plants the seed the dairyman who feeds alfalfa ha and ultimately the consumer of be and dairy products.

It all started when Nye (William] Nye of the USDA Bee Research Lal oratory at Logan, Utah) wanted

∴   ∴   ∴

S. E. MCGREGOR *is Chief, Apiculture Resear Branch, Entomology Research Division, Ag cultural Research Service.*

OTTO MACKENSEN *is a Bee Geneticist, also w the Apiculture Research Branch, at the B Breeding Research Laboratory, Baton Rouge, L*

110

Nectar-collecting honey bee on alfalfa blossom. Bee also picks up alfalfa pollen, which is the white mass packed on hind leg.

conduct a test that other bee scientists knew wouldn't work. He wanted to develop a bee to fit the crop. Everyone else said we should breed the crop to fit the bee. But, after he did it—with help from others, they wondered why they hadn't thought of it years ago.

The steppingstones toward development of a tailormade bee were many, but a critical step was the need to control mating of the queen. Ordinarily, she mates with any drone she happens to meet when she goes on her mating flight. But a breeding program cannot be conducted this way. So, the present method of mechanical insemination (hand mating) was developed. It is now a standard procedure in all USDA bee research programs. It is making possible the increased knowledge of bee genetics required for intelligent bee breeding.

Off to the side was another little steppingstone. Not in the direct path, but usable nonetheless. This was the pollen trap. Basically, it is a wire grid over the hive entrance that lets the bees get in, but scrapes off the pollen they are carrying to the hive in pellets on their hind legs. These pellets fall

111

into a container. When they are examined, the plant source can be determined. That tells the beekeeper where his bees are working.

A trap like this will yield 25 to 75 pounds of pollen in a year. The pollen is generally used as a supplemental feed for the colony during periods of the year when no pollen is available.

Many beekeepers have observed that traps on some colonies yield more pollen than others, and that not all traps at a location yield the same kinds of pollen even on the same day. There is scientific evidence that the foraging bees from different colonies become oriented to different areas where different plants grow.

Nye had noticed that certain traps had a lot of alfalfa pollen when others alongside had little. He wanted to know if this trait was inherited, regardless of arguments that existed to the contrary. To find out, he sent some of the queens to our Bee Breeding Research Laboratory at Baton Rouge, La., and we bred some daughter queens from them. These were shipped back to him and put into colonies near alfalfa fields. The trait persisted. Colonies that yielded a lot of alfalfa pollen produced offspring that did likewise, and colonies that yielded little alfalfa pollen were succeeded by colonies that yielded little.

Of course, the alfalfa flower is a bit unusual. It is largely self-sterile. It must get its pollen from another alfalfa plant, so it is dependent on the bee for this service. Its anthers and stigma (the male and female parts) are tightly enclosed by the petals and are released, or tripped, when the bee thrusts its head into the flower. When the flower is tripped, the bee is struck on the head by the stigma and by the anthers, bearing a mass of sticky pollen. When the next flower is visited, its stigma strikes the mass of pollen accumulated on the bee's head. Pollination results.

Some bees, only concerned with collecting alfalfa nectar, learn to get it from the side of the flower and avoid the light sock on the jaw caused by the tripping mechanism. They acciden-

tally trip a small percentage of th flowers they visit, but their pollinatic efficiency is low. Pollen-collecting bee on the other hand, trip nearly eve flower they visit. They are the on most valuable to the alfalfa grower.

After the observation was confirme in 1963 that alfalfa pollen collectic was inherited, the selection and bree ing program was increased. We test the colonies in the Utah fields of alfal grown for seed (some growers on produce hay and cut the plants befo seed is formed). We chose the ones th collected the most pollen, removed tl queens, and sent them to Baton Roug where the bee breeding work was don No alfalfa seed is produced at Bat Rouge, but it does have a long seaso long enough for queens to be reare mated, and shipped to Logan in tin to have worker bee progeny wh alfalfa blooms. In this way, one ge eration a year was tested.

Nye started out by testing 356 c onies near Logan. He didn't have th many traps, so he devised a vacuu cleaner to pick up pollen-laden be at the hive entrance and pull the into a killing bottle. Then the perce that carried alfalfa pollen was dete mined. This worked well for a qui test of a large number of colonies.

As the pollen preference study co tinued, another problem was create Inbreeding and selecting for one qua ity caused some of the other desirab qualities to gradually disappear. O bees lost viability and vigor, and th became more restless and difficult handle. So we had to breed out the bad qualities as we continued to sele for alfalfa pollen preference. The stra is much improved now, but not vigorous as we would like.

In 1963, the best colonies collect an average of 40 percent alfalfa polle Through the next three generation this increased to 85 percent. Not on the percent, but also the amount alfalfa pollen taken from traps w greater in our selected strain than in commercial strain. In addition to tl colonies showing a high preference f alfalfa pollen, we had also selected

112

Bees, the most important pollinators of our agricultural crops, also pollinate many wild flowers, shrubs, and trees. Other agents assist the bees. Nectar-feeding bat, *top,* is visiting agave. These bats also feed on and pollinate saguaro or giant cactus of Southwest. Bee, *below,* and whitewing dove, *left,* are pollinating saguaro.

group showing weak, or low, preference. In this line, the percentage decreased to 18 percent during the same period. Hybrids between the two lines were intermediate.

These results, together with those from backcrosses of the hybrid to the inbred lines, in which a lot of breeding and technical study was involved, confirmed that pollen collection was inherited and showed us that it was dependent on many hereditary determiners. This meant that efforts to develop still better strains for alfalfa pollination should be fruitful.

Further proof that the alfalfa preference was real was brought out by the 1966 tests. That year, we placed the test colonies where alfalfa was the main source of pollen (other pollens were scarce). Later we moved the colonies to a location where other pollens were abundant, but alfalfa was scarce.

We learned that where alfalfa pollen was abundant, 99 percent of the pollen collectors from the "high" line and 53 percent from the "low" line collected alfalfa pollen. Where alfalfa pollen was scarce, the corresponding percentages were 54 and 2.

This showed us that when other pollen sources were scarce, the low line was forced to gather alfalfa pollen to meet its need, while the high line got along fairly well with alfalfa pollen.

Where other sources of pollen were abundant, the low line almost completely ignored alfalfa. The bees from the high line were attracted away from alfalfa to a far less extent.

This also proved that the alfalfa pollen-collecting bee is most valuable to the seed-grower where it is most needed—in areas where there is much competition from other plants for the honey bee's services.

One question that came up repeatedly was whether the high line colonies gathered more alfalfa pollen because their bees ranged a shorter distance from the hive than bees of the low line. To answer this question, colonies of both lines were placed in three locations: In a field of alfalfa, 1½ miles from it, and 4½ miles from the field.

At all locations, colonies of the high line collected more alfalfa pollen than the low line colonies. This proved that the alfalfa pollen preference was real and not just a matter of convenience for the colony.

About 90 crops grown in the United States are dependent on bees for pollination. To develop special pollinating strains for each of these is not practical now. But a few crops are important enough and have a sufficiently difficult pollination problem to make development of a practical strain worth while.

One of the crops is red clover. Petals of the flower of this plant are united at the base to form a tube which is so long and narrow that honey bees have difficulty reaching the nectar in its base. However, we may have been led astray by too many references to the long corolla tube and the short tongue of the honey bee.

This tube length is a factor only in nectar collection. The honey bee can reach the red clover pollen when it wants to. The flowers of red clover are also self-sterile and require cross-pollination. Whenever honey bees are thick on red clover, the seed yields are good.

The alfalfa experiment indicates that when bees are placed on red clover some of them will probably show preference for its pollen.

Nectar-seeking bees have formerly been considered for red clover pollination, but pollen-seeking bees would be much better. The trait is doubtless present in certain colonies. We need only to ferret it out and develop it to have a tailormade red clover-pollinating honeybee.

Cotton is considered largely self-fertilizing, but it benefits from cross-pollination. And in the production of a hybrid cotton, large-scale insect cross-pollination is essential. As in alfalfa, the honey bee has been placed near cotton more for honey production than for pollination. A few colonies have been seen, however, that collected cotton pollen freely. A search is now underway for other colonies that demonstrate this trait.

114

There is no clear evidence now that bees inherit a preference for any pollen except alfalfa. Yet, when pollen traps were placed on colonies in New Jersey cranberry bogs in 1966, one colony consistently collected almost pure cranberry pollen, while others around it collected about half cranberry pollen with a mixture of other pollens. Daughters have been bred from this queen, and tests are underway to determine whether a preference for cranberry pollen is inherited.

Positive results would show that preference for pollen of a specific plant by bees may not be unusual, and that selective breeding for preference of certain pollens could be made. Or in less technical terms, we would say that we can tailor a bee to fit almost any crop.

Everything Is Automated These Days—Even Water

CHESTER E. EVANS

. . . .

Seedskadee, Wiggins, Maui, Yuma Mesa, alfalfa valves, fail-safe, and butterfly gates. They all add up to imaginative inventions, innovations, and developments for automating surface irrigation systems—important for all Americans through cutting food production costs while saving precious water. What's more, the future promises further exciting refinements for automation on an ever-increasing share of the nearly 38 million acres of irrigated land in the United States.

Dr. Howard R. Haise, water management research investigations leader for the Agricultural Research Service, headquartered at Fort Collins, Colo., has led the way in developing automated devices for surface irrigation systems. In 5 short years since 1963, Haise, his associates, and cooperators have automated and successfully operated underground pipeline and open-ditch irrigation layouts in six States.

This research has been guided by a basic concept: The farmer who automates a well-designed irrigation system to save labor will automatically save water.

Spiraling labor costs coupled with inexpensive water are major causes for inefficient use of irrigation water. Farmers are reluctant to use additional labor just to conserve water. Instead, the farmer may use his labor force for other more pressing jobs. Irrigating often becomes a second priority. It is frequently an around-the-clock job, and schedules for changing water are not always met at night. Besides, experienced or reliable irrigators currently are seldom available for hire.

Haise, with coworker E. G. Kruse, first invented devices to automate standard irrigation structures and turnouts and tested them at the Colorado State University Foothills Hydraulics Laboratory in Fort Collins. Basically, all systems developed consisted of four essential parts: (1) Gates or valves in irrigation structures that could be opened or closed, (2) a source of air

∴   ∴   ∴

CHESTER E. EVANS is Chief of the Northern Plains Branch, Soil and Water Conservation Research Division, Agricultural Research Service, Fort Collins, Colo.

or water pressure, (3) a valve and pipe system to direct the air or water pressure for opening or closing irrigation valves or gates, and (4) tone telemetry to transmit signals by radio or wire from a preset clock or hydraulic or soil moisture sensors.

These investigations proved that irrigation systems modeled on a prototype scale in the laboratory could be operated successfully with automated devices. But adapting the hardware and system to field conditions and situations was something else. Haise reasoned that the automated devices had to fit into established surface irrigation systems. Otherwise, costs would be prohibitive.

He selected two widely used types of irrigation water distribution systems—the underground pipeline with "alfalfa" valve outlets and the open ditch with manually operated slide gates on farm ditch turnouts. Systems on coarse-textured soils—or soils with high intake rates requiring frequent shifts in irrigation water from border to border—proved to be most ideally suited to automation. Irrigation "sets" of 6 hours or less necessarily require a relatively higher input of time by the irrigator.

First field test of devices for automating an irrigation system was accomplished by Haise and Agricultural Research Service Engineers E. G. Kruse and N. A. Dimick at the Irrigation and Dryland Field Station, Newell, S. Dak., in June 1964.

The fully automated system was installed on both pipeline and open-ditch distribution systems.

Heart of each system was an inflatable valve of nylon-reinforced butyl rubber. In irrigated fields served by underground pipeline, the inflatable valve is an O-ring mounted between the seat and lid of an alfalfa valve and held in place by a metal sleeve that slides up and down the valve stem. When the valve is open or deflated, the O-ring washes against the alfalfa valve lid so it rides on top of the water flowing from the pipeline. When the valve is closed or inflated, the O-ring seals the opening by filling the space between the alfalfa valve seat and lid.

In open-ditch systems, the inflatable valve is a tube with sealed ends that fastens in a turnout pipe. Inflated, it blocks the flow of water through the pipe. Deflated, it is held against the bottom half of the pipe by the force of flowing water.

Other essential components of this automated system are: (1) A three-way electric control valve that "inlets" or "exhausts" air from the pneumatic valve or closure, (2) air lines and a source of air pressure to inflate the closure, and (3) a centrally located, remote control system with timing device to actuate the three-way electric control valve by means of a signal transmitted by radio.

Both automated systems were controlled from the farm buildings, about

Howard R. Haise developing and testing four-way hydraulic valves, heart of the automatic irrigation system.

a mile from the graded border strips of grass-legume plantings being irrigated. A citizens-band radio transmitter was activated by a 24-hour preset timer with relays that beam signals to individual inflatable valves in the pipeline or open ditch.

At each valve, a battery-powered radio receiver tuned to one of the transmitter's channels receives the signal to open the valve. A relay in the receiver activates an electric valve that deflates the O-ring and allows water to flow into the border strip.

After water flows for a predetermined irrigation interval, the clock timer and relays again activate the transmitter which signals the receiver to close the valve. Compressed air—pumped to each valve in a flexible polyethylene tubing—then inflates the valve and stops the waterflow.

Four successive borders were irrigated by simply presetting the clock at headquarters to the time interval desired for irrigation water to flow onto each border.

Later in 1964, Haise, in cooperation with the Wyoming Agricultural Experiment Station, installed and operated the automatic devices in an open-ditch irrigation distribution system at the U.S. Bureau of Reclamation's Seedskadee Development Farm in south central Wyoming. Here, the radio transmitter was a half mile from the most distant receiver. After presetting the timer to trigger the radio transmitter at hourly intervals, 36 acres of forage crop were irrigated with lay-flat valves in ditch turnouts during a 9-hour period without touching the water or the system. A stream size of 10 cubic feet per second distributed water evenly to four graded borders, each an acre in size.

Although successfully demonstrated on a field-scale basis, the automatic irrigation system had some weaknesses. Air distribution lines developed leaks. Butyl rubber tubes placed in irrigation turnouts were damaged by gophers. And battery operation requires periodic replacement or recharging.

The scientists worked upon several modifications to correct these deficiencies. For example, the system at Seedskadee was operated remotely with a timer and relays that send signals through a pair of wires to the individual valves. When one electrical wire was added to the two signal wires, batteries to activate the receivers and solenoids were eliminated. However, electric valves could not be activated at distances greater than 3,600 feet with 35-volt capacity at the source using 18-gage wire.

Significant improvements followed initial design of remote control telemetry equipment. The transmitter was designed with electronic timers capable of sequencing water control valves for timed intervals ranging from 5 minutes to 16 hours. Or, if the farmer preferred, the timer could be bypassed by using instruments (sensors) such as electrical resistance blocks or tensiometers to measure the water content of soils. For example, valves on alfalfa risers or in farm ditch turnouts could be opened or closed by the soil water sensor when surface water reached a predetermined point of advance down the border strip or when soil water penetrated to a predetermined depth at the desired location within the irrigation run.

Cost of the redesigned telemetry system was reduced at least 50 percent by selection of alternative but equally reliable components and by redesign of circuits. These developments have been field tested at Mead, Nebr., by cooperating Scientists Paul Fischback and Howard Wittmus of the Nebraska Agricultural Experiment Station.

At Wiggins, Colo., 78 acres cropped to furrow-irrigated field beans, corn, and sugar beets were automatically irrigated by the farmer himself, utilizing pneumatic O-rings and the improved remote telemetry controls and timer. The inflatable valve or "O-ring" was modified to fit alfalfa risers equipped with hydrants and gated pipe as an adjunct to the underground pipeline distribution system already installed on the farm. Fail-safe features were incorporated to turn the

Automated surface irrigation system installed on 10 acres of citrus at Yuma Mesa, Ariz. *Above,* irrigator at stilling well, holding bleeder control valve in his left hand. *Below,* standard slide gate in ditch turnout, *left,* and standard turnout as modified with butterfly valve and piston, *right.*

Above, completed installation of automated devices in concrete-lined distribution ditch at Yuma Mesa. *Below,* automatic irrigation system in operation.

pump off when the last automatically timed valve had closed or a malfunction in the automatic system occurred.

On Maui, Hawaii, 13.4 acres of sugarcane have been automated on an experimental basis utilizing water-powered hydraulic cylinders to operate gates in an open-ditch distribution system. Haise has cooperated with Bill Reynolds of the Hawaiian Sugar Planters Association in Honolulu in field testing the irrigation system.

Driving a water piston in response to a float-controlled bleeder valve was made possible by combining four commercially available plastic valves—used to automatically irrigate lawns and turf grass—into a four-way hydraulic valve.

The four-way valve and float-controlled bleeder valve form the heart of this automatic irrigation control. It permits a continuous shifting of gate openings to maintain a constant depth of water either upstream or downstream from control gates in the distribution ditch. Present methods using electronic gear, batteries, and soil-water sensors to override the hydraulic controls when sufficient water has been applied appear to be too costly and impractical.

Recent modifications will permit automation with complete hydraulic control. Furthermore, gates now using large water pistons (2½-inch diameter and 18-inch stroke) have been operated with much smaller pistons using an improved gate design. These modifications should substantially reduce the cost of system control and provide for complete automatic operation.

Haise's most recent and successful field installation of an automated system is being used for irrigating citrus on Arizona's Yuma Mesa. John Scarbrough, owner of a 290-acre citrus grove, had been experiencing shortages of competent labor and steadily rising wages for irrigators in recent years. After observing a model of an automated system devised by Haise at the 1965 Convention of the National Reclamation Association in Kansas City, he wondered if water pressure and pistons might be used to open and close the gates instead of air pressure and rubber valves used by Haise in the model.

After 18 months and considerable correspondence, Haise and Scarbrough got together at Yuma in the spring of 1967. With the assistance of ARS Irrigation Engineer Leonard Erie from Phoenix, they installed a truly new and workable automated system on 10 acres of citrus on Scarbrough's farm. The system operates entirely on water pressure.

It features a newly developed, 12-inch diameter "butterfly" gate made of metal with rubber gasket that forms a watertight closure in turnouts already installed on Scarbrough's farm. These gates proved easier to install and were less subject to malfunctioning than the butyl rubber inflatable valves used in earlier field tests.

Then, too, the air compressor and air line system—so difficult to seal against leaks at connecting points—was no longer needed. Instead, float valves placed in the irrigation ditch, in the irrigation border near the turnout, and at a predetermined distance down each border were interconnected by ⅛- and ¾-inch plastic lines carrying water under pressure to pistons attached to the "butterfly" gates in the turnouts.

An electric-powered pump connected through a filter and storage tank to the ¾-inch plastic supply line maintained water pressure of about 60 pounds on a standby basis at all times.

The automated irrigation system works like this. The supply ditch to the 10-acre experimental tract contains 30 turnouts and has an automatically operated check below the last turnout. When the check is closed, the water level in the supply ditch rises, triggering a float valve that directs the water pressure through connecting lines to pistons connected to the first six gates. The gates open and water flows into the borders.

As the irrigation water reaches the end of the border, it flows into a sump containing another float valve. When water rises in this sump or stilling well, the float valve rises, actuating the second four-way valve that directs water toward pistons attached to the second set of six gates. These gates open, allowing water to flow between border dikes of second irrigated area. A third float valve in this area immediately adjacent to the ditch is triggered when water flows into a sump, causing the first set of six gates to close.

Thus, irrigation of the 10 acres of citrus is accomplished automatically, allowing water to flow from six turnouts on a 2-acre piece of land at any one time or "set." In sequence, the flow of water is automatically shifted to the other five sets.

Concerning the system, the *Arizona Farmer-Ranchman* for June 10, 1967, states, "IT'S SIMPLE. It works. It saves labor. It saves time. It saves water."

In contrast to remote controls requiring batteries, electrical tone telemetry systems, or radio transmission of earlier installations, the water-powered system has many advantages. It is on standby at all times, operates over a wider range of distances, and has many safety factors in its favor.

A recent feature of the automatic irrigation system—a water wheel-powered piston pump placed in the irrigation supply ditch to provide water pressure to the system—has been developed by Haise. Although not as yet field tested, the device has been operated successfully in a hydraulics laboratory. Field testing of the water wheel and pump is scheduled for the Yuma installation. If it's successful, the electric-powered pump to provide water pressure may not be needed.

Whoa and go for water—with water itself calling the signals—is here to stay.

ULV Brings New Benefits in Air War on Pests

JOSEPH T. KOSKI

. . . .

Aerial spraying of pesticides in amounts as low as 1 ounce per acre may well revolutionize the aerial war against insect enemies such as the mosquito and grasshopper. Among the benefits the public can expect are more effective pest and disease control with less toxicant; lower food production costs; and more enjoyable patio and vacation living with greater freedom from biting and stinging insects.

Development of the ultralow volume (better known as ULV) spraying technique reflects emphasis by the U.S. Department of Agriculture on increased safety in pesticides applica-

tion. Substantial reductions in the amount of toxic chemical applied to a given area also reduces potential hazards to people, animals, and the total environment including soil, air, and water.

Many farmers in Michigan and Indiana first shared this new development in the spring of 1964 when ultralow volume spraying became operational in this country. That year, infestations of the cereal leaf beetle, a dangerous pest of small grains, were controlled with aerial applications of an undiluted insecticide applied in a total volume of 5 fluid ounces per acre.

What is ULV aerial spraying? The U.S. Department of Agriculture defines it as applying an undiluted pesticide in volumes of 2 quarts or less per acre. A pesticide is considered undiluted if nothing is added to it after it leaves the manufacturer.

Actually, ULV is a relative term reflecting the progress of aerial spraying since its beginning during World War II. At that time, the generally accepted application rates varied from 30 to 40 gallons per acre.

Eventually, as pesticide formulations improved, the application rates were reduced to as little as a gallon an acre. Each substantial reduction in the total gallonage was referred to as "low volume" spraying.

For many years, pest control officials contended at least 1 gallon of spray per acre was the absolute minimum that could be applied by aircraft to adequately cover the acre, regardless of the vegetation involved. Thus, when the 1 gallon per acre barrier was broken, it was logical to refer to this as ultralow volume (ULV) spraying.

A principal feature of ULV pesticide application is reduction of costs associated with transporting, mixing, and applying the nontoxic portion of the spray mixture—diluents such as oil or water.

This is a major factor in remote areas beset by inadequate roads and other transportation problems. It was not surprising, therefore, that steps to eliminate diluents from aerial sprays were first taken in East Africa on desert locust control programs. While this did not constitute ULV spraying in the sense we know it today, it signaled a new approach to pesticide application by aircraft.

In the United States, feasibility of applying pesticides by aircraft with relatively little dilution was demonstrated in tests against the rangeland grasshopper in 1962. A chlorinated

∴   ∴   ∴

JOSEPH T. KOSKI *is Regional Supervisor, Eastern Region, Plant Pest Control Division, Agricultural Research Service, Moorestown, N.J.*

hydrocarbon insecticide was found to provide an excellent grasshopper kill whether applied in 1 gallon or 1 pint of fuel oil. However, before this discovery could be adapted to field use, rising concern over chlorinated hydrocarbon residues, such as DDT, in animals grazing on treated rangeland resulted in a switch to other insecticides.

Among the alternate insecticides field tested that year was malathion, an organophosphate compound of low mammalian toxicity. Again it was shown grasshopper control was not adversely affected by reduced amounts of diluent, a light oil in this case. The next logical step was to apply the material "straight from the drum" with no dilution at all. Results were outstanding. As little as 8 fluid ounces of undiluted technical malathion provided excellent grasshopper kill. This, then, marked the beginning of what we know today as ULV aerial spraying.

Since 1963, USDA's Plant Pest Control Division, in cooperation with the State agencies and affected property owners, has employed ULV to treat nearly 11 million acres of cropland and rangeland. The cereal leaf beetle has been controlled with as little as 4 fluid ounces of undiluted malathion per acre; the rangeland grasshopper with 8 ounces; the boll weevil with 12 to 16 ounces; and the Mediterranean fruit fly (Medfly) with 2 ounces in combination with a bait.

The Medfly was eradicated from the Rio Grande Valley of Texas in 1966 in a record 44 days.

Use of this technique is not limited to agriculture. During the summer of 1966, an outbreak of St. Louis encephalitis in Dallas, Tex., transmitted by the mosquito, *Culex pipiens quinquefasciatus*, was quelled with a single aerial application of 3 fluid ounces of undiluted malathion per acre. In just 8 days, nearly a half million acres in the Dallas area were treated by U.S. Air Force C–123 cargo planes, resulting in a 90 to 95 percent reduction of the disease-carrying mosquito population.

Elsewhere, residents and vacationers

in coastal areas plagued by pesky mosquitoes received relief from still another organophosphate insecticide, naled (Dibrom®), in ULV form. Amazingly, less than a single ounce of this insecticide distributed per acre by aircraft was sufficient to curb adult mosquito populations.

Advantages of ULV spraying in large-scale operations are many. The technique has decreased the number of aircraft and airstrips needed. Ferrying time has been drastically reduced. Transportation for water or other diluents and facilities for mixing insecticide formulations are no longer necessary. Fewer supporting vehicles, equipment, and personnel are needed. Besides, the relatively nonevaporative quality of the undiluted insecticide has permitted aircraft to fly higher, thus making it possible to double and triple effective swath widths. These factors have reduced aerial application costs on large-scale programs as much as 50 percent.

A striking example of cost savings can be illustrated by the boll weevil campaign on the high plains of Texas. Standard recommended application rate for this pest had been 3 gallons of insecticide mixture per acre. To spray the acreage involved would have required 80 aircraft and 16 airstrips and cost approximately $2 an acre.

Using ULV, 20 aircraft operating from five airstrips completed the program as scheduled for an overall cost of less than 85 cents an acre. Put another way, one planeload of ULV spray could cover 1,200 acres; whereas to spray this same area at the previously recommended 3 gallons an acre would require 27 planeloads. Other examples of substantial cost savings can be cited on the cereal leaf beetle and Mediterranean fruit fly programs.

These cost savings are based on large

By not having to dilute pesticides with water or oil, significant savings in aerial application costs on large-scale programs are possible. With ultra low volume (ULV) sprays, number of trips between airstrip and areas under treatment has been drastically reduced.

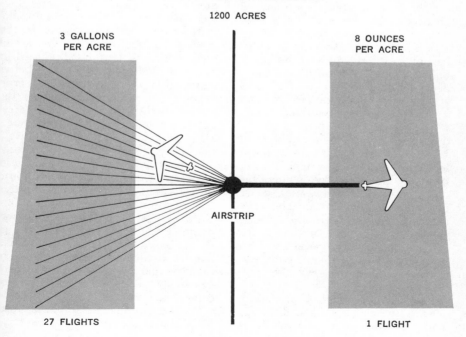

FERRY FLIGHT COMPARISON

1200 ACRES

3 GALLONS
PER ACRE

8 OUNCES
PER ACRE

AIRSTRIP

27 FLIGHTS

1 FLIGHT

123

area control programs and are not as pronounced for the local aircraft operator dealing with individual farmers. Since he must work smaller fields with diversified agricultural crops, some requiring different treatments, his application costs remain higher. Likewise, the expense he incurs in contacting growers and associated business transactions is generally constant, regardless of whether the sprays are applied in ULV or conventional form.

Besides the advantage of reduced application costs on large-scale programs, there is evidence of increased biological activity with ULV sprays. In the case of malathion, this is partially explained by the nonvolatile nature of the technical material and the distinct droplets which are formed on the surface of foliage. The compact droplets do not spread out upon contact as diluted droplets tend to do. Thus, less of the insecticide is exposed to degradation by plant enzymes and sunlight. In most cases, the increased biological activity of the undiluted insecticide has made it possible to reduce the amount of actual toxicant required per acre.

How is it possible to satisfactorily distribute only a few ounces of liquid over an acre of land? Uniform atomization is the key. Actually, if only a half pint of pesticide were broken up uniformly into a fine mist, the resulting deposit would contain approximately 75 drops per square inch of horizontal surface. If smaller cloud-type droplets were formed, nearly 10 times as many drops per square inch would result. In actual practice, this degree of droplet uniformity with available equipment is not feasible. Under field conditions, ULV sprays are dispersed in droplets varying in size. The largest droplets are wasteful; the smallest, subject to drift from the target area.

Recognizing the importance of uniform droplet sizes, manufacturers are striving to improve existing spray-dispersal equipment.

The current trend in nozzles is toward spinning cage and disk types, some of which are driven by the air-

stream, others by miniature electric motors. The latter are especially useful for helicopters whose forward speed is not sufficient to achieve adequate breakup of droplets using windmill-powered nozzles. Use of pneumatic atomizers, similar to those in paint sprayers, also is being explored.

Since the relatively sparse amount of liquid used in ULV sprays required finer atomization, one would expect the tiny droplets to drift farther than those produced by conventional sprays. However, there are indications this is not necessarily the case. Rate of evaporation is important. A small droplet of a relatively nonevaporative concentrate leaving the nozzle will remain the same size and should reach the ground within reasonable distance downwind from the point of release. On the other hand, a similar droplet of a water-diluted formulation decreases in size rapidly as it falls, especially under high temperature and low humidity conditions. Thus, as the droplet nears the ground, it may be only a fraction of its original size and consequently subject to extended drift.

Some degree of drift may be tolerated in remote areas where large acreages are treated, since more of the drifting particles will remain in the area being sprayed. As a matter of fact, under certain conditions drift may be desirable to obtain better penetration through forest or crop canopies. In recent tests against the spruce budworm, the U.S. Forest Service relied upon local mountain air currents to transport and diffuse a fine spray mist of Zectran®, a carbamate insecticide. Surprisingly, the tests have shown that spray broken up into droplets as fine as fog are most effective against this destructive forest pest.

Under most circumstances, however, pesticide drift is a serious hazard and should be avoided as much as possible. This is particularly true in areas of intensive and diversified farming where nearby forage and feed crops may become contaminated.

Pesticides should not be applied as ULV aerial sprays unless they have been registered for use in this manner by USDA's Pesticides Regulation Division. Pesticide manufacturers wishing to label their products for ULV aerial applications must submit data on effectiveness, drift, plant damage, residues, hazards to fish and wildlife, and hazards to the aerial applicator, including his ground crew.

At present, relatively few compounds have been approved for ULV application by aircraft. These include malathion for a fairly wide range of insect pests; azinphosmethyl (Guthion®) for boll weevil control in cotton and sugarcane insects, naled (Dibrom®) for adult mosquitoes on noncropland; a DDT-toxaphene mixture for a variety of pests of cotton and soybeans; and toxaphene for pests of bananas.

Numerous other materials have been tested as ULV sprays, many of them with promising results. It appears likely that additional chemicals ultimately will be approved for use in this manner.

Despite the progress with ULV aerial spraying, a concerted research effort will be required to fully exploit the technique. Aircraft spray dispersal equipment and pesticide formulations must be improved to permit better control of droplet size and, thus, drift. From the biological standpoint, optimum droplet sizes must be determined for each target pest. Likewise, more effective techniques are required to assess ULV spray deposits.

With the remarkable accomplishments recorded to date as a result of savings in application costs on large-scale programs, the increased effectiveness in control with less toxicant, and the speed of coverage against disease-carrying pests, ULV faces a promising future indeed.

Automatic Livestock Feeding

H. B. PUCKETT, K. E. HARSHBARGER, *and* E. F. OLVER

. . . .

Automatic systems for mixing and distributing livestock rations can reduce the man-hours required for feeding cattle by 75 to 80 percent. Such systems are now mechanically and economically feasible. That is, with sufficient capital available for the necessary investment, the environment can be created (buildings, equipment, etc.) and a profit realized. And if the general conditions most affecting this process continue substantially as at present, the profit potential is likely to become even greater.

Mechanization of crop production—as this affects the production of feed grains—and more practical adaptations of mechanical advancements in feed handling have made possible the breakthrough for radically increasing the efficiency of livestock production. This means livestock production can now join the ranks of grain production and other fast-changing agricultural production systems in the upward cycle of efficiency increase.

Examples abound:

Broiler production had an increase in productivity per man-hour of 538 percent between 1945 and 1965. In feed-grain production (using the 1940–1944 period as the basis for comparison), the productivity increase per man-hour has exceeded 700 percent. On the same basis, that of livestock and livestock products has increased only about 215 percent.

Mechanization of livestock production has progressed at a slow pace because of the large number of small and time-consuming operations that had to be meshed into a smooth and reliable system. Recently, however, livestock producers and equipment manufacturers have attacked the problem of mechanizing livestock production in earnest.

An example of the type of research and development unit that is serving to quicken the pace is the Dairy Mechanization Center at the University of Illinois. Established to explore the concept of automated, mechanized group feeding and handling of dairy cattle, it will take care of 80 dairy cows. And the system provides a precisely mixed feed ration.

A preset control system initiates all the actions automatically. The feed is mixed, ground, and conveyed to the desired points as directed by the automatic controls. One man can look after the whole operation—including grouping the cows for milking, feeding, and housing. Individual attention is required only during calving, breeding, or veterinary treatment for a particular animal.

To effectively apply modern, automatic equipment to dairying, the operator must accept the concept of group handling. Emphasis has to be placed on uniformly high production and on efficient use of labor.

The number of milk cows in herds of 50 or more increased 3.57 times between 1939 and 1959, according to the 1959 U.S. Census of Agriculture. Larger herds provide a more efficient base for mechanization.

One man can handle enough high-yield cows to produce 800,000 to 1,000,000 (or more) pounds of milk annually. The key is in arranging everything for maximum efficiency.

∴   ∴   ∴

H. B. PUCKETT *is Investigations Leader, Farm Electrification Research Branch, Agricultural Research Service, stationed at the University of Illinois, Urbana.*

K. E. HARSHBARGER *is Professor, Department of Dairy Science, University of Illinois.*

E. F. OLVER *is Professor, Department of Agricultural Engineering, University of Illinois.*

At present in the United States, most feed preparation and distribution systems are of the semiautomatic type—an operator is needed to initiate the actions and to change the pattern. Recent developments in solid-state devices—diodes, transistors, silicon control rectifiers—have created the potential for the kind of fully automatic control system that can be preset and that is both reliable and efficient. This is the kind of control system now being perfected and tested in units like the Dairy Mechanization Center in Urbana. The time-rate method of control best describes the controls developed for the system in the Illinois project. One of the new items developed was the electronic silo unloader control, which makes use of the high-power-amplification capability of the silicon control rectifier.

The University of Illinois system permits the dairy cows to be fed by automatic or manual control. Ingredients are removed from storage in the proper quantity and at the proper rate, mixed together to form a ration, and the ration fed in turn to each of the four lots.

Makeup of the ration for each lot and the quantity distributed are regulated by the control system.

Feeds handled are grass silage, haylage, corn silage, and a concentrate ration made up of a maximum of four ingredients or premixed combination. The concentrates are blended in an automatic hammer mill and are pneumatically conveyed to a concentrates tank, which is equipped with a volumetric feed meter that regulates the proportion of concentrates to the silage. The hammer mill unit operates independently of the main control system.

The silo unloaders are in the top of two concrete-stave silos and are supported by cables. The unloaders consist of a gathering auger to bring the silage to the center of the silo and a blower-thrower to discharge it from the silo. A bottom-silo unloader is used in the third silo, which is a sealed storage unit.

Overall view of Dairy Cattle Mechanization Center, *above*. Grass silage, haylage, and corn silage from three silos and concentrates from tall building provide the ingredients for feed ration. After mixing in low building, ration is conveyed on 90-foot raised horizontal cross auger to feed bunks. *Right*, cattle at feed bunk on one of four lots. Milking parlor is in background.

Since the combination and proportion of the ingredients are under full control of the operator, the finished ration may consist of any one of the four major sources, a blend of all four, or any combination.

The ration is assembled from the four sources and delivered to the feed bunks in turn.

The feed-bunk distributor is a 9-inch auger that can discharge material into several small "cells" beneath it. When the last of these cells has been filled, a switch causes a second auger to empty the cells into the feed bunk.

The ration can be delivered as often as every 2 hours or as infrequently as once each day. Delivery to any one lot is adjustable between zero and 30 minutes. After each delivery, the conveying equipment operates for a short time to completely clear the conveyors before feed is mixed for the next lot.

The control system includes safety features to prevent delivery of an improperly mixed ration. If a particular piece of equipment fails to do its job, automatic shut-off occurs and a warning circuit is energized.

Since 1936, mechanization in the field has increased by more than four times the work which one man can successfully perform in crop production. We are on the threshold of a similar upswing in efficiency (in terms of the human labor input) in livestock production.

The radical changes experienced in the broiler industry may only be a harbinger of what lies ahead in the production of livestock. And this, too, can be seen as taking its place in the massive pattern of change that has steadily increased U.S. agricultural production while steadily decreasing the number of people required to live and work on our farms in order to get the job done. It stands as a monument to the efficiency of mechanization, properly integrated into a total system which is dedicated to ever-increasing crop yields and ever-greater animal production.

Improved crop yields came first, followed by revolutionary changes in management practices and output in some types of animal production. The major holdout has been livestock production. Now, the means are at hand to begin to radically upgrade efficiency in that sector of agricultural production too.

H. B. Puckett at control panel for automated livestock feeding system.

City and Country

World's Largest Market Joins the Jet Age

KENNETH H. BRASFIELD

....

New York City is accustomed to being first, largest, or best known in a lot of things. It accepts innovation as commonplace, a part of daily life. But one of its innovations stands out as truly remarkable—even to New Yorkers.

On May 17, 1967, dignitaries and well-wishers from all over the world gathered at Hunts Point in the Bronx to witness dedication of the largest and most modern wholesale produce market ever constructed. The new $38 million market stands on 126 acres of land with buildings that would stretch almost 1½ miles if placed end to end. This is the new home for almost an entire industry that moved from its old, dilapidated home in lower Manhattan, 12 miles away.

Presidential representatives and other Federal, State, local, and industry officials, together with foreign ambassadors and private businessmen, heard New York City's mayor describe the new fruit and vegetable market as just the beginning of a giant wholesale food distribution center to be constructed at Hunts Point. He revealed that final plans call for filling 350 acres of land with facilities to handle all kinds of food for millions of people in the New York City area.

What New York's mayor called "just the beginning" for his metropolis would already be an avalanche for most other cities. Nearly 15 tons of fresh produce come here each minute of every daylight hour of every working day. About one in every eight carloads of fresh fruits and vegetables produced in the United States for sale in unprocessed form finds its way to this market where it joins with products from 35 foreign countries to be distributed to consumers.

This is the pricemaking market of the country, handling produce from nearly every State, as well as practically every kind of commercial produce grown in the world.

The individuality of this market did not come with the building of this new facility. This is something the New York wholesalers already had and had earned through generations of work and hardship.

Authorities believe it all started near the piers at the southernmost tip of Manhattan, for here is where ships brought goods to early New Yorkers.

A large part of the food arrived at these piers, and the original food handlers located near the place where it was unloaded.

For reasons known only to them, the food wholesalers gradually moved north to an area along Washington Street. They settled into any kind of housing that was available and stood their ground for over 100 years while the country's largest metropolis grew around them.

∴ ∴ ∴

KENNETH H. BRASFIELD *is Chief of the Marketing Facilities Development Branch, Transportation and Facilities Research Division, Agricultural Research Service.*

130

But while other industries adopted newly developed sources of power and applied assembly line techniques, fruits and vegetables continued to move from the crowded stores on the backs of porters and on handtrucks which the porters pushed down the cobblestone streets. The Nation's highways changed to multilane, high speed traffic arteries, yet Washington Street remained 30 feet wide and logjammed each night, when 20 miles of trucks tried to get into 2½ miles of street.

As mechanization became a basic requirement for the very survival of other businesses, Washington Street buildings were virtually without mechanization. Most of them had elevators, but many of the elevators were obsolete or mechanically unsafe.

A great many firms had no refrigeration to protect the quality of the foods they handled. Lack of sanitation prompted the writing of a series of popular magazine articles entitled, "Filth in Our Food."

Critics said the wholesalers let things stand because they were making huge profits. Other critics, in defense of the wholesalers, claimed exactly the opposite was true, that profits dwindled to almost nothing in the face of high operating costs imposed by deplorable conditions. Furthermore, they claimed, the volume of business had declined.

As a percentage of the total receipts of fruits and vegetables in New York City, the Washington Street market's share did drop from 76 percent in 1939 to 67 percent in 1956. This drop came despite large increases in the standard of living and a steady rise in the population the market could serve. One thing for sure, the net effect was an inefficient market that took its toll in greatly adding to the cost of marketing food in New York City.

Both public and private organizations attempted over the years to solve the market's problems. Some report that over 70 studies were made altogether, many in good faith by the wholesalers themselves. But these tended to treat the symptoms of the problem, not the problem itself.

In 1955, the Market Study Committee of the New York Branch of the United Fresh Fruit and Vegetable Association took the first step that led to the new Hunts Point market. As

Artist's sketch of new wholesale produce market at Hunts Point.

The old Washington Street market in lower Manhattan.

official representative of the industry, they opposed the popular belief that the Washington Street market should be rehabilitated and left where it was. They had new ideas.

The committee studied the work of William C. Crow, internationally recognized authority on food marketing facilities with the Agricultural, Research Service, U.S. Department of Agriculture. Bill Crow, author of a chapter in this Yearbook, directs a research program to find ways of improving efficiency in the physical movement of food from farms to consumers. Improving city markets is a part of this work, and over 30 city markets in the United States and many others in every continent have been designed after the principles he developed.

The Market Study Committee and the city of New York requested his assistance. They wanted to develop a plan that would once and for all clear up the mess in New York City.

"If any improvement is to be made. it is paramount to know exactly what exists and what is wrong with it." With this philosophy, Crow and his staff went to work assisted by the city of New York, New York State Department of Agriculture, Stanford Research Institute, and the food wholesalers themselves. In summary, here are some of the things they found.

There were 373 stores within the 24-block area known as the Washington Street Produce Market. Wholesalers used 213 of them in handling fresh fruits and vegetables. A total of $350 million worth of fresh fruits and vegetables moved through the wholesale channels each year.

Facilities for moving this produce were so cramped that a great part of it had to be stacked outside on the sidewalks and in the streets. Most of the buildings were old, antiquated relics from one to 10 stories high and never intended for marketing food. Some were built before the Civil War.

Little effort was made in recent years to modernize them. Eighty-eight percent were over 44 years old, 32 percent were over 100 years old, and only 16 percent were of fireproof construction.

Larger trucks were prohibited from entering the market area because of the knot of traffic that already existed. These trucks had to be unloaded on streets outside the area, and smaller trucks shuttled the loads on to the wholesalers. The market area did not have direct rail service, and yet over half its receipts came by rail. Railcars were unloaded some distance away, and their payloads also carted in on small trucks.

There was room for only about 400 trucks at the produce stores, and over 1,000 trucks were counted trying to get into the market at one time. Traffic snarls were indescribable. It took trucks an average of 4 hours to get into and out of the market.

The food wholesalers were crowded. Facilities were inefficient, wasteful, and unsanitary; handling methods,

outdated. Firms in the market lost business steadily to larger, more efficient firms outside the market. U.S. Food and Drug Administration inspectors seized tons of food each day as unfit for human consumption. In the words of one merchant, "The market was 50 years behind the times in 1900, and is now at least 100 years behind the times."

Findings of the study were presented at a public meeting in New York on Saturday afternoon, November 23, 1957. Over 150 people—city officials, food wholesalers, allied businessmen, and others—heard a comprehensive, detailed description of how food got to consumers in New York. They heard a listing of what was wrong and what should be done to correct it.

They learned that their present methods added $11 million too much each year to the cost of marketing food in New York City.

They also learned that this amount could be saved annually if they would improve their methods.

A great part of the produce had to be stacked on sidewalks or in the street.

At the new Hunts Point market, a USDA market news reporter on his early morning
rounds confers with a watermelon dealer.

"The deficiencies of the Lower Manhattan Market . . . cannot be corrected by remodeling the present market," the researchers pointed out. "Anything less than a completely new facility would be of doubtful value." They went on to propose that new, modern, and efficient facilities be built in a more suitable location outside congested lower Manhattan. They showed what such a market should look like, how much it would cost, how it could be bought and paid for, how much it could save in material and human losses, and even suggested five places where it could be located. One of these places was Hunts Point where the new market stands today.

Food wholesalers call it a "dream market." There are 252 individual stores each 25 feet wide and 100 feet long. Every store in the market can be served direct by both truck and rail simultaneously. The buildings are separated by streets 200 feet wide, and there is ample parking for the largest of trucks as well as for the automobiles of the workers and buyers.

The market is ideally located for motor transport, at the hub of New York State's arterial highway system. All 12 railroads that come to New York City can serve the market and deliver their cars direct to receivers or place them nearby in the largest rail holding yard of any wholesale produce market in the world.

Major airports are within easy reach for air freight shipments.

Every food handler has elevated loading platforms at both the front and rear of his place of business, and he can use the most modern handling equipment. The market is clean, modern, efficient; food can be refrigerated and protected; and it is a pleasant place to work.

Visitors from every corner of the world have come to see this market to get ideas they might use in their own country. But what they saw, as New York City's mayor put it, is just the beginning, and there will be more to see when they return.

During his study, Bill Crow had noted that other kinds of food wholesalers suffered with the same hopeless handicaps afflicting the fruit and vegetable wholesalers. "It would seem to be just as necessary to provide facilities for these (other) people as for the fruit and vegetable wholesalers," he remarked. "For this reason . . . the possible need for providing facilities for the wholesaling of other foods should not be ignored."

It was not ignored, for he was asked to continue and study the other kinds of food wholesalers. He found that an additional $15 million could be saved each year by eliminating the needless waste in marketing meat, poultry, eggs, butter, and cheese. He showed a plan of how this could be done.

Today you will see vacant land abutting the new fruit and vegetable market at Hunts Point. This is where a $160 million addition will be built to house the other kinds of food processors and wholesalers who will move there.

New York City is proud of its new wholesale produce market and anxious to complete the expansion into a vast 350-acre wholesale distribution center for all kinds of food.

It will be the market of markets that will go unchallenged for many years to come. But more important, it will provide an efficient, modern, and clean place to handle food for the tables of 15 million people.

For further reading:

"Hunts Point Opens! A Report on the Nation's Largest Market." *The Packer*, Packer Publishing Co., Section B, February 1967.

Rogers, Harold, "New York City the Biggest Market of Them All." *Produce Packaging Association Yearbook, 1964*, October 1964.

U.S. Department of Agriculture, *The 14th Street Wholesale Market for Meat and Poultry in New York City*. Marketing Research Report 556, Washington, D.C. 20250, 1962.

—— *Improving Market Facilities in New York City for Wholesaling Fresh Fruits and Vegetables*. Marketing Bulletin 6, Washington, D.C. 20250, 1960.

—— *New York City Wholesale Butter, Margarine, Egg, and Cheese Market Facilities*. Marketing Research Report 561, Washington, D.C. 20250, 1962.

—— *New York City Wholesale Fresh Fruit and Vegetable Markets*. Marketing Research Report 389, Washington, D.C. 20250, 1960.

Whitman, Howard, "Filth in Our Food." *Redbook*, McCall Corp., New York, May–July 1952.

New-Old Water Abracadabra Reverses Disappearing Act

LLOYD E. MYERS

. . . .

It's time to ring down the curtain on one of the world's oldest vanishing acts—by raindrops.

As our Nation's water needs soar, big new programs are being launched to find ways for desalting sea water, importing water from other regions, modifying weather to increase rain and snowfall, and reusing waste water. These techniques of modern scientific magic will work in some places, but not everywhere. Many areas have no water to import, desalt, or to reuse.

Where can they obtain more water?

One possibility lies in applying the wizardry of modern technology to an ancient practice called water harvesting—collecting and storing water from land treated to increase the runoff of rainfall and snowmelt. Grab the moisture before it vanishes right in front of your eyes!

Did you ever realize that two-thirds of the rain and snow falling on the continental United States never appears as streamflow? In the Colorado

135

River Basin, as a matter of fact, less than 10 percent of precipitation shows up as water in the river. Some of this precipitation is used by vegetation or replenishes ground water supplies, but much of it soaks into dry soil and then uselessly evaporates.

The amount of water falling as rain can be surprising. Ten inches of rain on 1 square yard amounts to 56 gallons of water. Our driest State, Nevada, receives average annual rainfall equal to a 50-gallon barrel of water setting on every square yard of land in that State.

Annual rainfall at many places in our wettest State, Hawaii, exceeds 1,200 gallons per square yard. Yet, Hawaii suffers from water shortages! The rain soaks into porous soils and cinders and percolates down to sea level. Pumped ground water is available at sea level, but is often contaminated by salt from the ocean. Large quantities of pure water could be made available by harvesting the rainfall before it soaks into the soil.

Water harvesting is not a new technique. During the Middle Bronze period, about 4,000 years ago, farmers cleared hillsides of rocks to smooth the soil and increase rainfall runoff. Ditches were dug across the hillsides to collect the water and carry it to lower lying fields. These systems were used to grow grain in the Negev Desert of Israel where average annual rainfall was about 4 inches. Collection and storage of water from rooftops was a common practice in the United States, until made obsolete by the development of central water supply systems and motor-driven pumps for small household wells.

Over the years, we have tended to forget the ingenuity—born of necessity—displayed by our ancestors. The recent urgent need to develop new water supplies has caused several agricultural engineers and scientists to

∴   ∴   ∴

LLOYD E. MYERS *is Director, U.S. Water Conservation Laboratory, Agricultural Research Service, Phoenix, Ariz.*

examine this old water harvesting idea in the light of modern knowledge. Results to date are highly promising.

An Australian, Hector Geddes, has built a modern version of the Negev Desert systems on the Badgery's Creek Experimental Farm in New South Wales, Australia. This farm receives an average of 26 inches of rain per year, but there are long dry spells that prevent growing good pasture and hay with natural rainfall alone. Geddes built ditches and reservoirs to collect and store runoff from two-thirds of the farm. The remaining third is sprinkler irrigated by pumping from the reservoirs. The farm now produces high yields of excellent forage and of hay. Water harvesting changed a marginal farming operation into a highly profitable enterprise.

Thousands of acres of rangelands in the western United States are not used efficiently because natural water supplies dry up during the grazing season. Drinking water for cattle often must be hauled in by truck. This is expensive; what's more, hauling water to some remote locations is impossible.

C. W. Lauritzen, a U.S. Department of Agriculture scientist at Logan, Utah, decided to attack this problem by using sheets of plastic and artificial rubber. He has developed a unit called a "rain trap." A 5,000- to 10,000-square-foot rubber sheet spread over the ground collects rain which is stored in a large rubber bag holding from 2,000 to 20,000 gallons. Water from the bag is piped to a drinking trough. These "rain traps" can be rolled up for transporting and are easily unrolled and installed at the desired location. Rain traps are now collecting water for livestock at a cost lower than prices paid for hauling water by truck.

Artificial rubber rain traps are useful in some locations, but they are still too expensive for wide-scale use. Our research at the U.S. Water Conservation Laboratory in Phoenix, Ariz., has been aimed at lowering the cost of water harvesting.

Materials under investigation for collecting and storing rainfall include asphalt, plastic and metal films, sodium salts, and water repellants.

Asphalt is a low-cost petroleum residue that has been used for hundreds of years to pave roads. Road-building is done by using large and expensive machines to mix asphalt with sand and gravel and then compact it into a pavement. We felt that asphalt water-harvesting pavements would be less expensive if we could build pavements by spraying asphalt on a soil surface without mechanical mixing.

Dissolved in a petroleum solvent such as kerosene, asphalt is sprayed on the soil surface. As the solution soaks in, it deposits the asphalt which binds the soil into a reasonably strong, but porous, pavement. The pavement surface is then sealed watertight by spraying it with a homogenized mixture of asphalt and water. Catchments of this type up to 10,000 square feet in area are now being used successfully to collect water for livestock. Sprayed asphalt catchments cost less than artificial rubber catchments, but they do require occasional repair.

Thin plastic and metal films can be used as low-cost ground covers to collect rainfall, but they are easily destroyed by wind. Brent Cluff of the University of Arizona has installed a catchment by covering plastic film with gravel. The gravel protects the plastic against both wind and weathering damage. However, it also reduces runoff by holding back part of the water, which is then lost through evaporation. These catchments should be useful where gravel is available and maximum runoff is not required. Plastic films can be glued to the soil with asphalt to stop wind damage, and low-cost spray coatings can be applied to reduce weathering.

Another promising material for use as a ground cover is aluminum foil, a thousandth of an inch thick, which can also be glued to the soil with asphalt. Catchments of aluminum foil are inexpensive and provide 100 percent runoff of rainfall. A small field installation has shown no sign of weathering damage after 4 years of exposure.

Spraying soil surfaces with chemicals that prevent water from soaking into

Spraying a waterproofing and stabilizing compound on soil to increase rainfall runoff for livestock water supplies.

the soil is another intriguing approach to building low-cost catchments. Only 40 pounds of one chemical tested was enough to waterproof an acre of sandy soil. Runoff from water-repellent soils has averaged more than 90 percent of the rainfall. Some erosion has occurred, but this can be stopped by using low-cost soil stabilizers with the chemicals.

Chemical manufacturers are now making many new materials that should be good soil stabilizers. One of these is a plastic that can be dissolved in hot water and sprayed on the soil. Once applied, it is no longer soluble. Water-repellent chemicals, combined with soil stabilizers, appear to be a major breakthrough in water harvesting.

Tanks or reservoirs are required for water harvesting systems to store water for use between rains. Good progress has been made in developing such storage facilities. Plastics, artificial rubber, and chemicals are now being used successfully for lining and covering storage reservoirs to stop seepage and evaporation losses. Size of storage structures needed will depend upon the rate of water use, the amount of rainfall, and the time that elapses between rainstorms.

New storage facilities will not always be required. Water can often be stored in existing reservoirs that are not adequately filled by natural runoff. It is also important to observe that the amount of rainfall available is not necessarily the amount that falls where water is needed.

For example, the average annual rainfall at Phoenix is only 8 inches. But, rainfall 25 miles north of Phoenix averages 20 inches per year. If desired, the water harvested from this higher rainfall area could be stored and transported to Phoenix in existing reservoirs and channels.

Water harvesting will not be detrimental to other land uses. The largest conceivable areas that might be converted to catchments would constitute only a small fraction of our millions of acres of timber and rangelands. Im-

proved use of rangelands resulting from water harvesting will more than offset production from land converted to catchments.

It is easy to demonstrate that water falling as rain on some forested land is worth more than the timber produced. A study at one site in Arizona showed that on a yearly basis, timber production was worth $1 per acre. Rainfall per acre at this site, if captured, would be worth $9.50 to $2 for crop production.

Tree clearing to increase rainfall

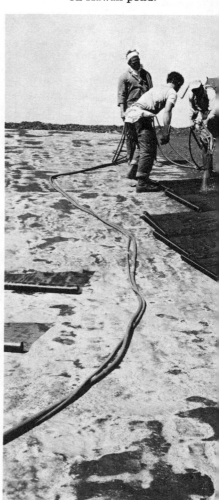

Fiber glass lining and spraying operation on Hawaii pond.

Reservoir site in Waiakoa, Hawaii.

noff is under intensive study. Rain-
l and runoff data from an 80-acre
ct of cleared forest in Arizona show
at more water could have been ob-
ned by building 4 acres of catch-
nt and leaving 76 acres of trees.
any other factors must be consid-
d, but these data imply that water
rvesting could be used to preserve
ne forested lands in areas where
ter yields must be increased.

Recreation can benefit from water
rvesting. There need be no eyesores
damage to scenery. Catchments can
made any size, shape, or color and
nouflaged or hidden from view if
s is desirable. Water harvesting can
used to establish and maintain land-
ping vegetation at strategic loca-
ns. Catchments are now being used
provide water for wildlife. Drinking

water for human visitors to some Hawaiian recreational areas is obtained
from catchments.

Water harvesting can be used to
make parks in our arid regions more
hospitable and attractive. Fishing
ponds can be built in areas where
natural runoff is inadequate for this
purpose. Recreational planners might
well begin to consider some of these
possibilities.

Proposals have been made to use
large-scale water harvesting techniques
to improve planned or existing water
resources. A sizable research program
is now directed toward increasing precipitation by seeding clouds with
chemicals. Land treatment to improve
runoff of the increased precipitation,
where increased runoff is desired,
seems logical.

139

Left. Gunite is sprayed to line re
ervoir in San Diego County, Cali
Step by step soil-cement linin,
bottom, of circular reservoir
Horsethief Canyon, Calif. Ceme
is spread with garden rakes. Rot
tillers are in action dry-mixin
cement with foundation materia
Operations are started in cent
and worked in circles towar
outside.

Butyl-lined ranch stockwater reservoir, with capacity of 5 million gallons.

Other suggestions relate to improving the quality of water in streams and rivers. Rainfall percolating through areas of salty soil and rock becomes highly saline. This water contaminates the streams it finally seeps into. Waterproofing the surface of these salty areas would cause water to flow into the streams without percolation and thus reduce stream salinity.

Similarly, water in some rivers, such as the Colorado, is becoming more saline as upstream water use increases. Pure water, obtained by large-scale water harvesting, could be used to dilute the present river water and improve its quality for downstream users. These proposals are just as feasible as the gigantic projects proposed for importing water from Canada and Alaska into the Western United States.

Estimates of the maximum water supply that can be developed at a given location should not be based on streamflow, of course, but on precipitation, which is many times greater than streamflow. All the precipitation cannot be captured, but a part of it can. The amount to be collected will depend upon the need.

Water harvesting will not be feasible in some areas. But in many areas, it offers the only practical way to develop new water supplies. Water harvesting adds a new dimension to resource planning.

141

Air Pollution Detectives

CHARLES R. BERRY *and* HOWARD E. HEGGESTAD

. . . .

Canaries once were widely used to detect methane gas in coal mines, and today plants are taking on the job of air pollution detectives in our smog-ridden communities. Even weeds are being recruited—ragweed and wild blackberry, for example. But field crops or ornamentals usually are signed for the job.

Air pollution injury to plants generally becomes evident before visible effects can be noted on animals or materials like paint, cloth, or metal. So plants make good detectives.

In a few areas, air pollution damage to crops has been so extensive that the effects for growers have been disastrous. For example, many citrus groves and truck crop acreages in the Los Angeles basin had to be abandoned after World War II when pollution rose to high levels. Today, estimates of damage to agricultural crops amount to more than $100 million annually in California and more than $500 million over the United States. A great deal of this loss is due to growth suppression without visible injury.

Virtually all principal types of plant crops have suffered economic damage from air pollution. Among these are citrus in California and Florida; grapes and orchids in California; peaches in Utah; tobacco in the East; and timber—especially pine—in the East, the West, and Canada. Because of pollution damage, it will be increasingly difficult to grow truck crops, particularly leafy ones like lettuce and spinach, near large cities.

But man has also made use of this sensitivity of plants. John T. Middle-ton first noted plant damage by smog in the Los Angeles area in 1944 and has carried out extensive investigations to better understand the nature of crop damage.

He has summarized the ways green plants are useful in combating air pollution. They assist man in:

• Recognizing the presence of air borne contaminants;
• Determining distribution of th pollutants;
• Estimating the level of pollution
• Providing a passive system for collecting pollutants for later chemical analyses.

Sometimes plants show a specific response to different air pollutants For example, P. W. Zimmerman and A. E. Hitchcock, at the Boyce Thompson Institute, have demonstrated that some plants—like tulip and field corn—are susceptible to fluorides, but resistant to sulfur dioxide while others—like alfalfa, dandelions and cotton—are susceptible to sulfur dioxide and resistant to fluorides. In addition, each type of pollutant tends to produce its own pattern of injury. Therefore, to the four uses set forth by Middleton, we can add a fifth: Direct identification of differen air pollutants on the basis of plan species injured.

⁝ ⁝ ⁝

CHARLES R. BERRY *is Principal Plant Pathologi at the Southeastern Forest Experiment Statio Forest Service, Asheville, N.C.*

HOWARD E. HEGGESTAD *is Principal Plant Pa thologist in the Crops Research Division, Agricu tural Research Service.*

142

This is not to say green plants will soon eliminate the need for sophisticated instrumentation in combating foul air. There are limitations, of course, particularly those brought about by the environment. For example, high temperature, low humidity, or a soil moisture deficit can sometimes alter a plant's response. And sometimes air pollution injury to vegetation is often similar to markings caused by fungi, bacteria, viruses, or insects. Eventually, however, plants grown under standardized conditions and located in strategic areas will serve as silent sentries and provide an inexpensive way to keep tab on air pollution. Instrument analyses are usually more meaningful when injury to plants is also considered, particularly with complex mixtures of toxic gases.

The five toxic gases that are the easiest to identify are sulfur dioxide, ozone, peroxyacetyl nitrate (PAN), ethylene, and the fluorides.

Before 1940, "air pollution" often meant only two things, smoke and sulfur dioxide. Smoke had been a nuisance since the first fire, and sulfur dioxide had been causing trouble since the first use of coal as fuel. In recent years, engineers have learned how to remove most of the post-combustion particles from stacks, thus making possible the elimination of smoke. Early in the century, sulfur dioxide pollution was so severe around smelters that practically all plant life was killed for miles downwind from the source. Because of improved technology, such severe pollution is essentially non-existent today.

But sulfur dioxide remains a problem. A modern electric powerplant may burn thousands of tons of coal or thousands of gallons of oil each day. Sulfur, an impurity in most coal and oil, is changed in the process to sulfur dioxide. It is not uncommon for a single large powerplant to produce several hundred tons of sulfur dioxide each day. Other sources are copper and iron smelters. Leaf injury from sulfur dioxide appears as light to dark brown blotches between the larger veins, which tend to remain green. Both leaf surfaces are affected.

The blotching may be extensive and, of course, decrease the plant's productivity and value.

mog trapped by temperature inversion that settled over Los Angeles. Inversion layer—layer of warm air which lies above a layer of cool air near ground—prevents natural ispersion of air contaminants. Upper portion of City Hall is exposed in clear air bove base of the inversion.

Plants sensitive to sulfur dioxide are alfalfa, barley, cotton, wheat, and beans. Resistant plants are potatoes, onions, corn, celery, and boxelder.

Ozone, a very active form of oxygen, is produced by both man and nature. In nature, ozone is found in the stratosphere where it acts beneficially as a filter, screening out most of the ultraviolet radiation coming from the sun. Without this screening, sunlight would be intolerable.

But more important for agriculture, ozone is also a product of air pollution. It is produced when sunlight shines through the products of combustion of coal or petroleum fuels, especially automobile exhaust gases. Because sunlight is necessary for its formation, pollution-generated ozone is also called a "photochemical product." Levels are usually highest about midday and relatively low at night.

Injury caused by ozone is very distinctive. Lesions are small and appear either as a dark stipple or a light fleck on the upper surfaces of leaves. A microscope shows that ozone first damages tissue—the palisade layer—just under the upper epidermis.

USDA Plant Pathologist Howard Heggestad checks graph from a met which measures concentration of ozone the air.

Plants sensitive to ozone are tomatoes, tobacco, pinto beans, spinach, potatoes, and lilacs. Tobacco variety Bel–W3 appears to be at least as sensitive to ozone as any plant species. Resistant plants are mint, geranium, gladiolus, and peppers.

Peroxyacetyl nitrate (PAN), like ozone, is also produced when the sun shines through various exhaust gases. It causes a silvering or bronzing of the lower surfaces of somewhat younger leaves than those affected by ozone. The tissue just under the lower leaf surface, spongy mesophyll, is injured most easily. Frequently, a banding pattern is noted; for example, injury may be restricted to either the tip, mid-area, or base of a leaf.

Plants sensitive to PAN are petunias, romaine lettuce, pinto beans, and annual bluegrass. Resistant plants are cabbage, corn, wheat, and pansies.

Fluorides—compounds containing the element fluorine—are produced by

aluminum and ceramics industries a fertilizer factories. These compound though highly toxic, are usually fou in toxic amounts only in very localiz areas. Losses have been extensive these areas, and some plants are i jured by concentrations as low as 0 part per billion.

Unlike other phytotoxicants, flu rides will build up inside the plant, ev though the concentration is low in t air. Once absorbed in the leaves, the compounds move toward the edges tips where a distinct marginal killi of tissue occurs. However, resista plants may accumulate several hu dred or even several thousand pa per million of fluoride without leaf i jury. Fluoride injury may be reveal by chemical analysis and is probab the most distinctive and easiest to dia nose of all pollutants.

Plants sensitive to fluorides are gla iolus (light colors generally more sen

ve than dark colors), Chinese apricot,
alian prunes, and pine. Resistant
ants are alfalfa, roses, tobacco, cot-
n, and tomatoes.

Ethylene, a gas that once plagued
eenhouse operators using manufac-
red gas for heating, now is recog-
zed as part of the growing problem
urban areas because it is also one of
any products of auto exhaust. Eth-
ene interferes with plant hormones,
growth regulators, resulting in
owth retardation, abnormal growth
ch as downward curvature of shoots
d leaves and leaf and flower drop.
Plants sensitive to ethylene are to-
atoes, orchids, carnations, snapdrag-
s, and cotton. Resistant plants are
asses and lettuce.

The U.S. Forest Service began stud-
s of air pollution effects on forests in
e late 1950's under the leadership of
eorge H. Hepting at Asheville,
.C. Deaths of eastern white pines in
ennessee stimulated these studies,
hich at first sought to determine
hether fungus or bacterial pathogens
insects was the cause. As work pro-
essed, each experiment seemed to
dicate air pollution as the culprit.
inally, by using grafted susceptible
hite pines as "detectives," Hepting
d Charles R. Berry showed that
r pollution was the cause.

Because white pine is unusually re-
tive to several known pollutants,
ork is now underway to determine
hether individual white pine seed-
gs with the proper genetic constitu-
on can be found for use in a wider
nge of detection problems. Spotted
eedles, yellow needles, or needles with
ead tips are the most common symp-
oms of pollution damage, although
ot all symptoms will be seen on each
ffected tree. One tree may display
ne kind of symptom, while another
ee nearby might display a com-
letely different, but equally harmful,
ind of injury.

These various symptoms may be
ifferent reactions, characteristic of
dividual trees, to the same pollutant.
r each kind of symptom may indi-
ate a different pollutant.

Sensitivity of white pine to some
gaseous pollutants has been established. The concentration of ozone
that causes injury to white pine is
about the same as that needed to injure some annual plants, like sensitive
varieties of tobacco or beans. Recent
work has also shown that some white
pines are very sensitive to sulfur dioxide. Sickly white pines are frequently found along heavily traveled
highways, presumably injured by auto
and truck exhaust. Therefore, it seems
likely that pines, grown as evergreen
ornamentals, could serve as air pollution detectives throughout the year.

The use of plant detectives has been
more than just a curiosity. Extensive
use of annual bluegrass was made in
Los Angeles County during the 1950's
in monitoring oxidant smog.

Research on the cause of the tobacco

Leaf of ozone-sensitive tobacco variety,
Bel–W3, shows light fleck characteristic
of ozone damage.

145

Contrast between grafted eastern white pines after 7 months exposure in a pollut area, *left,* and in an area free of pollution, *right.*

leaf spot "weather fleck" led to the identification of phytotoxic levels of the air pollutant ozone in the Eastern United States. Prior to this discovery in 1958 by Heggestad and Middleton, the problem of ozone injury to vegetation was generally known to exist only in California. R. H. Daines made plantings of Bel–W3 tobacco at 14 widely separated locations in New Jersey in 1959 and established the presence of phytotoxic levels of ozone at all locations. It was injury of the PAN type to the lower surface of leaves, especially of plants such as petunia and romaine lettuce in California, which led to the identification by Middleton and others of a photochemical air pollution problem in the Los Angeles basin. Similarly, varieties of gladiolus, such as Snow Princess, have been used a great deal in monitoring fluorides near aluminum plants. Tomato plants have been used many times to provide a simple means of testing for leaks of manufactured fuel gas containing ethylene.

Injury to orchid blooms, however, is usually the first evidence of high levels of ethylene in urban areas. Cattleya orchids are very sensitive to ethylene. Exposures of pines by the Forest Service provided dramatic evi-

dence of the presence of air polluti in concentrations sufficient to cau mortality of natural pine in the are

We still don't know how useful the plant detectives may become, b many people are carrying on resear testing of many species. In the mea time, the Forest Service, Agricultur Research Service, Public Health Ser ice, and many State and private ins tutions are making much use of pla to detect air pollution.

Perhaps the feature most liked abc plant detectives is that as living org nisms they are more closely related people and animals than instrumen Injury to a plant is frequently a mc convincing indication of injurious p lution than a trace on a piece of chi paper. Thus, plants from the low lichen to the stately pine can be use in combating the rising tide of a pollution.

For further reading:
Brandt, C. Stafford, and Heck, W. V "Effects of Air Pollution on Plants." *Pollution,* Academic Press, New York, 196

Darley, Ellis F., Nichols, Carl W., a Middleton, John T., *Identification of Pollution Damage to Agricultural Crops.* Ca fornia Department of Agriculture Bullet Vol. 55, No. 1, 1966.

Thomas, M. D., "Effects of Air Polluta on Plants." *Air Pollution,* WHO Monogra 46, 1961.

146

PEG Is the Sweetheart of the Wood Craftsman

HAROLD L. MITCHELL

. . . .

If you visit the office of a Congressman from California I know, you will see a log cross section displayed on the wall, beautifully preserved and finished. It came from the base of a large red fir, the 1966 national Christmas tree, which was a perfectly formed forest giant grown in the Congressman's home district.

This cross section is distinctive. It is free from the checks and the pie-shaped cracks that normally develop when a cross section is dried by conventional means.

The perfection of the Congressman's wall display is due to a new chemical stabilization treatment developed by USDA's Forest Products Laboratory at Madison, Wis. It is one application of knowledge gained from basic research aimed at finding ways to prevent wood from changing in dimension (shrinking and swelling) with variations in moisture content.

The chemical that has shown the greatest promise, and is now widely used in processing specialty wood products, is polyethylene glycol-1000—PEG, for short.

PEG is a white, waxlike chemical that resembles paraffin. It is nontoxic, dissolves readily in water, and will not discolor wood. When a piece of green, undried wood is soaked for an appropriate period in a 30 to 50 percent water solution of PEG, the wood does not shrink appreciably when it is dried. Because there is little or no change in dimension, treated wood has less tendency to warp and is usually free of the checks and splits that so frequently develop in wood, especially thick stock, during the drying process. Equally important, wood thus treated and then dried swells very little when exposed again to high humidities.

PEG attacks the problem of changes in wood dimension where they start by bulking the microscopic, latticelike structure of the individual wood fiber walls. Heavily treated wood is thus permanently restrained from shrinking, swelling, or warping regardless of atmospheric humidity.

Treatment with PEG permits efficient processing of green or partially dried wood, which is relatively inexpensive and plentiful.

It is ideally suited to the manufacture of salad bowls, large serving trays, candlesticks, art carvings, gunstocks, and similar products that normally require thick pieces of the highest and most expensive grades of kiln-dried hardwoods.

Although wood is easily adaptable and widely used, its tendency to shrink and swell causes many problems. Almost everyone has been plagued by doors that swell and stick in hot humid weather. Fine rifles lose their pinpoint accuracy due to a warped stock. Straightedges too often ripple during

∴ ∴ ∴

HAROLD L. MITCHELL is Chief, Division of Wood Quality Research, Forest Products Laboratory, Forest Service, Madison, Wis.

147

"dog days." For more than 30 years, the Forest Products Laboratory has been searching for a solution to problems such as these.

Early research was directed by Dr. A. J. Stamm, now of North Carolina State University.

At the Forest Products Laboratory, his work was largely securing fundamental information. This included impregnating veneer and wood with phenolic resins, high-molecular-weight polyethylene glycols, and various other promising chemicals, and modifying wood with heat and pressure.

More recently, other scientist-researchers—following the leads developed by Dr. Stamm—have developed practical applications of stabilization methods for high-value wood products such as gunstocks, art carvings, tabletops, and bowls.

Among these scientists are George Englerth, Harold Wahlgren, Ray Seborg, and the author.

Specialty wood products are traditionally made by relatively small, cottage-type industries located in rural communities near the source of their raw material. These industries have been hurt by the spiraling cost of kiln-dried turning stock. Few can afford dry kilns of their own. PEG seemed to offer an economically feasible solution to this particular problem and has been widely adopted by many small woodworking industries as well as by thousands of wood hobbyists.

Typical of the users of this new process is Delavan Designs, Interbrook Farm, Interlaken, N.Y. This small family-owned and family-operated business produces a high-quality line of exquisitely designed and crafted serving trays, bowls, bookends, candlesticks, table and floor lamps, and other woodenware items.

Formerly these products were made from kiln-dried mahogany and other tropical hardwoods. As these imported woods became scarce, and increasingly expensive, the company turned to native hardwoods. Now all their products are made from black walnut, butternut, and cherry grown on the

farm woodlots in the Finger Lakes are of New York State.

The change to native species at firs caused some production problems Since the company lacked adequat facilities for kiln-drying the local lum ber, large trays and other items wer made from green or poorly seasone walnut. As the wood dried, the tray warped and checked badly and wer unsalable. A local sawmiller, who ha heard of PEG, suggested its use t Nelson B. Delavan, Jr., owner of th woodcrafting business.

Delavan contacted the Forest Prod ucts Laboratory and a commercia supplier of PEG for technical data an advice on the PEG process. H followed their recommendations; an he is well pleased with the results.

Delavan, a professionally traine and highly talented artist, has an ap preciation of wood and a deep love fo it as a material for artistic expressior Following Navy service in World Wa II as an officer on a destroyer, he ma jored in art at Bard College at Annan dale-on-Hudson, N.Y. About the tim that he received his B.A. degree, h acquired a wife—an Alabamian at tending nearby Vassar. He continue his studies at the Cranbrook Academ of Art, near Detroit, where he earne a master of fine arts degree. With thi preparation, he accepted a teachin assignment at Berea College, Berea Ky., where he taught fine arts an humanities from 1952 to 1956.

About this time, Delavan decided t give up teaching to start his own wood craft business. Although raised in De Moines, Iowa, Delavan had deep root in the Finger Lakes area, where he ha spent most of his summers with h grandparents and other relatives. seemed natural to return, and he pu chased a farm near Interlaken over looking Lake Cayuga.

The old barn became a workshop equipped with lathe, bandsaw, an jointer. The comfortable farmhous became the home for the family which by then included four daugh ters, and it also housed the office.

Under present practice, raw ma

Artist and Designer
Nelson B. Delavan, Jr.,
displays a finished serving tray.

rials—logs, half-logs, and thick anks—from local sawmills are transrted to the shop. There Delavan, sisted by one full-time, skilled helper, nverts log, half-log, or thick plank to blanks of appropriate size for the tended product. The green blanks e next placed on the lathe and ugh-shaped into trays, bowls, lamp sts and bases, and other products. he rough green turnings are then aced in a homemade vat where they e soaked for an appropriate period—pending on size and species—in a percent water solution of PEG. llowing this, the green wood turngs are slowly air-dried to 6 to 8 rcent moisture content in a homeade conditioning room maintained about 75° F. and 30 percent relative midity.

As orders come in, the rough turngs, dried to flawless perfection, are placed on the lathe, shaped to final mensions, sanded, given several coats a special polyurethane finish, waxed, d polished. Although processed from een wood, the finished products are mpletely free of seasoning degrade—ecks, splits, and warp. Moreover, anks to the PEG treatment, they will y in that condition regardless of bsequent exposure to widely fluctuing relative humidity.

The sanding and finishing operations provide temporary employment to high school students in the area.

Farmers who grow the trees, loggers who harvest them, and sawmills that do the primary processing likewise all benefit economically from this small business enterprise.

Delavan exhibits his products frequently and has received many awards for excellence of design and craftsmanship. His products are marketed by about 20 retail stores throughout the eastern United States.

This craftsman emphasizes beauty, originality of design, and superb workmanship. He employs methods and products that enhance the inherent properties of fine woods. A key to his success, undoubtedly, is his understanding and appreciation of the material he works with. He states it thus:

"Wood has always been one of the most rewarding of materials, with endless variations of line, color, and texture. Wood invites the hand as well as the eye to explore it, to feel its warmth. In the grain pattern of a bowl one discovers the history of a living tree: The lines are a path of action, a record of forces at work. This organic quality must be kept alive by the craftsman as he shapes his material in the service of human needs."

149

Land Price 'Ticker Tape'

WILLIAM H. SCOFIELD

Land is many things—it is space to park your car, a place to build a patio, or the site for an office building. On a Sunday drive, it is a view, a roadside park, or a hiking trail. But only 3 percent of the total land area of the 48 contiguous States is taken up by cities, industry, highways, and similar uses. About three-fifths is used for crops and livestock production. The 1.1 billion acres in farms, including the buildings, had a market value of nearly $200 billion in early 1968. Such rural lands account for nearly a fourth of all taxable real estate outside our major cities.

The value of a commodity as versatile as land is intertwined with its use. It can be priced by the square foot, the acre, or by the square mile. A square foot located on a choice corner in Manhattan, New York City, may be priced at $200; in Manhattan, Kans., perhaps $1; and in Illinois corn country, 1 or 2 cents. There are 43,560 square feet in an acre—in a square plot each side is 211 feet. Up to 25,000 corn plants can be grown on 1 acre or 2 square feet per plant. The land for each plant would cost a nickel and produce about 6 ounces of corn.

Go westward to Arizona desert country where land is priced by the section—1 square mile or 640 acres. The price figures out at about a tenth of a cent a square foot. But even 10 square miles would represent just a modest cattle spread. It would provide grass for only 300 to 400 cattle.

Take this block of land and lay it out in 1-, 2-, or 5-acre plots. Put in a water system, roads, draw up plans for a shopping center, a golf course, and recreation center. Advertise your ne city in national magazines as a de sirable retirement community an price the land at $500 or $1,000 a acre. The original desert has becom a new commodity.

California has the widest range i land prices of any State. Topping th list for agricultural uses are avocad groves, upward of $7,000 an acre. Ci rus groves in the path of subdivisio may bring even more, but are value at around $3,000 where alternativ land uses are not important. Irrigate lands suitable for cotton and veg tables carry price tags of $1,000 $1,500 an acre.

Rangeland in the northern part the State is more likely to be price according to the amount of forag produced than by the acre. Eigl hundred dollars worth of land to car one animal would be typical.

Or take land in the East, within commuting distance of our larg cities. If it has frontage on water, will sell by the front foot, only infr quently by the square foot or acr Along a small lake or stream, the pri may be $20 or $30 a foot or $50 to $1 if it can be used for commercial pu poses. Prices go on up to $200 or mo for ocean frontage with good bea and highway access.

If you are thinking of a summ place in the mountains, you may ha

⁖   ⁖   ⁖

WILLIAM H. SCOFIELD is an Agricultural Econo mist in charge of research work in farm real est values and valuation in the Economic Resear Service.

choice of building a cabin on a small
y-size lot in a planned community
of finding an abandoned hill farm
th a house that can be fixed up for a
nmer home. The land in the farm
ll cost less per acre, and you'll have
ore space, but the total investment
n be a lot more. And don't forget to
ure the interest lost on the money
u put into either kind of place as
rt of the total cost of owning a
nmer retreat.

Land prices are by no means a con-
rn only of farmers. Many important
cisions in the business world involve
me aspect of land valuation. A major
mmunications firm needs estimates
land costs on which to build relay
tions scattered across the country.
en in the space age, a spot on earth
needed to launch satellites and to
ceive their messages. A life insur-
ce company in Hartford, Conn.,
vests a part of your insurance pre-
ums in farm mortgages throughout
e country. The company needs to
ow the level and trend in farmland
ices and the income farmers are
ely to earn to repay their loans.
A writer for a national business mag-
ine wants to compare returns from
ming farmland with returns from
cks and other investments. A public
lity company needs to update the
lue of its assets in order to adjust the
te structure. The utility wants cur-
nt market values for the land its
werlines are built on. The admin-
rator of a Federal or State agency
budgeting the probable costs of ac-
iring rights-of-way for a highway,
land for an airport or a sewage
sposal plant.

Letters and phone calls posing such
estions flow to an office of the Eco-
mic Research Service in Washing-
n, D.C. Here, three research econ-
ists have access to a large volume
statistical data on farmland values
most areas of the country. And
ey are constantly adding to their
ckpile of information with the aid of
nationwide corps of special reporters.
This reporting system has some rath-
interesting features. One group of

reporters consists of the regular crop
reporters—mostly farmers—who provide a regular flow of crop and livestock information to State offices of the
Statistical Reporting Service. This
agency, assisted by a large "staff" of
voluntary reporters, serves farmers and
consumers by issuing regular reports
on a wide range of farm subjects. Crop
conditions, acreages, yields, livestock
numbers, and prices are covered in
these reports.

Twice a year—March and November—these reporters, who represent
the eyes and ears of the U.S. Department of Agriculture, send in their estimates of the going market values of
farm real estate in their localities.
State statisticians review these reports
and send on to Washington summaries
for each reporting district. These are
the data we use to measure changes in
market values State by State.

This reporting system was first
started in 1913 and provides an unbroken chain of readings on land prices
every March since then. The November reporting date was added in 1942.
Let's take as an example the reported
values per acre for March for the 12
counties in northwest Iowa—1913,
$140; 1920, $301; 1933, $73; 1941,
$102; 1967, $430.

We use these figures chiefly to measure the relationship between prices at
different points in time. Because the
area is quite large, they can't be applied to particular farms. Selling prices
can vary greatly within a township or
a county. It takes a detailed appraisal
to determine what any particular tract
of land is most likely to sell for. So,
this is a job for specially trained ap-
praisers, not something that can be
done in our office.

This is why we express the reported
dollar values as index numbers—a
kind of "ticker tape." Like the cost of
living or the wholesale price indexes,
the land price index is simply a statistical device to permit easy comparison of where prices stand at any point
in time in relation to the base period.
We use average values for 1957, 1958,
and 1959 as a base or 100 to facilitate

comparisons with other statistical series published by Federal agencies.

There is nothing mysterious or complicated about using index numbers. Let's take our index for Iowa for March 1, 1967, 147 (1957–59=100). It means average values on that date were 47 percent higher than the 1957–59 average. Now, take the index number for 1933, 27. This means that values in 1933 were only 27 percent of the 1957–59 average.

Dividing the 1967 index by the 1933 index, we find values in 1957 were 5.4 times higher than in 1933 or an increase of 444 percent.

How can you use these figures to solve problems? I have a letter on my desk which reads as follows: "My father died in 1938 and left me 160 acres in Osceola County, Iowa. I sold the land last spring for $360 an acre. I need some information to help me put a value on the property in 1938 so I can fill out my income tax return."

He is referring to schedule D of the Federal Income Tax Return, Form 1040, which calls for "Cost or other basis" of property. What was the fair market value of this property in June 1938 when his father's estate was settled and title passed to him?

This is how I'll answer his letter. The index for Iowa for March 1, 1938, was 34 and for March 1, 1939, also 34. It was a period of quite stable prices, and there is no need to make an adjustment to a June date. Then, I divide the 1938 index by the 1967 index and find that values in 1938 were 23 percent of the 1967 level. Multiply this percentage by the 1967 sales price and we have $83 as an approximate value at that time.

The agricultural census for 1940 showed an average value of $95 an acre for this county.

I must stress that this is only a starting point in arriving at the capital gain for tax purposes. Other adjustments have to be made to comply with tax regulations. But it is a fair and objective starting point when no other basis is available to solve the problem.

We have another source of informa-

tion that is perhaps unique for a government research agency. More tha 40 years ago, an annual mail surve was started to tap the knowledge of local people in every community whos work brings them into contact with th farm real estate market. About ha the 8,000 names on our mailing li are real estate brokers and the rest ar local bankers, lawyers, abstractor county officials, and others. All serv as real estate market reporters, volun tarily and without pay. Many have r ported regularly for a decade or mor

A mail questionnaire goes to th group every March and October whic asks for their opinions as to recer changes in market conditions and als for facts about specific land transfe with which they are familiar. We g a sample of about 15,000 land sal each year, including the selling pric terms of sale, occupation of the sell and buyer, and related information.

Data obtained from these surveys ar reviewed by the research staff an made ready for analysis by compute No two surveys are identical becaus we are constantly seeking new bits information in order to improve ou analysis and interpretation of ne developments.

In the early 1960's, for example, w began to receive inquiries as to th effects of expanding cities on rur land prices. What is land for ope spaces, parks, highways likely to cos How should land still in farms bu with value for other uses be assesse and taxed?

A few years later, realization of th future recreational needs of an ir creasingly urban population focuse the attention of local, State, and Fe eral agencies on the steady rise tha had occurred in rural land prices.

The development of long-range lan acquisition programs required info mation on the range in land prices fo various purposes. We were able obtain this information from our r porters, thereby filling an importar gap in data.

But many facets of the rural lan market cannot be studied at the n

onal level. We need local "labora-
ories" where 100 or 200 land transfers
an be studied in greater detail than
possible with our national surveys.
To do this, we team up with econo-
ists in the State agricultural experi-
ent stations and work out procedures
r special studies. These may be con-
erned with land purchases by Ne-
raska farmers or prices paid for cotton
nd in South Carolina, the Mississippi
elta, and in California. Results of
ch studies are published by the co-
perating States. On other occasions,
e have provided technical and finan-
al assistance to graduate students
ho wish to study a particular aspect
farm real estate.

Collection, analysis, and interpreta-
on of information obtained from the
miannual survey and from farmer-
porters is a continuous process. Sta-
stical tables coming from the com-
uter must be checked for accuracy,

compared with results of previous
surveys, and condensed into understandable form for publication.

Twice a year a summary report is
issued which carries up-to-date information and analysis of changes in land
prices, rates of farm transfers, sources
of the land supply, and the demand
for land. Entitled "Farm Real Estate
Market Developments," and available
upon request without charge, this report is only one of a whole family of
publications that are products of the
ongoing research program of both
State and Federal research agencies.

Our research is concerned with the
economic behavior of people as they
go about putting a price tag on a very
special commodity—land. Our laboratory is the entire Nation. The better
this complex process can be understood, the more information people
have to guide their decisions, the better
our economic system will perform.

New Look Trees and Shrubs
for Homes, Communities

H. F. WINTERS *and* J. L. CREECH

. . . .

In the 21st century, as well
s during the immediate future, we
ill need an increasing variety of trees
nd shrubs genetically tailored or self-
mited to shape, size, and use. The
rchitectural styles of our houses have
anged. Properties are smaller. Our
opping malls, apartment communi-
es, and individual homes all need
ndscaping with plant materials that
ow to these specified shapes and
zes, then remain so for years.

Landscape materials for the future
ust be "smogproof," since even
ough great efforts are being made

to reduce atmospheric pollution, it is
doubtful if smog can be entirely eliminated in the near future. Landscape
materials also must be highly adaptive
to climate and soil. They must be as
resistant as possible to other factors of

∴   ∴   ∴

H. F. WINTERS *is Investigations Leader, Horti-
cultural Crops Investigations, New Crops Research
Branch, Crops Research Division, Agricultural
Research Service.*

J. L. CREECH *is Chief of the New Crops Research
Branch, Crops Research Division, Agricultural
Research Service.*

153

Traditional residence landscaped with carefully chosen materials.

today's environment including compaction of the soil by trampling and vehicles; and limitation of root growth because of encircling pavement, sewers, and utility lines.

Landscape materials for the future must also be resistant to attack by disease organisms and insect pests. Control measures are expensive and in many instances are undesirable as well due to location of the plants close to human habitations.

Ease of maintenance will become more important as a factor in selecting landscape materials for all purposes. Even now most homeowners personally care for their lawns, shrubs, and trees. Yard maintenance is a favorite weekend occupation of most American families today.

Future landscape materials must not create litter problems from fruit and

leaf drop. There is considerable room for improvement in this characteristic of many of our present trees and shrubs. The simple problem of leaf disposal is often overlooked in present tree selection programs of cities.

Needs for landscape materials have changed almost without our realizing it. In the first place, styles in architecture have changed. The three-story Victorian house with gingerbread decorations and porches all around has not been built for nearly a century. Still, the one- to two-story houses on smaller plots of land which replaced it were surrounded by the same tall elms and maples. Arborvitaes, hemlocks, and junipers frequently were used as foundation plantings. Consequently, these smaller properties were often damaged by clogged gutters, tree breakage, and tree roots. In many ases, foundation plantings grew taller ¡an the houses.

Everyone admires the shaded resi-ential street, too, but how long be-›re the wild seedling trees grow out of ›ounds? How much does it cost prop-rty owners and taxpayers each year ¡st to repair curbs, sidewalks, and reets broken by tree roots? Vigorous •ee growth is a real and costly problem ¡ the maintaining of utility lines, also. What is the solution? The need for ¡ndscaping has not changed. And the ¡ral background of the majority of ¡mericans prevents the acceptance of ¡are brick and concrete as their en-ironment.

Can we avoid costly and sometimes nsightly mistakes in the future? U.S. ›epartment of Agriculture scientists elieve so. In the first place, we Ameri-ans can choose our landscape mate-als more carefully in the future.

There already is a greater variety of plant material than we realize.

Nurserymen always have been eager to identify and propagate plants for specialized uses. A few shade tree varieties originated from well-planned tree breeding projects. Examples are several recently patented varieties of honeylocust, linden, and sugar maple. Many more originated as selections from seedling plantings in arboretums and along city streets.

Fifty-one deciduous shade tree va-rieties had been patented by Decem-ber 1966. A few nurserymen specialize in propagating them asexually for lawn and street planting. Such trees are predictable as to ultimate shape and size. Most nurserymen, however, lack time and facilities to grow seed-ling populations of shrubs and trees to maturity simply with the hope of se-lecting desirable individuals.

Contemporary residence landscaped with plants that will stay within bounds.

USDA scientists long have been aware of the need for selected shrubs and trees for specialized landscape use. Several Department programs are aimed at testing introduced and native plants. The Agricultural Research Service, the Forest Service, and the Soil Conservation Service routinely evaluate plant introductions for a variety of purposes and in doing so have the opportunity to select outstanding varieties for landscape use.

The New Crops Research Branch has overall responsibility for introducing and testing foreign plants. It has performed this function since the end of the last century. Among over 300,-000 plants brought to the United States, many have shown outstanding ornamental value. Perhaps the best known example is the Japanese flowering cherries, for which Washington, D.C., is famous.

A more recent development is the 'Bradford' ornamental pear, a non-spiny selection from a seedling population of *Pyrus calleryana* Decne.

In 1918, a search was conducted for improved rootstocks for commercial pear varieties. More than 100 pounds of Callery pear seed was collected in the mountains around Ichang, China, by the famous plant explorer, Frank Meyer. At the U.S. Plant Introduction Station, Glenn Dale, Md., large quantities of this seed were planted. The seedlings were tested for vigor and uniformity of growth, value as rootstocks, and resistance to diseases and insects.

One of our early horticulturists noticed a vigorous seedling that was different. It was entirely without spines, in contrast to normally spiny seedlings of the species. The young tree was removed from the nursery and planted on the main grounds near the station office. Here it developed to maturity without pruning. By the age of 44 years, the tree had an approximate height of 50 feet. Its broad oval form had a spread of 30 feet. Unfortunately, the original tree no longer survives, but its identity continues through the hundreds of trees grafted from it.

Long before the original tree wa destroyed, it was propagated on seec lings of the same species. In 1954, test planting of 180 grafted trees alon the streets of University Park, Md provided the opportunity needed observe the growth and developmei of this variety.

Performance of the trees was so ou standing that the variety was name 'Bradford' in honor of the superii tendent of the Glenn Dale Station wh first became interested in the Callei pear. It was released for general prop gation in 1960. Repropagations of th 'Bradford' are uniformly vigorous i growth and have produced mediun sized, dense-headed trees when traine as street trees. In early spring, the tre produce myriads of spurborne, sma white flowers.

In summer, undulating margins the thick glossy-green, broadly ov leaves of the 'Bradford' pear add the attractiveness of the foliage. A tumn is its special season for colo The foliage undergoes several chang from green to dark purple-bronze rosy-red, and the leaves are retaine later than with most trees.

The small, brown inedible fruits ai not troublesome since they hang c the trees until they disintegrate durii the winter or are eaten by birds.

Recent investigations have show the variety to be self-sterile. It will n fruit at all unless planted near oth pears.

Exact hardiness range of the 'Brac ford' pear has not been establishe It is now recommended for plantii throughout the Southern and Easte United States, including hardine zone V as delimited by the U.S. N tional Arboretum in Miscellaneo Publication No. 814. It has not prov dependably hardy at St. Paul, Minr in zone IV. Neither has it performe well in the interior valleys of Californ or other warm sections of the Sout west. Under these conditions, t trees fail to develop the brilliant f foliage so characteristic of them the Eastern United States. Also, r foliation in the spring may be delaye

156

J. L. Creech examines a rhododendron during a USDA plant exploration trip to Japan.

Reports indicate the 'Bradford' ornamental pear is adapted to a wide range of soil and other environmental conditions, a fact noted long ago by the collector in China.

Other kinds of trees which have received recent attention and may offer the greatest promise for future development are coniferous evergreens, crapemyrtle, honeylocust, magnolia, certain species of maples, and Chinese pistachios.

American nurserymen have been particularly active in propagating new varieties of the evergreens and honeylocust. Widespread planting of honeylocust varieties during recent years has shown a need for varieties with disease and insect resistance.

The National Arboretum's program of hybridizing magnolias already has produced the 'Freeman' with considerable promise for the South. Others are being tested.

Several new crapemyrtle varieties were released this year from the breeding program. Only widespread planting will show their worth.

As a result of USDA plant introduction activities, several new tree species appear particularly promising for certain areas of the Nation. Recent introductions of the purpleblow maple (*Acer truncatum* Bunge) under test at Chico, Calif., appear particularly desirable for lawn and street trees. At maturity it seldom exceeds 25 feet, which would make it suitable for use under powerlines. The autumn foliage is brilliant even in the warm interior valleys of California. This species needs to be tested more extensively in the upper Midwest and Eastern States where it should be cold hardy.

Street tree plantings of *Pistacia chinensis* Bunge in Wichita, Kans., indicate this introduced species may be of value for areas that experience hot, dry weather in late summer and autumn. Under such conditions, it produces brilliant leaf coloring.

The greatest need for ornamental

The thornless honeylocust is an excellent low-litter tree for patio and street planting provided a barren clone is chosen.

trees at present and probably for some years to come is in the Northeast. In this area, millions of American elms have died because of the Dutch elm disease. Although several agencies of the Federal Government have cooperated in attempts at control, it appears most elms eventually will need to be replaced. Various kinds of lindens, maples, and oaks appear particularly promising as replacements. Meanwhile, investigations with resistant elm varieties are being conducted at the Shade Tree and Ornamental Plants Laboratory, Delaware, Ohio.

Shrubs, because of size, are even more closely observed than trees. It is in this group of plants that many varieties were selected and propagated in the past. Nurserymen did most of

the work aided by homeowners an gardeners. The nurserymen have bee particularly active with varieties of th easily propagated arborvitaes, jun pers, and yews.

Americans have a nostalgic fondne for spring flowering deciduous shrub but comparatively few are plante now. They are considered old fasl ioned. Perhaps the basic reason is the grow out of bounds too quickly, occur too much space, and require too muc maintenance. They were replaced to large extent by evergreen shrubs. Th modern homeowner likes year-rour greenness. Still, there is a place fe deciduous shrubs. Government age cies may play a greater part than i the past in selecting tailored varieti for future planting.

The research program of the National Arboretum is concerned with development of shrubs as well as trees. Several varieties of viburnum were recently released for further propagation and testing. Those which prove to have merit in the different climatic zones of the country will soon be available from nurserymen. Another breeding program is aimed at improvement of the Rose of Sharon (shrub Althea).

Many foreign shrub species have been introduced for testing by the New Crops Research Branch. After quarantine and propagation, they are distributed to cooperating arboreta, experiment stations, nurserymen, and private individuals for testing.

Examples of new varieties originating from this program are 'Gulftide' Osmanthus and nine variety selections from an introduction of *Ilex cornuta* Lindl. & Paxt. One of the latter, the 'Rotunda' holly, is outstanding for its dwarf habit and compact shape. This rugged plant was used in landscaping near the Library of Congress and in planters on the main streets of Tulsa, Okla.

No doubt, many more "modern" varieties will result from the program.

Perhaps the most outstanding example of the effectiveness of a planned improvement program for landscape shrubs is to be found in the Glenn Dale hardy azaleas.

Here, the planned objective was to produce by plant breeding a race of azaleas that would be cold hardy at Washington, D.C., and have the flower characters of the tender hybrids.

Beginning in 1929 and continuing for several years, plant introductions were crossed with locally available varieties in all combinations. The progeny were grown first in the greenhouse, then tested outdoors for cold hardiness. About 1 percent of the

Checkout line at a nursery near Greenbelt, Md.

This 13-year-old Dwarf Burford holly, *above,* is only slightly taller than 4-year-old Gil Marx of Hyattsville, Md. Several varieties of low-growing holly have been developed by USDA. Camellia, *right,* makes beautiful and low-growing shrub for many landscaping situations.

seedlings were saved. Of these, 453 had been named and released by 1953 when the project was terminated.

In addition to cold hardiness, the Glenn Dale series of azaleas were selected for season of bloom, bush type, and flower character such as color, number of petals, and size. The selections were propagated and distributed to cooperators throughout the country for further testing.

Reports indicate Glenn Dale azalea varieties differ considerably in cold hardiness. Most survive winters of the Washington, D.C., area. Some are dependably hardy as far north as Columbus, Ohio, and Hartford, Conn. Many have been propagated for sale by nurserymen.

Some varieties have been used as parents in further breeding tests.

As with most groups of plants, these azaleas had to be grown under many varied conditions to reveal their good and their bad points.

Widespread planting has revealed the need for further breeding programs. The varieties available should be more resistant to petal-blight disease and the foliage to injury by the lacewing fly. Some are not truly evergreen. Many other varieties maintain their foliage in rather unsightly condition through the winter months.

On the other hand, the Glenn Dale azaleas proved tremendously popular with the homeowning public. Nothing could be more like fairyland than a residential neighborhood in the spring with the individual properties heavily planted to azaleas and dogwood. Several such neighborhoods have been developed in the National Capital area. Besides, the Glenn Dale azaleas are well adapted to park landscaping.

For further reading:

U.S. Department of Agriculture, *Plant Hardiness Zone Map*, Miscellaneous Publication 814, U.S. Government Printing Office, Washington, D.C. 20402, 1965. 20¢.

A 'Cure' for Concrete Soothes Motorist Too

JOHN C. COWAN

. . . .

Each spring the ravages of winter appear on our bridges and highways as concrete scaling and spalling. We see the damage as we drive over the Nation's highways and feel it where we sit on our pocketbooks.

Scaling occurs when thin pieces break away from the surface of the concrete, and spalling when thick pieces break away. New developments with linseed oil on concrete promise help to reduce this "winter" damage.

Concrete is a complex material formed by the reaction of water with

cement in a mixture also containing sand and gravel. This reaction, called curing, occurs rapidly during the first few hours while the concrete sets or hardens. Curing continues at a reduced rate, and the strength of the concrete may continue to increase for over a year. Roads and bridges usually

∴ ∴ ∴

JOHN C. COWAN *is Chief, Oilseed Crops Laboratory, Northern Utilization Research and Development Division, Agricultural Research Service, Peoria, Ill. He is President, American Oil Chemist's Society and recipient of its A. E. Bailey Award.*

161

Section of Interstate 55 in Illinois, *above,* that had been coated with linseed oil solution. Roadways and bridges were in excellent condition after two winters of exposure. This section is salted frequently. *Right,* scaling damage to another road from salt and freeze-thaw cycles.

attain sufficient strength within 28 days to bear traffic.

Reactions other than curing do occur. In the winter, alternate freezing and thawing happen many times, and the concrete surface may scale and spall. Salt used to melt a covering of ice or snow accelerates this action. As the surface of the concrete deteriorates, it becomes weaker. Exposed reinforcing steel bars corrode. More and more pieces of concrete break away from the original structure.

Extensive damage is the result.

Air bubbles improve concrete's resistance to scaling and to damage from salt and freeze-thaw cycles. By the suitable addition of a variety of materials, air bubbles are trapped in the mass when it is mixed. This air entrainment delays concrete scaling in all structures. It is particularly desirable in structures that become saturated with water and are exposed to salt and to freezing and thawing. But despite adoption of air entrainment in specifications for our concrete highways, scaling damage continues.

Concrete scales more often on bridge floors, associated curbs and sidewalks, and cloverleaves than on roads. Our new expressways have many bridges and cloverleaves.

Unfortunately, repair of these susceptible areas is more costly than the repair of uncomplicated roadway.

Salting of our streets and highways removes ice and snow, and makes motoring safer and easier. Salting also increases scaling and the cost of bridge and road maintenance. Salt accelerates scaling regardless of whether the concrete is air entrained or not. Between 1960–67, the use of salt on our Nation's thoroughfares increased from 2 million to about 6 million tons.

One treatment besides air entrainment shows clear-cut cost benefits. A coating of linseed oil on the concrete retards entrance of water and salt and prolongs resistance to scaling.

When the Northern Utilization Research and Development Division (NU) initiated cooperation with the National Flaxseed Processors Association on the protection of concrete in the early 1960's, air entrainment was already established as the best procedure for protection against scaling. The Portland Cement Association had also established that linseed oil protected concrete not entrained with air. Highway officials and numerous reports suggested that air-entrained concrete needed improvement. So, NU undertook further linseed oil studies.

Linseed oil, diluted with solvents or emulsified in water, coats and penetrates the surface of concrete. Laboratory tests sponsored by contracts from the U.S. Department of Agriculture at Kansas State University and at the Ohio River Division Laboratories, Corps of Engineers, show linseed oil delays appearance of scaling. Coated air-entrained or nonair-entrained concrete beams retained their surface and strength four to eight times longer than uncoated beams in the presence of 2 percent salt. Recoatings prolonged their resistance.

Field tests in Illinois, Kansas, Ontario, New York, and Connecticut show that linseed oil coatings preserve bridges and have value where salt is used. Scaling damage occurs usually in the concrete's early life, particularly the first two winters. It may also come later with prolonged use of salt and many freeze-thaw cycles.

More than 35 State highway and many toll and bridge authorities report use of linseed oil on bridges and roads. The Bureau of Public Roads now endorses the application of linseed oil where deicers like salt are used. Specifically endorsed is the coating of new bridge decks, including curbs, sidewalks, and other splash areas; new pavements-on-grade placed late in the fall; and existing nonair-entrained bridge decks and pavements.

Linseed oil may be applied as a solution or an emulsion.

Linseed antispalling compound is available from members of the National Flaxseed Processors Association. It is a solution of equal volumes of mineral spirits (inflammable paint solvent) and boiled linseed oil.

The emulsion contains equal volumes of boiled linseed oil and water. Our NU emulsion also contains minor amounts of soaps, fatty alcohols, and stabilizers. After homogenization, our emulsion has remained stable through five freeze-thaw cycles and more than 2 years of storage.

Diluting linseed oil with solvent or water reduces viscosity and helps the oil penetrate the concrete's surface. We developed our NU emulsion to avoid fire hazards associated with the solvent mixture and for use in studies on curing concrete.

Both the solution and emulsion contain 3.85 pounds of oil per gallon. Either should be applied to new concrete in two coats, about 28 days after the concrete is poured.

Either the solution or the emulsion can be sprayed from a variety of rigs, including a garden sprayer, a paint gun, or spray-bar rig mounted behind a truck. Recoating at a reduced rate may be desirable in 1 to 2 years. The time interval and amount will depend in part on the severity of traffic and salt applications.

Emulsions offer distinct benefits when large enclosed areas need to be coated. They avoid fire and explosion hazards and exposure of personnel to solvent fumes.

The Chicago Park District applied an emulsion similar to ours to the new Grant Park Underground Garage-South in 1965.

Linseed oil shows promise in another way. Emulsion applied 2 to 4 hours after pouring the concrete aids in its curing. Application of the oil just after the free water disappears gives best results. Tests at NU, Kansas State, and the Ohio River Division Laboratories disclose that protection against

Highway engineering technician for District of Columbia applies linseed oil emulsion to a freshly poured concrete sidewalk.

freeze-thaw cycles and salt also results. The oil forms a coat that retains moisture necessary for curing. Retention is six to 19 times better with oil than without. In subsequent freeze-thaw tests with 2 percent salt solutions, concrete cured with a linseed oil coating had four times the durability of air-entrained concrete cured by more conventional methods.

These successes in the laboratory have led to a number of successful field trials of curing in places like Washington, D.C.; Peoria, Ill.; Colorado City, Tex.; and Wichita, Kans. Appearance of popouts was reduced from 155 to 20 per 100 square feet on sidewalks in Peoria, Ill. Popouts are pieces of concrete forced out of the surface by freezing of porous moisture-absorbing rock. These results show that oil used for curing also protects. Scaling resistance lasts longer with oil coatings applied after 28 days, but no curing benefit is realized.

Curing with linseed oil has been used on six bridges in Wichita. Specifications for bridge construction in Wichita now require use of linseed oil as a curing aid. Results are continuing to be encouraging, and show protection for the concrete.

Treating concrete with linseed oil gives unexpected dividends. Abrasion resistance increases; and paint adheres much better.

In laboratory tests devised by the California Division of Highways, linseed oil increased abrasion resistance of concrete 20 to 40 percent. Linseed treatment reduced concrete wear regardless of whether the concrete was laid under standard or adverse conditions. Better abrasion resistance should give the concrete longer life and retain its rough braking surface even where no freeze-thaw cycles occur.

Paints adhere longer to concrete previously coated with linseed oil. Studies by the Ohio River Division Laboratories show that the life of traffic markings increased in accelerated weathering and field tests. Paints applied to uncoated concrete became loose, blistered, or lost from the surface long before those paints applied to coated concrete.

It is difficult to estimate how much these protective procedures aid the taxpayer, but it must be considerable. The cost of a square yard of concrete pavement varies from $5 to more than $13. Replacement costs run still higher. Repairs usually require removal of some of the previous pavement or preparation of concrete to receive a new load-bearing surface.

The cost of a treatment with linseed oil will run from 6 to 13 cents per square yard. At least two treatments of the concrete appear desirable—one in the first 28 days and the other 1 to 2 years later. A third treatment appears desirable in areas of high stress, with salt applied often, freeze-thaw cycles frequent, and traffic heavy.

These three treatments cost less than 6 percent of the original cost of the concrete pavement. This is a small price to pay for extending the pavement's life for an indefinite period or until other factors cause replacement.

Linseed oil aids in curing concrete. It protects from salt and freeze-thaw damage. In the bargain, the oil improves abrasion resistance and paint adherence of concrete.

Driver, let's go!

For further reading:

California Division of Highways, *Factors Affecting Abrasion Resistance of Concrete Surfaces.* Research Report M and R 250908–1, Sacramento, Calif., 1965.

Cordon, William A., *Freezing and Thawing of Concrete—Mechanism and Control.* ACI Monograph 3, American Concrete Institute, Detroit, Mich., Iowa State University Press, Ames, Iowa, 1966.

Kubie, W. L., and Cowan, J. C., "Linseed Oil Emulsions for Protecting Concrete." *Journal of American Oil Chemists' Society,* Vol. 44, 1967.

National Academy of Sciences-National Research Council, Highway Research Board, *Effects of De-Icing Chemicals on Structures.* Bulletin 323, Washington, D.C., 1962.

National Flaxseed Processors Association, *Stop Concrete Damage with Linseed Oil Antispalling Compound.* Bulletin 103, Chicago, Ill., 1967.

Scholer, C. H., and Best, C. H., *Concrete Curing and Surface Protection With Linseed Oil.* Special Report 60, Kansas Engineering Experiment Station, Kansas State University, Manhattan, Kans., 1965.

Easygoing Hardwoods Taught a Faster Pace

JAMES F. BURRELL

Centuries ago, when the tortoise and the hare staged their big event, they lined up a whale of a good press agent. We've been hearing about it ever since.

But the tortoise in that race was a Parnelli Jones "whooshmobile" compared to the slow boy in one very special modern-times race. This 20th century classic has been going on for years, and it's a race that could use some press agentry even better than the ancient tortoise.

This is a race with trees—trees that once upon a time required from 100 to 300 years to grow to maturity. It might have been practical for Methuselah, but wood researchers today aren't sitting around waiting for the trees to catch up with *them*. Waiting a couple of hundred years would be pushing your luck a bit.

Instead, the technologists are prodding, pushing, teasing—trying different foods and chemicals to make the slow boy move faster, clearing the ground for him so that nothing will impede his progress. And they're noticeably stepping up his r.p.m.

These are important trees. They are our native hardwood species. As proof of the importance of this race—in the grandstands, watching patiently, is a very large segment of the American economy: The thousands of factories which use hardwoods to manufacture tables, chairs, stereo and radio cabinets, dining room furniture, beds, bureaus, kitchen furniture and cabinets,

wall paneling, toys, games, woodenware, sporting goods, plywood, novelties, architectural woodwork, office furniture, institutional furniture, bookcases, store fixtures and displays—to identify just some of them.

Other watchers are the U.S. factories producing industrial woodworking machinery, conveyor lines, abrasives, adhesives, tools, fasteners, paints, enamels, lacquers, coatings of many types, paintbrushes, spray guns, home workshop equipment—and even pushbuttons.

At home, sitting around the radio listening to the sports announcer, are millions of Americans whose welfare is totally dependent upon paychecks received from all of these factories.

They listen, and sharp and clear from the loudspeaker comes the excited voice of the sportscaster: "Here's a late flash! Since my last remarks a few months ago, Seedling No. 1B2 in the Kaskaskia Experimental Forest in Illinois grew 3.8 feet under the stimulus of intensive care and culture."

And that ain't hay! Seedling No. 1B2 is a young walnut tree.

American black walnut is the king of cabinet woods—beautiful, machinable, enduring. No. 1B2 is located at the first official "racetrack" established in 1963 (specifically for genetic improvement of walnut trees) at Car-

⁘   ⁘   ⁘

JAMES F. BURRELL *is Editor and Publisher of* Plywood & Panel *Magazine.*

166

bondale, Ill., by Southern Illinois University and the American Walnut Manufacturers Association, in cooperation with the U.S. Forest Service. At dedication ceremonies for this research facility in August 1966, Edward P. Cliff, Chief of the Forest Service, looked forward to success in this genetic research and the ultimate expansion of similar research in behalf of other hardwood species.

Seriously, of course, there is no "race." There are no grandstands. Factories can't go to races anyway! The factories we mentioned are all spouting smoke, are fastened quite firmly to their foundations, and the workers aren't home listening to a radio, but are at their stations crafting the fine wood products which have made this vital industry great.

Long-needed attention is now being given to hardwood research, upgrading, and planting. The move to direct dedicated research efforts into hardwood genetics is a move to perpetuate the natural beauty of real wood in our surroundings. This beauty cannot be duplicated mechanically. The warmth and attractiveness of real wood will always be with us.

This is a nation of huge forests. If you drive through—or fly over—the mountains and rolling lands and plains of 48 States just about every year as I do, you'll know the country abounds in timber. Forest products represent approximately 5 percent of the gross national product, and that fact alone points up this industry's importance.

We can foresee that at some far future date—50 years hence perhaps—this Nation could be in real trouble with respect more to quality rather than quantity of our hardwood timber. This obviously will not happen, however, if we look ahead and solve the problem before it arises, and that's the best possible description of this modern-day tortoise-and-hare "race."

Look around your homes and you will see such hardwood species as walnut, cherry, oak, pecan, birch, elm, maple. We simply need more information on the manner in which all these

species, and many more, can be grown faster to best advantage. And we're getting it!

Trees constitute a harvestable crop. They are planted—by nature or by man—and they grow to maturity and become useful to mankind as do corn, soybeans, and cabbage.

If allowed to become overmature, trees rot and die. While they are growing they are beneficial in many ways to man, beast, and bird.

Our best grades of hardwood trees are becoming more difficult to come by. Loggers are having to move out farther to get them and must sometimes settle for less than the best. Harvesting costs are up. And with increased land value, stumpage costs everywhere are higher.

How did this come about?

Such costs were of little concern way back in 1620 when the Pilgrims landed. The hardwood trees which met them at the shoreline had to be cleared away for the cultivation of food crops. Besides, this tree cutting amply filled their requirements for building materials, furniture, and firewood.

The stream of colonists which followed pushed the frontiers ever westward. The time came when clearing activities alone did not satisfy the Nation's need for lumber, and gradually all the virgin stands were logged.

We had the expanse of a vast continent, most of it wooded. And most of it is still covered with trees, for nature reseeds itself. But there's a difference in the quality of the resulting tree from a seedling which takes root deep in a dark forest and fights its way straight up to sunlight vs. second growth seedlings (many from the seeds of cull trees) which struggle for existence against competing weeds and shrubs in old clear-cut, logged-over areas. Man must fight against competing undergrowth, just as the forests discouraged it. Man has already acquired knowledge that can now make our existing trees grow much faster and straighter, and he can plant millions of additional seedlings annually, just to insure constant supplies for generations of Americans still unborn.

This is a Nation which prides itself on beautiful homes, attractively furnished. The degree of warmth and beauty in our surroundings, provided by our hardwoods, is a major factor in creating this pride.

That's why today's researchers are looking ahead. If you live in Nevada or Oklahoma, for example, where trees are a bit scarce due to climate or soil, then the problem may seem remote. Or if you live in the Pacific Northwest where softwoods are king, again the seriousness of the problem facing our future generations may be dimmed.

But if you live in Pennsylvania, Indiana, Michigan, North Carolina, or many other States, the problem hits home hard.

Actually, there are two problems— or, rather, situations. Number one involves the need for educating owners of private timberlands to take better care of the Nation's existing broad stands of hardwoods, which cover most of our States in the northeast, eastern, central, and southern regions.

These trees can use a little attention. They respond to pruning, fertilization, and clearing just as corn, soybeans, and cabbage respond to plowing, cultivating, and fertilizing.

And where the farmer gets pennies for a few plants of these latter crops, one good quality, valuable, hardwood tree can bring hundreds of dollars— sometimes thousands.

The day is gone when a man plants a hardwood grove as an investment for his grandchildren. That's old fashioned, dating back to the era when you were sure that a walnut seedling, for example, couldn't be ripe for harvesting until the next century. From data already secured by researchers, a 25-year-old farmer can now plant a walnut grove and start banking the money when he's 60. Or, if he gets a later start, it's a cinch for Junior. In fact, Junior will be interested in rolling up his sleeves and helping with the project, for with controlled harvesting there can be a fortune in valuable hardwoods.

Problem number two concerns the desirability of putting more of our finer species into the ground, just to be sure of meeting demands of a far larger population five decades ahead.

One very notable step forward in this direction is concerted action by one of the largest single organizations in the United States—the bubbling, energized army of more than 5 million Boy Scouts of America. Our boys know how to dig holes and plant trees. A planned program for hardwood reforestation by the Scouts took definite shape in 1967 and will expand in 1968 and future years to include plantings of all important species on public lands, Scout lands, and private property in hardwood-growing regions.

Foresters—State and Federal, the Soil Conservation Service, and industry are combining to provide training programs to show Scouts how and where to dig the holes and plant the trees. Industry will pick up the tab for the seedling costs—and this can well grow to a million-dollar-a-year project. Of all the men and firms and organizations behind this program, the boys themselves are the only ones who will really benefit. For even with today's assured faster growth in hardwoods, these boys will reach maturity ahead of the trees they'll plant.

Liaison between Scouts and industry is being handled by the newly formed United Hardwood Forestry Program, sponsored jointly by the Fine Hardwoods Association and the American Walnut Manufacturers Association. It is supervised by Forester Larry Frye with offices in Columbia City, Ind.

And what is the scope of this new research with hardwoods? Who are the men questing for unknown facts about our trees, determining the characteristics of different species, grafting, seeking stronger strains, and testing different techniques in cultivation? It's encouraging that they have made such headway in the growth rate of walnut alone, for this in itself greatly simplifies later problems.

168

Conceivably, if you must work in the tortoiselike atmosphere of a woody plant which insists on taking 150 years to grow up, you might succeed in proving or disproving little more than two or three theories in an entire lifetime! A band of dedicated technologists is now far more assured of success. The tortoise has been prodded into relatively high speed. This speed has had no effect on wood coloration, grain configuration, or machinability. Our fine hardwoods have simply been put into high gear.

F. Bryan Clark had been principal silviculturist for the North Central Forest Experiment Station, Forest Service, U.S. Department of Agriculture, stationed at the Carbondale, Ill., research center. But effective January 1, 1968, Clark was advanced to assistant director for timber management of the North Central Station, headquartered in St. Paul, Minn., and he continued to shoulder the responsibilities for the special research activities in walnut at Carbondale.

Working with him are such men as Willard H. Carmean, principal soil scientist; Raymond F. Finn, principal plant pathologist; and Calvin F. Bey, associate plant geneticist.

Research in hardwoods is not new at this Southern Illinois University facility. As far back as 1954, a plant for pilot research operations in low-grade hardwood utilization was started here. Now, following the 1966 establishment of additional facilities aimed at genetic research in walnut, numerous "plantations" of walnut seedlings can be found not only on Southern Illinois University grounds, but on numerous tracts in the Kaskaskia Experimental Forest and the Shawnee National Forest in Hardin County and the Crab Orchard National Wildlife Refuge in Williamson County.

From row to row in plantation after plantation, different techniques have been employed with respect to mixtures of walnut seedlings with other species, distances between seedlings, and variations in fertilization formulas. Old walnut stands in the forests have been accorded varying degrees of release from surrounding vegetation and trees.

Records have been carefully kept, and due to stimulation of the seedlings on these test tracts in Illinois, results have been secured in 2 years which formerly could not have been gained in a decade.

Definite forward strides have already been made in the light of facts revealed through these many combinations of environment and cultivation.

The genetics project at Carbondale is aimed at producing straight, fast-growing, insect- and disease-resistant, high-quality walnut trees of timber type. The seeds planted here have been gathered from select trees spread variously across 12 different States.

Research on physiology is underway at Ames, Iowa, and research on silviculture and soil and water relations in Illinois and Indiana, administered from Carbondale.

Other Forest Service experimental stations throughout our hardwood areas are compiling data on additional important species.

In this situation involving our hardwoods, I have been only an observer, for I am not a manufacturer or a researcher. Observation comes easy when, in the natural course of your work, you personally visit hundreds of wood products operations from coast to coast each year. You watch them seek farther and farther for log supplies, with log hauls moving up to the 200-mile mark and beyond. The shortage is in quality, and not in quantity. Logs are smaller; they have more defects. Some species acceptable today would have been refused 15 or 20 years ago. Shortages are spotty, but are prevalent in most of the important species in the Central, Eastern, and Southern States, with some in the north as well.

And in this situation, I am little more than a reporter, closely watching those who see need for action and are acting. More than 2 years have elapsed in bringing the Boy Scout reforestation program forward, from an idea in

1965, to a point of definite organization today.

I've watched this program grow and have reported on its growth through many conferences conducted in such faraway places as New Brunswick, N.J., Washington, D.C., Carbondale, Ill., Syracuse, N.Y., Indianapolis, and Chicago.

I've reported it from the field, from Boy Scout training sessions, and from actual field trips made by troops of Scouts with their buckets of water, spades, and bundles of seedlings.

I have enjoyed my share of helping to organize the first Boy Scout pilot planting program, working with the Central Indiana Council at Indianapolis. It was this test effort, in the spring of 1966, which proved to Scout executives at New Brunswick that industry would support such a program and that foresters, conservationists, and soil scientists could teach boys—in boy language—the rules that have developed from the knowledge gained by our researchers. This one council, in the Indianapolis area, planted 25,000 walnut seedlings in the first 9 days of April 1966.

Other wood industry men are at work with groups such as the Future Farmers of America and our 4–H Clubs—all very practical avenues for progress in making Americans more knowledgeable about the Nation's future needs in valuable hardwoods.

We're not out of the fine woods yet. And with the race getting faster, we never will be!

Rebuilding Rural America— An Ozarks Case History

MELVIN R. JANSSEN

. . . .

In the mid-1950's, few would call the Ozarks a land of opportunity. Certainly not Amos Butcher. *His small 165-acre Missouri farm, half in woods, didn't provide much income. There was no chance for his two sons to farm. There were no other jobs either, so they went to St. Louis to find work.*

Neither would Bill Jennings, a miner until the lead and zinc mines closed down after the war. *His only income came from a few odd jobs and a welfare check because he doesn't know much except mining. His son now works as a laborer in Kansas City.*

Joe Miller would agree. *One of the small businessmen in the many small towns, he saw his business slowly drop as two-thirds of his younger patrons moved away. His daughter teaches school, but her pay is far below that of teachers in Oklahoma City.*

All over the Ozarks, the hills and valleys were nice to see, but produced a poor living for most. The 79-county area had only two economic bright spots—Springfield, Mo., and Little Rock, Ark.

That was what Ronald Bird saw when he came to Columbia, Mo., in 1956 to work on Ozark problems. With

∴ ∴ ∴

MELVIN R. JANSSEN *is Assistant Director, Field Research Coordination, Economic Development Division, Economic Research Service.*

In his chapter, the names of the researchers are real. Other names are fictional.

The pump and daffodils are the only reminders that a farm family migrated from the rural Ozarks to an urban area. Between 1950 and 1960, over one-third of the farm families left the land, a migration that continues.

Frank Miller, of the University of Missouri, he studied farms to learn what types would provide more adequate farm incomes.

Farmers with enough good land and capital were doing well, but there were too many Amos Butchers in the Ozarks who weren't. Ronald learned it would be necessary to consolidate several farms and reduce the number of farm families to improve farm incomes. Those remaining would have better income, but only if their management ability was improved.

The Missouri Extension Service, through the Balanced Farming Program, used results of the research to develop the management capacity of operators. However, without job opportunities farmers were loath to give up their land, and only a few improved their incomes. Yet, between 1950 and 1964, three-fifths of the farms in the Ozarks disappeared.

The Lake of the Ozarks and other areas seemed to provide an answer. Thousands of tourists were seeking recreation experiences on lakes and streams. They needed goods, services, and accommodations. Would these provide suitable employment for people in the Ozarks? What was the impact of the tourists upon the economy of the area?

Ron Bird studied motels, restaurants, and other businesses to learn the level of gross and net incomes from the tourist trade. And of course, he learned the level of employment and the expenditures of the tourists.

Clearly some employment was provided. But frequently businesses were run by outsiders, like Roy Johnson from Chicago. He brought capital and know-how when he built his motel and restaurant. He hired local people as maids and waitresses at low pay, some with only part-time employment. The tourist trade provided employment and income, but could employ only a few of those who needed jobs.

In another part of the Ozarks, Max Jordan, working at the University of Arkansas, sought to learn if farmers could develop profitable recreation enterprises. He found that a few farmers like Pete Newlin were successful, but others like Ralph Jones lost money. Few farmers have a good location, managerial capacity, and can get along well enough with people to make money with a farm recreation enterprise. Most tourists want a combination of facilities and activities, not usually found on farms. Again, employment was created and some income improved, but only a fraction of the needs were met.

Other employment potentials were analyzed by a newcomer, O. Wendell Holmes, Jr. He studied the effects of a large Government installation, Fort Leonard Wood, on Pulaski County, Mo. This is one of the few rural counties with a large net immigration of males, age 20–24, from 1950 to 1960, many of whom were fresh recruits like Jimmy Grant. In addition to the 1,950 civilians employed directly on post, construction and military payrolls influenced the business of the small nearby towns. In turn, other businesses

171

benefited. But the growth in retail sales of the county was $23 million. In Boone County, with an increase in student population and services at the University of Missouri and Stephens College in Columbia, retail sales had risen by $31 million during the same period.

As the number of problems identified grew, interest in low-income areas such as the Ozarks led to designation of the Ozarks Economic Development Region. It was clear that before economic development of the region could be stimulated, a concise inventory of the natural resources, people, community facilities, transportation, and problems was needed.

Max Jordan and Lloyd Bender of the University of Arkansas prepared such a summary—"An Economic Survey of the Ozark Region." This guides legislators, program specialists, extension workers, researchers, and community leaders. It pointed to the needs for private and public investment to create employment, especially in recreation and service industries. Important needs are highway development to improve access to industry and markets and education to train the labor force to attract industry.

Subsequently, Bender joined the U.S. Department of Agriculture's Economic Research Service staff and worked closely with personnel of the Missouri Experiment Station to identify potential growth centers. The objective was to locate centers where public or private investment will generate further private investment and more jobs. Only four or five highly promising centers were found. Springfield, Mo., and Little Rock, Ark., were obvious. But less obvious were centers based on the recreation industry. Bender also worked to delineate functional economic areas based on growth centers. These can form the basic planning unit for development based on new investment to create some of the many jobs needed. But this indicates we must be careful in choosing the location for investment.

Recently, Gerald Doeksen began a study to learn the intricate flows of goods and services among industries of the Ozarks. He will learn which industries show the greatest promise for growth.

Ozark farmers with good management and enough land can have adequate income, comfortable housing, and a satisfactory level of living.

In the meantime, Jordan evaluated the effects of a shirt plant established in northern Arkansas. The industry is generally considered mobile because it requires a small fixed investment and utilizes semiskilled labor that can be trained easily. The plant, located in a building constructed with local funds and a development loan, employs 750 persons, mostly women. Beulah Jones has a better family income, but her husband works only part time. This condition creates family and social problems that can be solved only if a job can be found for her husband. Thus, it is necessary not only to provide jobs, but also in a mix with employment for those needing it.

Bird projected employment, wages, and output of the timber industry and agriculture in the Missouri portion of the Ozarks. In 1960, some 14,800 workers were employed in timber cutting, hauling, and processing. Since many persons like Fred Long were employed part time, an equivalent of only 6,800 workers were employed full time. The forest production is improving, and output is projected to increase. While the number of part-time workers may decline, the level of equivalent full-time employment will remain constant. As new technology is incorporated, output per worker will increase and wages will rise, but few new jobs will be found.

In a similar study of agriculture, it was found that there would be 25,500 equivalent full-time farms earning $3,000 or 19,100 earning $4,000. In 1964, there were 56,000 farms, some of them part-time farms.

Even modestly higher levels of income will reduce the employment in the industries studied.

It is clear that bringing mobile industry to the local area cannot hope to provide enough jobs. Some migration will have to continue. But unless young men and women are prepared with skills that can be used in other areas, they will be moving from a low income rural area to an urban area where their earnings will be low. How well are they prepared?

The Natural Arch Recreation Area of the Ozark National Forest attracts many visitors every year.

Jordan and Bender, working with James Golden of the University of Arkansas, studied rural high school boys in Arkansas. Lee Casper had high aspirations, but his expectation of becoming an engineer or a doctor was slight because his family couldn't pay even the first semester of tuition to college. Most, and especially Negroes, were poorly prepared to earn a living in an urban area or even to take vocational training after high school.

The team concluded that a two-pronged program is needed in any area to deal with Ozark poverty. First, the economic conditions must make jobs available, and then programs must help people like Lee Casper to prepare for the jobs. But little was known about the people in the area. Census data provide a description, but do not give individual data needed for some analyses.

Two new members of the team, Bernal Green at Arkansas and Herbert Hoover at Missouri, undertook a study of the characteristics of the people to

Skill training can start early. *Left,* Ozark girl waits outside her home for Extension Service bus workshop. *Right,* these girls used sewing machines in workshop to make dresses. Besides learning new skills, girls will be more apt to stay in school if they have suitable clothes to wear to class.

include education, employment, housing, income, debts, family composition, and assets. This knowledge will give better information to develop programs to help Lee Casper, Fred Long, and Beulah Jones' husband. Many programs have been based on a limited knowledge of individuals, did not fit the needs, and had modest success at best.

As an outgrowth of the main study of the people, Fred Hines joined the team. He wants to learn how education can best be applied to aid the Ozark people to secure and hold skilled jobs. This is one important key in the effort to bring new manufacturing and service industries to the area. A community that has trained workers or can train them has an advantage over one with an ample supply of unskilled, untrained laborers.

Another way to improve the overall level of skills of the labor force in an area is to have skilled workers and managerial personnel like Roy Johnson, the motel owner, come to the

area. In some areas of the South, large losses of Negroes have occurred, but there was net in-migration of whites. Most studies do not identify the people or the characteristics of those who move in both directions.

Bender and Green, in cooperation with Rex Campbell of the University of Missouri, are studying in-migrants to Missouri and Arkansas. This project will take 2 years to complete. But we will know if the Roy Johnsons raise the levels of skills of the working force. Also, will the influx of skilled outsiders—to include former residents of the area—bring new ideas and attitudes that will help develop the area?

Many homes in the Ozarks are generally substandard. Hughes Spurlock is trying to learn how the housing of the area can be improved. It is also his goal to help housing program administrators and regional planners make sense of our present hodgepodge of housing location. Frank Brewer lives at the end of the road that should be abandoned. He drives to work on

174

the 2 extra miles of road that must be maintained, while the schoolbus drives 9 extra miles each day. Water and sewer systems are less feasible. And the area's scarce tax dollars are stretched badly.

Two other team members are seeking to learn the relationship of highway development in area development. They are studying the location factors for new firms in relation to various types of highways. Also, they seek to learn how recreation developments can best benefit from highway improvements. John Kuehn is working with personnel of the Missouri Experiment Station. James P. Miller is working with the Texas Transportation Institute at College Station, Tex., to solve these problems.

The cooperative ERS-experiment station team has conceived of the Ozarks region as a multicounty, four-State activity in which planning of the region and its subregions must be integrated. The research has not made the region a Garden of Eden. But it has uncovered problems, focused upon them, and pointed the way to program action.

It will take public and private investment over a period of several years to improve incomes of the people. Education takes years, and job skills take time to learn. Communities will have to revamp the educational system and upgrade the present schools. This will take time and effort, but Amos Butcher, Bill Jennings, and Joe Miller will have to see the problems and take action. What can be done about upgrading the unskilled? There are opportunities for Joe Miller's schoolteacher daughter to help. But unfortunately, some Ozark residents are getting too old to learn or for Roy Johnson to hire them. For these, a welfare program will need to supplement their low incomes to lift them beyond poverty.

With research guidance, the programs can guide the investment in human resources, natural resources, plants, and community facilities to improve the incomes and living levels of people of the Ozarks.

Progress will be slow, because the problems did not develop overnight. But the ingredients for economic progress in the Ozarks have been isolated.

Left, boys display wood articles they made with power tools in bus workshop. *Right,* a work session underway inside the bus.

Beautifying Highways
Helps Make Them Safer

ANSON R. BERTRAND

. . . .

How can a county save $1 million in highway costs and yet come up with roadside beauty spots with high recreation potential? Washington County, Nebr., did it by replacing 200 wornout bridges with roadway dams; it was $1 million cheaper to fill channels than to build bridges. Shelby County, Iowa, saved $750,000 the same way.

Many new lakes are being created beside highways in other counties in Nebraska and Iowa and in Kansas counties, too. Roadway dams conserve water and often lead to moneymaking recreational enterprises, besides slashing highway construction costs in these areas. They are an outstanding example of putting research know-how on soils to work.

These new beauty spots are the result of cooperation between the State highway commissions, local landowners, and USDA's Soil Conservation Service. Highway engineers, using SCS and other data, found that soil and water runoff characteristics made roadway dams practicable.

Miles of oleanders line highways in California, Texas, and Florida. Here again, research played a role in selecting this flowering evergreen for a dual role: To beautify the highways and make them safer.

Beautiful highways are safer because they provide restful and scenic views that reduce the monotony of driving. A beautiful and safety-enhancing feature of modern highways is a wide landscaped median. A median reduces headlight glare from oncoming traffic and provides a quieter, more pleasant ride with less distraction from surroundings. Such medians are numerous on our interstate highways.

An outstanding example of a median that is functional and beautiful may be seen on parts of Highway 95 in Virginia. Native evergreens and flowering plants were wisely selected in landscaping these medians. In a few places where the traffic lanes are widely separated, rest parks are provided in the median area.

When the United States Interstate System is completed, it will be a 41,000-mile network of the finest roads in the world. All roads—interstate, State, and secondary—require maintenance. Highway engineers have learned that maintenance of the traffic surface is impossible unless erosion is prevented on the road shoulders and backslopes. Experience has also shown that the best and most economical protection for roadsides is provided by living plants—grass, shrubs, and trees which incidentally provide beauty along the highways.

Public interest in beautiful roadways has been slowly increasing for about 30 years. Interest reached a new peak during the 1965 White House Conference on Natural Beauty. This confer-

.·.   .·.   .·.

ANSON R. BERTRAND *is Head of the Department of Agronomy, University of Georgia, Athens.*

176

ence was a milestone in the history of American conservation.

The day after the conference closed, the President sent to Congress proposals for legislation to require the use of a portion of Federal highway funds for landscaping, beautification and recreation, and to eliminate outdoor advertising signs and junkyards along interstate highways.

That the conference spawned a new level of activity in roadside stabilization and beautification cannot be denied, but this new activity would not have been possible without the foundation provided by research and action programs of the past 30 years. One of the earliest studies of erosion control on roadsides was conducted by USDA's Forest Service in the Yazoo-Little Tallahatchie basin in Mississippi nearly 30 years ago. The Forest Service has also conducted education and demonstration programs to show lumbermen how to prevent erosion during logging operations.

Erosion control on roadsides is receiving major emphasis in small watersheds everywhere. An example is the Haynes Creek-Brushy Fork watershed, a Public Law 566 watershed in Georgia. The Soil Conservation Service assisted local people in stabilizing 52 miles of roadsides by planting grass, shrubs, and trees.

Highway departments in most States now employ agronomists and landscape architects to plan and promote roadside erosion control and beautification. Federal agencies such as the Soil Conservation Service, Bureau of Reclamation, Bureau of Public Lands, and National Park Service promote highway beautification. Plans for development and preservation of natural beauty, observable from highways, are an integral part of every conservation plan prepared by SCS.

Landscape preservation, including highway beauty, is of prime concern to river basin planning commissions and to area development and planning commissions throughout the country. Expressions by civic groups, garden clubs, church groups, PTA's, and others have made it unmistakably clear that the general public wants erosion controlled and the roadsides made attractive and pleasant. The response by State highway departments and county road commissioners has been positive. These professional highway planners and supervisors are applying available knowledge and seeking new knowledge at a very accelerated pace.

Highway engineers have three objectives in planning and construction of today's heavily traveled transportation arteries—greater safety, reduced maintenance costs, and general roadside attractiveness.

Natural beauty contributes strongly to this threefold objective.

Highway architects have learned to fit the highway to the landscape by disturbing the natural landscape as little as possible. A highway that fits naturally into its surroundings gives the user the feeling that he is a part of and belongs to the land. Interstate Highway 24, northwest of Chattanooga, Tenn., is a beautiful highway designed in such a way as to give the traveler a feeling of fitting into the hills while enjoying a panoramic view of the countryside. Landscape architects have learned to use plantings to outline hills and curves and introduce vertical and horizontal dimensions which tend to make driving safer.

Roadway designs require hundreds of bits of specific information for every mile of roadway. For example, they must have accurate and reliable information about the soil over which their road will pass. Soil surveys provided by USDA are used by highway planners in deciding on locations and engineering features and identifying problem areas along the route. They also use soil surveys to select locations that have beauty as well as utility. In this way, soil surveys reduce the number of soil borings needed, cut costs, and speed up highway planning.

From soil surveys, the design engineer may also secure information concerning physical and chemical characteristics of the soil material and its suitability for various uses. Physical

Mixture of lovegrass, sericea, fertilizer, and wood cellulose fiber mulch is sprayed on a steep roadbank in East Ellijay, Ga.

characteristics of the soil, including texture, structure, and arrangement of layers, determine the grades which must be established to provide sidewalls in cuts and slopes in valley fills that are stable.

Research scientists studying the physical and mechanical properties have learned that some soil material is unsuitable for roadways because it shrinks and swells too much. They have learned that permeable material over-lying dense clay or shale is susceptible to slippage, and cuts through hills must be designed to avoid this danger.

Highway designers use soil information to select suitable sources of surface soil and to locate rest and recreation areas. Roadside rest areas present many unique problems because they must be accessible, functional, and beautiful. The soil and its grass cover must be able to withstand heavy pedestrian traffic. The soil must contain plant nutrients and have physical characteristics which prevent it from becoming soft and spongy during the rainy periods.

Establishing and maintaining grass, trees, and shrubs on highways is difficult and requires considerable knowledge and experience because soil and site conditions along highways vary more than natural conditions in the surrounding area. The environment in which plants must grow may be drastically different on slopes with different aspects.

A north-facing slope may freeze early in the fall and remain frozen until late spring, while the south-facing slope directly across the highway may be subjected to dozens of freeze-thaw cycles during one winter.

A slope with a westerly aspect will frequently be quite droughty and present a soil climate typical of conditions several hundred miles removed from the actual area. At the same time, the opposite slope with an easterly aspect may be shaded much of the day, and the soil is often relatively moist and cool.

Problems of incorporation of lime and fertilizer in the soil and the placement of seed and mulch are numerous and challenge the ingenuity of research agricultural engineers. Engineers have developed many unique pieces of equipment for soil preparation, fertilizer application, seeding, mulch placement, shrub and tree planting, and mowing and trimming which lower the cost of roadside stabilization, beautification, and maintenance.

A widely-used piece of equipment mixes together, in a large tank, seed, fertilizer, water, fiber mulch material, and an adhesive. The mixture is then blown on hard-to-get-to roadbanks. In warm weather, only a few days are required before a green carpet of grass begins to emerge. Other interesting equipment includes such things as rotary tillers, mowers, and tree trimmers attached to long arms and operated by a person many feet from the working mechanism.

Creating a Big Industry to Save Small Towns

D. L. FASSNACHT

. . . .

Natchitoches, near the Red River in western Louisiana, in many ways is typical of hundreds of southern towns. It is a quiet place. With a population of about 15,000, it has no urban crowding, midcity blight, or tenement living. Nearby are good hunting and fishing spots.

Natchitoches is a fine place to live and raise a family—if you can find a job, that is. If you can't, there's little choice but to pack your family off to the big city where jobs are plentiful, even though the smog is thick and the living crowded.

Jobs are a little easier to find today in Natchitoches and 32 other towns from Maryland to Texas because of a new industry—the manufacture of southern pine plywood. In its 5-year existence, this industry has brought investments of over $100 million and at least 6,000 permanent new jobs to small towns.

179

Of course, the natural resources and technology on which the southern pine plywood industry is based took more than 5 years to develop. Creation of the conditions needed for the industry is a complex story with hundreds of heroes—conservationists, resource managers, local business and civic leaders, members of trade associations, and U.S. Forest Service research scientists. Each of them forged an essential link in the chain of events that led to a better life in some southern towns.

Natchitoches provides a good example of the developing industry and its importance. It is an old town, older than New Orleans. It was the last civilized outpost between French Louisiana and Spanish Texas. Traveling the 150 miles from Natchitoches to Nacogdoches beyond the Sabine River in Texas was once a matter of courage, luck, and guaranteed trouble. Both became important way stations on "El Camino Real," the King's Highway that tied together Spanish possessions from St. Augustine, Fla., to San Antonio, Tex., and thence to Mexico City or California.

The bottom land along the Red is flat and fertile; it helped Natchitoches become the center of a wealthy agricultural community. The rolling hills farther back from the river once supported a virgin stand of longleaf pine. Forty years ago, the last of the longleaf pine whirred its way through the sawmills, and most of the lumber industry moved West. The hills were cleaned of trees, and frequent fires reduced the vegetation to scattered grass and worthless brush. Small wonder that land here was cheap during the great depression.

That was a long time ago. Today, the southern pines again stand straight and tall. Seedlings were planted, and fires were fought to protect them. The young trees were tended and nurtured. The fine stands of today are rewards

∴   ∴   ∴

D. L. FASSNACHT *is Assistant Director in charge of resource, economics, engineering, and products research at the Southern Forest Experiment Station in New Orleans, La.*

for yesterday's hard work, dedication, and know-how.

Certainly, some credit must go to the research scientists who, early in the century, anticipated many of the problems that would arise in reforesting the South. When people asked when, where, and how seedlings should be planted, these men had answers. Their studies showed at what age seedlings are most sensitive to fire. Thus, firefighters knew where their efforts should be concentrated. Entomologists learned how to control outbreaks of bark beetles, and pathologists, to prevent cataclysmic losses to diseases like cankers and root rots. Results of silvicultural research made it possible for foresters to keep the young stands growing vigorously.

Plywood technology was developing at the same time as the trees. U.S. Forest Service scientists at the Forest Products Laboratory in Madison, Wis., studied problems involved in making thin sheets of veneer and in gluing them together. Appropriate machinery was developed to convert the huge trees found on the west coast into plywood.

By the early forties, excellent plywood was being made for walls, panels, and cabinetry. At that time, the Crossett Co. in Arkansas and the Southern Forest Experiment Station supported a study at the Forest Products Laboratory to assess the value of southern pine for plywood. The results were not promising. Southern pine logs could not then compete with the virgin "peelers" from the West.

The postwar years brought important changes to the industry. The Forest Products Laboratory developed the stressed-skin method of construction, in which the sheathing provides structural support. Research at Madison showed that plywood was ideal for this purpose, and today, more plywood is sold for construction components than for decoration.

Again, the southern station sent sample logs to Madison. Dr. H. O. Fleischer and John Lutz tested veneer and plywood made from the samples, and in 1956, the laboratory announced that southern pine could be used for sheathing grades of plywood.

U.S. Forest Service resource analysts reported by 1960 that the trees were ready. Forest surveys in the Southern States had revealed that growth was far exceeding cut, and that a vast supply of wood was available. Wood was accumulating so rapidly that there was some concern about future markets.

In September of 1960, Edward G. Locke, the late director of the U.S. Forest Products Laboratory, and Philip A. Briegleb, director of the Southern Forest Experiment Station, met and determined to promote a softwood plywood industry in the South.

During 1961, promising evidence was collected and summarized. That fall, staffmen from the laboratory and the station visited several industrial locations to collect logs representing extremes in the characteristics of southern pine. At each location, favorable evidence for the future of a plywood industry was discussed with the mill managers.

Southern pine logs were sent to western mills for production trials. This time, the results were highly encouraging. Pine logs gave high yields of acceptable veneer; knots stayed tight in the dryer. It was found that southern pine required heavier glue spreads than western species, but this was not economically crippling.

Timber was available in the South to support a new industry, and it could profitably be converted into plywood. Fleischer, later to be director of the Forest Products Laboratory, outlined these findings in a speech before the mid-South section of the Forest Products Research Society in October 1962. Representatives of prospective manufacturers had been invited to attend, and their response was immediate and favorable. A committee was formed to set up commercial standards that would assure a product of quality equal to that made in the West.

Word that a smalltown industry was about to be born spread quickly to progressive towns in the South. The people of Natchitoches drew comfort from a wise decision they had made a few years before. In 1957, leading citizens had contributed and collected enough money to buy and set aside an industrial park in the hills just east of town. Their faith in their community, and in the pine forests surrounding it, was soon to be rewarded.

An engineer from Shreveport, La., looked over the town and told its leaders he could design and build a mill—if Natchitoches could provide a plantsite, money, and an assured supply of timber.

The land for construction was already available. A timber supply could be assured by getting landowners to agree to reserve some of their trees for plywood. But money was another matter. Who in Natchitoches could prudently invest $2½ million in a new manufacturing idea? The answer came to those who foresaw the value of a new plant to the community. If a few individuals could not afford the initial investment, the community could—with municipal bonds. The enterprise could pay back the loan, with interest, in 15 years.

So, the Southern Plywood Corp. was formed. Presidents of the local banks, a lawyer, a real estate developer, and the engineer and officers of an eastern lumber company that agreed in advance to sell 80 percent of the plywood produced were elected to the board of directors. Plans for the new mill were prepared and presented to the Police Jury, governing body of the parish (or county). Tentative arrangements with landowners for a timber supply were drawn. The time came to present the plans to the people of Natchitoches Parish for their approval or rejection.

Tuesday, July 27, 1965, was the day set for the voting. On Sunday the 25th, the opposition thundered "Vote No!" in a full page advertisement in the Natchitoches Times. "The public should not be asked to support private enterprise." Another full page replied "Vote Yes!" "The public will gain much from the new industry—in jobs—in opportunity."

181

Steam rises from veneer block being peeled in plant at Darlington, S.C. Blocks are heated in water before cutting, to soften them.

The people read, discussed, and thought, then gave their decision: FOR, 1,459 votes; AGAINST, 376 votes. The money was at hand.

Now people were needed to lead the enterprise. Two Texans who were addicted to 16-hour workdays had just helped build a plant in their home State. One accepted the position of vice president and general manager. The other, a longtime associate, was placed in charge of production.

Construction began in the fall of 1965. By May 1966, the Natchitoches Times displayed pictures of substantial progress in construction. On December 22, local dignitaries celebrated the first shipment of plywood. During August 1967, design capacity was attained; in that month, over 4 million square feet of plywood were manufactured and shipped.

The past 5 years have witnessed activity unequaled in the history of any forest products industry. Problems of all kinds have been investigated and resolved. Southern manufacturers joined the Douglas Fir Plywood Association in the American Plywood Association.

Western firms made available their considerable knowledge of manufacturing technique and quality control. The U.S. Department of Commerce issued a tentative commercial standard for southern pine plywood in 1964, and since then a combined standard for all softwood plywood has been agreed upon and published. Dr. Peter Koch, working at the Southern Forest Experiment Station's laboratory in Alexandria, La., discovered and reported many important determinants of quality in the new product.

A total of 33 mills are now operating; they have a combined payroll of between 6,000 and 7,000. A new payroll in a small town means increased prosperity for a host of people—grocers, filling station operators, schoolteachers, even veterinarians. Residents of overcrowded cities must be included among the beneficiaries, since their numbers have not been swelled by contingents from Natchitoches or the other towns where plywood is manufactured. For the plywood industry has not moved to the city; it has stayed in the country, near the forests.

Natural
Resources

Pillow on the Mountain Eases Water Forecast Headaches

WILLIAM G. SHANNON

. . . .

A snow surveyor sitting in an office in Portland, Oreg., can tell you if it has snowed in the past hour on Mount Hood 50 miles away, what the air temperature there is, and how much water is in the Mount Hood snowpack. The information comes automatically by radio every hour from a "snow pillow" high on the mountain.

With snow pillows now being installed at other points in the Cascade Mountains, the Soil Conservation Service snow surveyor in Portland will be kept posted on conditions at key mountain sites and as far away as Cold Springs, Oreg., a distance of 240 miles. This is the new method of snow surveying.

Under this system, readings of basic data are made by instruments installed at observation sites called snow courses. A signal sent out from a base station located in a town or city asks the observation sites for current information. This information is then sent back by radio to the base station. It is not necessary for anyone to be around during this operation. The system operates by itself, and the data are recorded for a permanent record.

The regular way of snow surveying is by manual means. Snow survey teams of two men each are sent to the mountains to obtain forecast data by taking measurements. They measure the depth of the snowpack about once a month beginning in January and ending in May or June. All measurements, taken at about 1,200 fixed locations, follow a set schedule and exact measurement procedure. This network is spread over the mountains in 11 Western States.

Snow surveyors are specially trained for this work. They must be able to ski or snowshoe, drive oversnow machines, avoid avalanches, survive in the snow under severe cold, wind, and blizzard conditions. The possibility of being caught in an avalanche is a constant danger. Shelter cabins with food, wood, and bedding are usually provided if trips take more than 1 day. Sometimes the cabins are completely buried under the snow.

Information collected by snow survey teams or by electronic devices provides the basis for making water supply forecasts. Each State has a unit of two or three people who analyze the data and then prepare the water supply outlook.

Years ago, farmers and ranchers could only look toward the mountains in spring and surmise that the snow cover was heavy, average, or light.

Now, snow surveying provides good estimates of water that will be available for irrigating crops and pastures, for industry and power generation, for municipal and recreational uses. Water as snow is in storage on the great

∴   ∴   ∴

WILLIAM G. SHANNON is Chief, Water Supply Forecasting Branch, Engineering Division, Soil Conservation Service.

mountain slopes until the warming temperature of spring begins to melt it. Snow surveying provides information about the water supplies several months before runoff occurs. This means better planning and more efficient use of the water that is available.

In 1958, R. A. Work, then head of the Soil Conservation Service's Snow Survey Unit, and I discussed the need for a better and safer way to obtain forecast data from remote mountain locations during the winter. We recognized that a simple and inexpensive device to translate, in place on the mountain, the depth of snow cover into equivalent inches of water was the first step necessary.

In 1959, the Agricultural Research Service agreed to assist with this work. ARS contracted with the University of Idaho to research past efforts and to develop a device to provide water content of snow in units adaptable to radio transmission.

A device now called the snow pressure pillow was first tried at the university's test site in Idaho.

The pressure pillow translates weight of snow into water equivalent. It is designed so it actually weighs the snow that accumulates on it.

The pillow is of flexible material, and if it is round, resembles a large pancake. It is usually filled with water and enough methanol or ethylene glycol to prevent freezing. An outlet permits connection to pressure measuring devices. Pillows that have been used are from 1 to 5 inches thick and have a top surface area of 20 to 125 square feet.

They have been made from butyl rubber, neoprene, rubberized fabric, sheet metal, and fiber glass.

In 1961, the Soil Conservation Service began experimenting with different sizes and shapes of pillows at its Mount Hood, Oreg., test site where snowfall is deep and testing conditions good.

For testing, the ground is leveled at the data collection site so that the pillow is flat. A pressure hose is attached, and as snow accumulates on the pillow, its weight exerts a pressure.

Snow pillows and measuring instruments being installed on Mount Hood test site.

The change in pressure is proportional to the weight of the snow upon the pillow and also to the equivalent inches of water.

Experiments with different sizes and shapes show that a 6-foot pillow provides good results in shallow to medium depths of snow. In heavy snow country, 8 to 25 feet deep, and where quick response to snowfall is required, a pillow 10 to 12 feet in diameter gives best results.

The pillow may be round in shape or have four or more straight sides.

With testing of the pillows well underway, the next requirement was a means to get the information from the mountain to the office station. We considered a number of methods. One was to reflect radio signals from data sites off ionized meteor trails so that the signals could be received at the base station.

Another method was to fly over the data sites and record the signals with equipment mounted in the airplane. And the use of satellites as repeater stations also offered possibilities. We decided to use a base station, mountain repeater station, and one or more data collection sites as segments of a telemetry system.

By 1965, system requirements became more clearly defined, and components were being designed and constructed to do the snow surveying job. Instead of sending two men up into the mountains to collect data, pushing a button in the office would provide the information in a few seconds.

Essentially, the telemetry system—consisting of electronic and mechanical devices—must be able to collect many kinds of data from mountain sites, transmit the data through a repeater station, and receive and record the information at the base station. The repeater station, consisting of a radio receiver and transmitter, passes information in both directions between the base station and the data site. The radio frequencies being used require that there be line-of-sight from the repeater station to the base station and to the data site. A repeater station is usually located on a high peak. The whole system has to operate unattended for at least 9 months of the year under adverse weather and temperature conditions and provide accurate readings.

This was the job undertaken by scientific instrumentmakers and electronic experts. Electronic snow surveying materialized as a joint effort. Snow survey personnel set forth the requirements, carried out the tests under winter snow conditions, and provided actual measurements for calibration purposes. Electronic engineers designed and assembled the telemetry hardware.

Three groups have assisted from the beginning in designing and developing electronic and telemetry components. These are the Leupold and Stevens Instruments, Inc., Portland, Oreg.; Utah State University at Logan through the Electrical Engineering Department and Montana State University, Bozeman, through the Electronics Research Laboratory.

Leupold and Stevens developed the Mount Hood system which reports three channels of information to the Portland office on an hourly basis. The readout is in digital form on a printed tape.

Utah State University designed and installed the system operating in the Wasatch Mountains. This system has six data sites, one repeater site, and a base station at Logan. The data sites are interrogated from the base station, and numerical readings are displayed on a panel.

Montana State University designed and installed the system operating in the mountains south of Bozeman. This system has two data sites, a repeater site, and a base station at Bozeman. Information is reported hourly, received by teletype, and punched on a paper tape. The university also has a comprehensive system working between Bozeman and the Bridger Bowl Mountains.

The prototype systems that have been installed have served for testing and development purposes. The cooperating groups are continuously seeking ways to improve and simplify the equipment. Eventually the entire snow course network can be controlled by a computer which will ask for and receive data, make analyses and computations, provide a printout, and store the information on tapes.

Segments of the telemetry systems have been installed for the Soil Conservation Service in Oregon, Nevada, Wyoming, Colorado, and Idaho by commercial contractors. Plans are to instrument entire mountain ranges so water supply forecast information can be obtained at any time interval.

Information received from the mountains permits forecasting the water supply for western rivers well in advance of the summer use season.

Great river systems like the Columbia, Missouri, Colorado, and Rio Grande originate in high mountain country. The entire economy of the West is tied to its water resources since there is just not enough water for all purposes.

Approximately 17 million acres of land are irrigated from surface water sources in the Western States. There are approximately 380 major reservoirs. These reservoirs are used to regulate flood flows, to provide storage for irrigation and power, and to provide water for municipal, industrial, and recreational purposes. There are thousands of irrigation reservoirs with usable storage less than 5,000 acre-feet.

About 35 farms of 100 acres each can apply water 6 inches deep three times in the summer to their crops with 5,000 acre-feet of water.

Information obtained from the SCS

snow course network readily shows the mountain areas that have the heaviest snowfall and produce the greatest volume of runoff during the melt season. The highest water-producing areas in the West include the Cascade and Sierra Nevada Mountains and the high elevation ranges making up the Rocky Mountains. The Wasatch and Uinta Ranges provide water for the interior basin of Utah and contribute to the flow of the Colorado River system. The Gila River system of Arizona receives snowmelt water from Mogollon Plateau and Mountains.

Forecast information is released to

Snow pillow construction in mountains near Juneau, Alaska. Pillow filled with 250 gallons of methanol is connected by plumbing system to standpipe within tower built from empty drums. House atop drums contains recording instrument. Blades of copter used to transport men and equipment can be seen at far right.

The new way in snow surveys. Electronic equipment inside shelter house in Rocky Mountains sends data to Steamboat Springs, Colo., base station from snow pillow which is buried beneath the snow.

the public by newspapers, radio, and television. Special State and local reports are supplied to water users having a need for detailed information and basic data. The forecast period and type of forecast are selected to fit the needs of a particular area or water use interest. Basic data summaries are updated and published periodically.

The amount of available water has always been of great concern in parts of our West. In its early settlement, possession of springs and flowing streams meant control without possession of large areas of grazing land. With the influx of settlers, pressure developed for possession of both water and grazing land. Disputes were com-

mon, often resulting in shootouts. The Johnson County, Wyo., range war in the 1890's is an example of armed conflict between ranchers. With the coming of statehood, laws were established to protect the water rights of settlers and to provide an orderly procedure for the control and use of the water in the streams.

There isn't enough water in all places for everyone to use as much as he may like. Determining the amount that will be available in any given period permits advance planning. This allows better management and use of available resources.

Water supply forecasts have no regulatory function, but provide a basis for regulation. Each major water interest needs the basic data so it can plan its operation.

Irrigation water users adjust their water use or demand to the supply forecast from the winter snowpack. Reservoir levels are adjusted to either conserve water or release it in anticipation of flood flows. Space in a multiple-purpose reservoir can be managed more efficiently with advance information on reservoir inflow. Power companies can plan the adjustments that will be necessary between hydropower generation and other sources of power.

Interest is rising in the possibilities of increasing precipitation through artificial means. The Soil Conservation Service, under agreement with the Bureau of Reclamation, is making measurements of snow accumulation in the Park Range area near Steamboat Springs, Colo., in connection with the Bureau's Atmospheric Water Resources Program. This is a program to determine, through research and field operations, if there is a practical way of increasing the precipitation at any time or place.

In this Colorado network segment of 21 snow courses, six are equipped with pressure pillows, onsite recorders, and radio telemetry. Data are transmitted via a repeater station to the base station at Steamboat Springs. The operator at the base station can obtain data at any time from the mountain by pushing a button. Similar work by the Soil Conservation Service is also being done in Utah and elsewhere.

Efficient use of the West's water depends upon advance knowledge of water on the mountain.

. . . .

Porcupines and Deer Problems. Phil Farnes, snow survey supervisor at Bozeman, Mont., observed some peculiar readings coming in by radio from one of the data collection sites high up in the mountains.

Normal readings from this site give the water equivalent of the snow cover, total precipitation in the snow gage, and the air temperature. The peculiar readings showed that there was something on the pressure pillow, the device that weighs the amount of snow at the site and transmits a reading. But this was in the middle of summer—there was no snow.

The only likely answer was that wild animals of some kind were walking onto the pillows and standing or prancing around, thus producing the false readings. A quick trip to the mountain by Phil and examination of the ground and pillow showed many deer tracks.

We expected some bugs in operating the snow pressure pillows and we got them. But we did not expect that wild animals would be a problem. During the 1966–67 winter season, five pillows were severely damaged—one by a bear in Washington, two by deer in Montana, and two by elk in Oregon. The bear chewed a hole, and the deer and elk apparently ripped holes with their antlers. The pillows were filled with 250 to 300 gallons of antifreeze. This escaped through the holes and flowed down the slopes.

Porcupines are chewing the bottom out of the instrument houses that are used to protect the radio equipment and recorders.

The butyl rubber pillows are about 12 feet in diameter and when filled with antifreeze are about 5 inches thick. Walking across them produces a bouncy, floating feeling. There is a question as to why the wild animals are attracted to these installations. Maybe they like this crazy way of walking.

Thus, the search continues for a damageproof pillow or some simple means of preventing damage. Tests are being made using sheet metal pillows. Also, woven wire placed under and over the top of pillows may provide protection.

. . . .

Gyro Trail Hauler
Makes Mules Blush

IRA C. FUNK

. . . .

More than a decade ago, Herbert K. Harris slogged his way by foot and horseback over 200 miles of mountainous forest trails in planning the forest fire protection system for national forests in northern Idaho and Montana. As he plodded along, he often thought, "There must be a better way!" Now, thanks to Herb's persistence, there is a better way.

It is the gyroscopically stabilized cargo carrier. This looks like a cross between a large box and a motorcycle. The gyroscope, like a child's spinning top, keeps it upright even on steep, mountainous terrain. It carries the load of four pack mules, but unlike mules you don't have to feed it except when it's working.

Forestworkers, firefighters, miners, campers, hunters, farmers, and others will benefit from its use. It will speed rescue and firefighting operations when weather makes use of planes or helicopters unfeasible.

Largely through Herb Harris' urging, many people, privately and in public organizations, developed and tested machines for constructing forest trails and the vehicles for carrying men and cargo on them. Special scooters and motorbikes have been developed to transport one or two workmen and a few handtools over trails with only 18- to 24-inch tread width.

Special machines to take the place of handtools are now under test for constructing and maintaining these narrow trails.

Gasoline-powered cargo carriers with one wheel or with two wheels in line have been used for several years. These carriers require two husky men to operate and balance them with their 250- to 350-pound payload. Mules are still being used extensively, but can pack less than 200 pounds per animal.

Harris, who now directs the Forest Service Equipment Development Center at Missoula, Mont., was still not satisfied. "There must be a better way to transport cargo on trails," he told his small staff.

In 1959, he and his crew began studying gyroscopes and previous designs of gyroscopically stabilized vehicles. Although gyroscopes were successfully used in guidance of aircraft and missiles, no one had succeeded in developing a successful gyroscopically stabilized land vehicle. Nevertheless, Herb's studies of models of gyroscopic balancing systems and the cargo hauling problem showed that a gyro-stabilized cargo vehicle would give the most promise of success. A vehicle that could carry about 800 pounds and require only one operator was needed.

Realizing he and his staff did not have the outstanding capability in gyro-balancing system design needed to develop a successful vehicle, Harris made a countrywide search for the

∴   ∴   ∴

IRA C. FUNK is Staff Engineer for Equipment Studies, Forest Service.

190

man or organization that could succeed where all others had failed.

He found Tom Summers, a gyroscope systems designer and inventor. Tom had over a hundred gyroscope patents to his credit and was president of a small organization in Van Nuys, Calif., called the Summers Gyro-Car Co. He was already actively engaged in developing a gyro-stabilized vehicle. It appeared that much of the work Summers had done could be applied to the trail vehicle.

Under a series of contracts, Tom Summers and his small organization teamed up with the Forest Service's Equipment Development Center at Missoula. An experimental model of a gyroscopic stabilizing system was designed and tested in 1963. This demonstrated that the needed stabilizing system was feasible.

The first pilot model of the carrier was completed in 1965. This brought an opportunity to study the problems in a full-scale working model and important progress in development of the gyro control system. After 5 years of teamwork, the second pilot model was undergoing 200 hours of grueling tests on the center's proving ground and along forest trails.

On July 7, 1967, at a gathering of civic and forestry leaders and officials at Missoula, the battered and worn second pilot model, refreshed with a new paint job, was unveiled to the public. It was described as the first successful gyroscopically stabilized land vehicle on record.

Those attending saw for the first time a trail vehicle that could pack four times as much as a mule over the same narrow forest trail. Since its speed was 2½ times the mule's speed, it could transport 10 times the amount of cargo a mule could transport in a given time. Its designers had done an excellent job.

The forces that hold a child's spinning top upright keep the gyro cargo carrier from tipping over. Its 20-inch

Cargo carrier's narrow tread and gyro stabilizer permit crossing on log bridge.

Gyro carrier climbs a steep slope.

diameter, 180-pound gyroscope spinning at 5,500 revolutions per minute is similar, but much more complicated than a toy gyroscope that balances on a string or tip of a pencil. A hydraulically operated parking stand keeps the vehicle upright when the gyroscope is not functioning.

All controls are at the rear of the machine. The operator may ride standing on a steplike platform or may fold the platform against the vehicle and walk behind it with his hands on the controls.

Each wheel is driven by a small hydraulic motor in its hub. A pump operated by a gasoline engine supplies hydraulic power to these motors and to the motor driving the gyro. The same power source also provides power steering. All three wheels are in line and have 9.50 x 8 low-pressure tires for maximum traction with minimum tread width.

Bogey or "rocking chair" suspension of the two rear wheels plus 10-inch ground clearance give good perform-

ance in climbing over the obstacles frequently found on trails. Overall dimensions (length, 8 feet, overall width, 32 inches, overall height, 59 inches) and 1,700 pounds empty weight permit easy transport via highway or forest road in a pickup truck. A narrow gangplank is all that's needed for the carrier to load or unload itself.

The carrier's forward speed up to 5 miles an hour, reverse speed up to 1½ miles an hour, and 6-foot turning radius are adequate and safe for mountain trail travel. It will climb a 60 percent slope on pavement and travel side hill on a 60 percent side slope. (A 60 percent slope is one that rises 60 feet in a horizontal distance of 100 feet. Maximum grades on mountain highways are generally 7 percent and rarely exceed 15 percent.) An 800-pound load can be carried on the carrier's 15 square feet of cargo deck.

Having successfully reached their original objective, Herb Harris and Tom Summers still were not fully satisfied. Since July 7, 1967, they have made several major improvements in the gyro-stabilized cargo carrier. These include improvements in utility and reliability and reduction of cost. Essential refinements should be completed by the end of 1968, and production of the carriers started soon after.

When gyro cargo carriers become available, many will be faced with deciding the question, "Shall we use gyro carriers or pack animals?" The decision in most cases will be based upon cost versus benefit studies. In some private situations, cost may not be a consideration or mules will be used because of a person's love for the animals.

Use of motorized equipment in designated wilderness areas is prohibited. Therefore, in these remote areas, horses and mules will continue to be the main means of transportation. However, there are 88,000 miles of trails in the national forests exclusive of wilderness areas.

For those who must transport much cargo on the forest trails where use of motorized vehicles is permitted, the gyro-stabilized cargo carrier will probably become the favorite.

That Forests May Live—
The Smokejumpers

WILLIAM C. WOOD

. . . .

Twenty-eight years ago, a Ford trimotor airplane droned 2,000 feet above a forest fire smoldering in the Selway-Bitterroot Wilderness. The pilot cut its motors briefly. Rufus Robinson, Kooskia, Idaho, and Earl Cooley, Hamilton, Mont., stepped from the plane, parachuted earthward, became the world's first smokejumpers, and revolutionized firefighting in the back country. A month later, Francis Lufkin, Winthrop, Wash., and Glen H. Smith, Bakersfield, Calif., parachuted to a small fire in the Northern Cascades in the State of Washington. These young Forest Service aerial frontiersmen were pioneering a feat that would be repeated nearly 40,000 times by 1968.

In 1968, Cooley and Lufkin were still with the Forest Service as supervisors of smokejumping bases in Montana and Washington.

The key to successful forest firefight-ing lies in speed of attack. "Hit 'em while they're small" has been the byword among Forest Service firefighters since the organization was founded in 1905. Unless a forest fire is put out while it is still small, it can grow to catastrophic proportions with losses reaching millions of dollars.

Lightning is nature's own special fire starter. Each year, about 7,000 forest fires are caused by lightning throughout the Western United States. Many of these occur in remote, mountainous areas where helicopters cannot land, and ground travel is slow and difficult. Since the earliest days, foresters have searched for ways to speed the attack. Smokejumping was born of this need.

The art and science of parachuting to fires is truly a Forest Service innovation. The idea of parachuting men to fires in inaccessible back-country areas was conceived in Utah in 1931 by an imaginative early-day forester, T. V.

193

Pearson. Pearson proposed and started the first experiments in the use of parachutes by forest firefighters. He hired a professional parachutist to conduct a few demonstrations and experimental dummy drops, but the idea was abandoned as being too risky.

For the next few years, the thought of parachuting men to fires was only a glimmer in the minds of a few other foresters who had heard of Pearson's experiments.

In 1935, the U.S. Forest Service established an aerial fire control experimental project. The immediate plan was to experiment in use of air-dropped water and chemical bombs. Fire bombing experiments were begun in California.

After several years of intensive experimentation to establish a feasible method of fire control from the air, it began to be more and more apparent that suppression of fires with water or chemicals delivered by aircraft was, at the time, impractical. The planes and equipment then available simply did not have the capability to deliver an effective blow to even the smallest forest fire.

In the latter stages of these aerial bombing experiments, the project was transferred from California to the Pacific Northwest. David P. Godwin, assistant chief of fire control for the Forest Service, recommended that the bombing tests be discontinued and the balance of project funds be spent on a parachute jumping experiment. Parachutes, protective clothing, and the services of professional parachute riggers and jumpers were contracted. The experiment was conducted at Winthrop, Wash., on the Okanogan National Forest during the fall of 1939.

A small group of exhibition parachutists (barnstormers in those days, skydivers today), with Frank M. Derry in charge, conducted a number of

∴   ∴   ∴

WILLIAM C. WOOD *is an Equipment Specialist in the Division of Fire Control, Pacific Northwest Region, Forest Service, Portland, Oreg. He has served as a parachute rigger and smokejumper.*

dummy tests and made approximately 60 live jumps. Toward the end of the experiment, Lufkin and a few other Forest Service firefighters volunteered to jump into open fields and timbered areas. The tests showed that smokejumpers could land safely in all kinds of green timber common to the Pacific Northwest at altitudes ranging from 2,000 to 6,800 feet above sea level. Jumps were also made in mountain meadows, open ridge tops, and on steep, boulder-strewn slopes.

Equipment used in these early trials was designed and built by Derry. Basic designs have remained almost unchanged to this day, attesting to the thoroughness of these early experiments and suitability of the jumping gear developed. Over the years, only minor revisions have been made to incorporate modern textiles and hardware. Silk, cotton, and linen have gone by the way; nylon is the thing. Felt padding has been replaced by modern foam plastics especially designed to absorb bumps and jolts.

The parachute is somewhat larger, and, of course, the business of getting down out of tall trees has been simplified by modern snaps and quick-release buckles.

As a result of the successful experiments in 1939, two small squads of smokejumpers were organized for the 1940 fire season. One squad was located at Winthrop, the other in Montana near the Idaho border. Each squad was made up of regular forest firemen (some of whom had volunteered to jump during the 1939 experiments) and a few of the professional parachutists who were employed by the Forest Service and then trained as firefighters. Derry was retained as technical adviser to both squads.

Due to a light fire season in the Pacific Northwest, the Washington squad saw action on only two fires, but the Montana-Idaho jumpers handled nine back-country fires that season. Careful analysis of these fires indicated a net saving amounting to nearly three times the cost of outfitting and training both squads.

Top, smokejumpers ready for a mission. Padded suit, special football helmet, and mask help prevent injury if they land in trees or rough terrain. A 150-foot nylon line in leg pocket is used for sliding down out of tall trees. *Right,* smokejumpers drop from plane to fight a fire. *Below,* smokejumpers work out on the "torture rack" to strengthen their back and belly muscles.

The Johnson Flying Service, an aviation pioneer enterprise famed throughout Montana and Idaho for daring hinterland flights, contributed much to the development of aviation equipment and techniques in support of smokejumping. An outstanding accomplishment was development of the parachute static line, a length of webbing fastened to the airplane to automatically open the parachute as the jumper falls away.

Bob Johnson, bush pilot, and Howard Flint, forester, had invented a static line to drop equipment and supplies. Derry successfully adapted this principle to the man-carrying parachute. The static line greatly improves the reliability and performance of parachutes. There is no ripcord to pull. The parachute opens a short distance below the aircraft, eliminating the possibility of the jumper tumbling or spinning prior to opening of the canopy. The static line has become the lifeline of today's paratroopers who must jump at extremely low levels in combat action.

Smokejumping demonstrations were made during the visit of four U.S. Army officers to the parachute training camp in Montana during the 1940 fire season. One of these, Major William Cary Lee, later employed Forest Service techniques and ideas in organizing the first paratroop training at Ft. Benning, Ga. Lee subsequently commanded the 101st Airborne Division which he took to England and trained for the Normandy invasion. He became the first chief of the Airborne Command and is regarded as the father of U.S. airborne doctrine.

Shortages of textiles and hardware created by World War II affected the growth of smokejumping almost from the start. War priorities and shortages eliminated the special maneuverable silk parachutes used by smokejumpers. To offset this, Derry experimented with standard military-type parachutes, modifying them so smokejumpers could glide and turn to land on a target on the ground. He cut a pair of long slots in the rear portion of the parachute which allowed air to escape in a rearward jet imparting forward thrust on the canopy. Guidelines were attached to the slots to enable the jumper to turn the parachute by closing one or the other of the slots. The Derry-slotted parachute, still in use by smokejumpers, is the forerunner of the highly complex, vented canopies used by sport skydivers throughout the world.

In recent years, the smokejumping program really paid off during the 1967 fire season, which stands as one of the worst on record throughout the States of Idaho, Montana, Oregon, and Washington. A long summer drought set the stage for a series of lightning fires which began to occur in early August.

During the early morning hours of August 10, lightning storms started more than 400 fires along the crest of the Cascade Mountains in Oregon. Smokejumpers were flown in from California, Idaho, Montana, and Washington to back up the Oregon squad. On this day, 149 smokejumpers landed on fires that occurred in the most rugged and remote parts of the Cascades. Other crews using helicopters and trucks manned the more accessible fires. Lightning storms continued throughout the summer, and the smokejumpers broke all previous records when they made 4,440 jumps to 1,247 fires. Since the beginning of smokejumping, nearly 40,000 jumps have been made to suppress over 11,000 fires.

Modern smokejumpers have a number of advantages over the oldtimers. Whereas the early smokejumpers had only the shovel and ax-mattock, today's smokejumpers have aerial retardant bombers to aid them in suppressing fires. World War II bombers, converted to carry up to 2,000 gallons of fire-retardant slurry, can be ordered out to drop on strategic parts of the fire to back up the smokejumpers. Time and time again, the combined attack of smokejumpers and aerial retardants has stopped small, explosive fires dramatically.

196

Helicopters are a boon to the smoke-jumpers. They can lift ground crews in to help after smokejumpers have cleared landing spots (helispots) near-by. After a fire is out, smokejumpers can also clear a landing spot so a helicopter can come in and retrieve men and tools. The smokejumper can be lifted by helicopter back to the base where he can be ready to go on another fire, often the same day.

Except for a small nucleus of career personnel, most smokejumpers are seasonal employees. College students, many of them aspiring foresters, comprise the majority. They are the elite of forest firefighters, most of them coming up through the ranks after having received training and experience in regular fire crews. Upon reporting for duty in early summer, they are put through a strenuous 1-month regimen of calisthenics, jogging, parachute training, advanced firefighting tactics, and first aid training.

During the summer of 1968, about 450 smokejumpers were stationed throughout the large wildland forest areas of the Nation. Smokejumper bases were located at Redding, Calif.; Grangeville, Idaho City, and McCall, Idaho; Missoula, Mont.; Silver City, N. Mex.; Cave Junction, LaGrande, and Redmond, Oreg.; Winthrop, Wash.; Yellowstone National Park; and Fairbanks, Alaska.

A Living Filter
for Sewage

LOUIS T. KARDOS, WILLIAM E. SOPPER, and EARL A. MYERS

Some 23 billion gallons of sewage effluent were discharged daily during 1967 by municipal treatment plants in the United States. This effluent, generally considered as waste, may represent a hidden resource for many communities. It is somewhat paradoxical that communities experiencing water shortages will at the same time discharge millions of gallons of effluent into local streams for rapid removal from the area. Is this the most efficient use for our water resource, or simply a pattern inherited from the past?

At the turn of the century, less than 1,000 communities in the United States had sewer systems, and most of these discharged untreated waste directly into the nearest watercourse. As a result, many streams, lakes, and coastal areas became health hazards. But with advances in science and engineering and the development of modern waste treatment plants, discharge of properly treated sewage effluent into natural watercourses for dilution became an acceptable technique.

However, recent rapid population and industrial expansion along with urbanization have placed a greater demand on the Nation's water resources and have accentuated waste disposal

∴   ∴   ∴

LOUIS T. KARDOS is Professor of Soil Technology at Pennsylvania State University.

WILLIAM E. SOPPER is Associate Professor of Forest Hydrology.

EARL A. MYERS is Associate Professor of Agricultural Engineering.

Detergent residue foams up a Pennsylvania stream.

and water pollution problems. In many areas, dilution is no longer the answer to pollution. With today's complex society, ever-increasing water needs can be satisfied only by use and reuse of all available water resources. And methods that ignore the right of downstream users can no longer be tolerated.

Sewage effluent discharged from efficient waste treatment plants looks much like ordinary tap water and when properly treated with chlorine is theoretically safe for human consumption. But unlike ordinary water, this effluent is usually highly enriched with plant nutrients and undesirable synthetic detergent residues.

Discharging effluent into natural bodies of water alters the normal balance of life in the stream or lake, often with harmful effects on fish and other aquatic life. Prolific growth of aquatic vegetation generally occurs as a result of the increased nutrient level, and unsightly foam may appear as a result of the detergent residue, both of which detract from esthetic and recreational values of the water resource.

Water pollution and water supply problems in State College, Pa., are typical of many communities in the United States. Effluent from the sewage treatment plant, which services a population of approximately 30,000 people, goes into Spring Creek—the area's main watercourse.

Population growth continually increased the volume of waste to be treated and, likewise, the volume of effluent discharged. As a result, less dilution occurred, and nutrients were carried at higher concentrations into Spring Creek. Increased nutrient level caused excessive growth of aquatic weeds that choked the waterway and depleted the water of lifegiving oxygen necessary for fish life. Mounds of foam floated downstream.

A second problem in the area is water supply. Almost the entire supply comes from the ground water reservoir whose level gradually fell due to a prolonged 7-year drought that started in 1960. During the 7 years, there was a total deficit of 50 inches of precipitation, which is almost equivalent to 1⅓ years of normal precipitation. In the same period, millions of gallons of effluent were discharged daily into Spring Creek and thus not available for reuse as a water resource in the immediate locality.

Both problems led to investigation of the feasibility of applying large volumes of effluent on the land. Diversion of the effluent from local streams would certainly help lessen pollution. And if the effluent could be renovated by the land and recharged to the ground water reservoir, it would be retained in the area for a longer period of time and be available for reuse. Increased growth and yield of crops and forest products as a result of irrigation with the nutrient-laden effluent might also result.

Land disposal of effluents has been used by man for centuries. Domestic sewage, after various degrees of treatment, was applied directly to the soil through surface ponding or by sprinkler irrigation techniques. For the most part, the goal was disposal of waste water without producing a health hazard, rather than pollution abatement, increasing the ground water supply, or improving the productivity of farms and forests. The soil was used primarily as a mechanical filter and in most cases was overloaded beyond its biological capacity.

A more practical method would be to use the soil with its microbes and vegetative cover as a "living filter."

The Waste Water Renovation and Conservation Project was established in 1962 at Pennsylvania State University to investigate the living filter concept. Adding one or more inches of waste water, weekly, to a complex natural system of soil, microbes, plants, and animals may trigger a multitude of actions and reactions. So, a team was assembled to attack all aspects of the problem. It consisted of agricultural and civil engineers, agronomists, biochemists, foresters, geologists, microbiologists, and zoologists.

Preliminary studies indicated two potential disposal sites were available on university farm and forest land and adjoining State gamelands within 4 miles of the sewage treatment plant. At one site, the soil was high in silt and clay, at the other it was high in sand. Soils at both sites were well drained. Forested areas were red pine and white spruce plantations and natural regrowth of mixed hardwoods of different ages. The farmland involved rotations of corn, small grains, and hay for animal feed. The terrain was generally undulating.

For 1 year, beginning in April 1962, water samples were collected monthly from a network of 50 private and public wells, six large flowing springs, and one stream, all within a 10-mile radius of the proposed project site. Chemical and bacteriological data from these samples showed the quality of the water supply before the first application of waste water in May 1963. This network continued to be sampled in subsequent years as part of a monitoring system.

Waste water came mainly from domestic sewage that had received primary and secondary treatment. After chlorination, it was pumped through a buried, 6-inch pipeline to the disposal sites and then distributed through fixed, quick-coupling, aluminum surface lines and revolving sprinklers. Suspended solids ranged from 14 to 32 mg. per liter, and biochemical oxygen demand ranged from 7 to 18 mg. per liter. Such waste water would be regarded as excellent in quality. The weekly application of 2 inches for 31 weeks in 1965 was equivalent to applying 1 ton of a 7–14–12 fertilizer per acre, worth about $70.

About a half million gallons of waste water was disposed of daily at a rate of a quarter inch per hour. Various experimental areas received 1 to 6 inches (27,154 to 162,924 gallons per acre) at weekly intervals. During severe winter weather, the main and submain lines were kept from freezing by continuous operation of a small sprinkler at the end of each submain.

To protect the lateral lines from freezing, each was placed on a uniform grade of 2 percent to facilitate rapid drainage by opening the end of the line immediately after its operation ceased. Special nonrevolving sprinkler heads were also developed to operate at subfreezing temperatures.

To determine changes in the quality of the waste water as it passed through the living filter, samples were obtained by pan lysimeters and suction lysimeters to a depth of 30 feet, by shallow sand-point wells to a depth of 52 feet, and by ground water wells to a depth of some 300 feet.

Has the living filter worked?

Results from 1963–66 show the soil with its microbes and vegetative cover can satisfactorily renovate waste water from a sewage treatment plant provided we work with nature rather than overpower her.

After a red pine forest received 2 inches of waste water weekly for a total of 174 inches (4.7 million gallons per acre) over a 3-year period, water samples taken at a 4-foot depth showed a 97 percent decrease in concentration of detergent, a 92 percent decrease in phosphorus, and a 49 percent decrease in nitrate nitrogen. Larger decreases in detergent and phosphorus occurred in the cropland areas receiving 2 inches of waste water weekly. When only 1 inch was applied weekly, cleanup was better. Where 4 inches were applied, cleanup was poorer, particularly of phosphorus. Six inches weekly on the sandy soil resulted in unsatisfactory removal of both detergent and nitrate.

Nitrogen and phosphorus, the two nutrients primarily responsible for excessive weed growth in streams and lakes, are removed from the system in large amounts when crops like corn and hay are harvested. A 111-bushel corn crop removed 112 pounds of nitrogen, 41 pounds of phosphorus, and 39 pounds of potassium. These amounts were equivalent to 105 percent of the nitrogen added by the 1.57 million gallons of waste water applied to each acre in 1965, 47 percent of the phosphorus, and 15 percent of the potassium. The 5 percent excess in removal of nitrogen represents a net loss from the soil supply of nitrogen.

Winter application of sewage effluent creates ice statuary.

Forest vegetation also removed nutrients during the growing season, but much of these nutrients are redeposited annually in the leaf and needle litter rather than being hauled away in harvested crops. Hence renovation of the waste water in forested areas is not as effective as in cropland areas.

The microbial portion of the living filter in both cropland and forest land destroys the complicated organic molecules, such as the "hard" detergents, if the applications of the effluent are controlled to permit them to remain for about 1 week in the well-aerated, microbe-rich topsoil.

To these living systems, the plants and the microbes, the soil adds a safety valve in the tremendous adsorptive capacity of its organic and inorganic colloids. Of special importance is the large capacity of the soil to fix phosphorus. Adsorption experiments in the laboratory indicate the upper 5 feet of fine-textured Hagerstown soil from one disposal site had an adsorptive capacity equivalent to 20,000 pounds of phosphorus or more phosphorus than would be added in 100 years if 2 inches of effluent were applied weekly.

Another benefit from using the farm and forest land as a living filter occurs as the cleaned waste water trickles down to help fill the ground water reservoir. Ultimately, this water, which now meets the U.S. Public Health Service standards for drinking water, works its way back to the streams or lakes or to the wells and springs of the region. Data at the Penn State project during a dry year indicated 80 to 90 percent of a weekly application of 2 inches of waste water was recharged to the ground water. During a normal or wet year, even larger amounts of water would be added to the ground water reservoir.

Would a living filter system require too much land in this era of increasing competition for space?

At application levels of 2 inches weekly, which looks very promising in the Penn State project, only 129 acres of land would be needed to dispose of 1 million gallons of waste water per day. This is about the output of a sewage treatment plant that serves a community of 10,000 persons.

Land disposal of large volumes of sewage effluent is feasible. It offers a way to prevent pollution of streams and lakes, replenish water resources, and improve the productivity of forest and farm land.

Secondary benefits can also be expected from increased yields of farm and forest products. In 4 years of operation, average increases in hay yields due to weekly applications of 1 or 2 inches of effluent were 2 to 3 tons per acre. Increases in corn yields were 30 to 50 bushels per acre in conventional 38-inch rows and over 100 bushels per acre with larger plant populations in narrow (19-inch) rows.

Young hardwoods and white spruce responded favorably to effluent by becoming larger in diameter and taller than the unirrigated trees. Red pine trees did not increase in girth, but did grow taller if only 1 inch of effluent was applied weekly, and they produced a denser shade with 2 inches.

Since any disposal system must operate throughout the year, in northern climates when the temperatures are low, the system must rely more on the adsorptive capacity of the soil and less on the microbes and roots. Forested areas fit into the system well by providing better winter infiltration conditions and larger phosphorus adsorptive capacities under the acid conditions associated with forest soils. Combinations of cropland and forested areas will provide the greatest flexibility in the living filter concept.

For further reading:
McGauhey, P. H., Krone, R. B., and Winneberger, J. H., *Soil Mantle as a Waste Water Treatment System.* SERL Report 66–7, Sanitary Engineering Research Laboratory, University of California, Berkeley, 1966.
Parizek, R. R., and others, *Waste Water Renovation and Conservation.* Penn State Study 23, Pennsylvania State University, University Park, Pa., 1967.
Robeck, G. G., and others, "Factors Influencing the Design and Operation of Soil Systems for Waste Treatment." *Journal of Water Pollution Control Federation,* Vol. 36, No. 8, 1964.

Loggers Fly Balloons, Trees Ride the Breeze

WILLIAM K. NELSON

. . . .

Two fishermen in a pickup truck sped toward the Cascade Mountains east of Eugene, Oreg. They were headed for their favorite fishing site at the end of a side road that had been used for logging.

When they turned into the logging road, they were met almost immediately by a truck loaded with logs. As they pulled over to the edge of the road to allow the truck to pass, they both wondered where these logs could be coming from. Logging in the valley had stopped years ago after timber on the gentler slopes close to the road had been taken out. The only access to remaining timber stands would be by expensive winding roads up the steep higher slopes.

Gradually, they heard the roar of a diesel-powered yarder used to pull logs into roadside piles. Suddenly, they saw the large silver balloon floating serenely high above the ridgetops.

Drawn by the yarder, the balloon turned and slowly moved down the slope, deposited its load of three large logs, and glided again toward the ridgetops. Scanning upward, one could barely make out the work crew that would fasten the next load of logs to the tether line on the balloon.

The two fishermen got out of their truck and introduced themselves to the logging boss. "Yes," the boss acknowledged, "this is a new concept in logging. It is still a cable system—but instead of dragging logs, the balloon lifts them off the ground and carries them to the landing near the yarder."

He said this timber could not have been harvested economically with conventional cable systems because of the high cost or impossibility of road construction. Roads would have to be close together, taking a lot of timberland out of production and creating unsightly scars on the landscape.

"Roads on steep slopes," he explained, "expose large areas of mineral soil." Now, glancing at the logged areas, the fishermen could see no ground disturbance—only the absence of trees and the usual litter of branches and tops. It was almost as if some giant hand had plucked the trees from their growing places and deposited them at the landing below.

The usual scars from road construction and the dragging of logs with conventional cable systems were simply never made.

In a few years, the slopes would again be green with young trees. Meanwhile, no erosion threatened their fishing spot, and the scenery would not be impaired. Mature timber was simply being removed from the slopes above and the land left in condition for a second crop of trees. The fisherman could still enjoy his sport. And soil, water, and esthetic values were being protected.

Credit for original experimentation

.·.   .·.   .·.

WILLIAM K. NELSON is Branch Chief of Engineering Research with the Forest Service.

n balloon logging goes to Prof. Ulf
Sundberg of Sweden, who first conducted trials in 1956.

The trials were on flat ground, and
the balloon provided only enough lift
to hold one end of the log off the
ground while it was being dragged.
However, an idea was born.

In September 1963, the director of
the Pacific Northwest Forest and
Range Experiment Station (PNW)
was asked to assume leadership in applying balloons to forestry needs. PNW
was then investigating the use of helicopters and aerial cableways for harvesting timber from inaccessible areas.
Hilton Lysons, industrial engineer in
charge of this research, reported favorably on the possibility of using balloons for aerial logging.

The Canadians had also been studying balloons, and in October of 1963
logged experimentally near Vancou-
ver, British Columbia, with helium-
filled barrage-type balloons connected
in tandem.

Balloon logging.

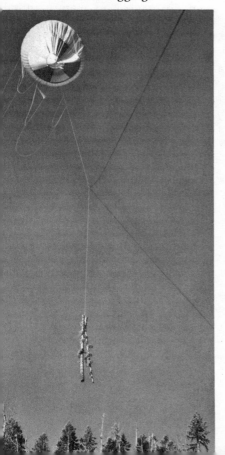

The Canadian trials were the first in
which logs were flown in the air. Their
experiments showed that the idea
would work, but a logging system for
the various wind and load conditions
could not be designed without engineering data. To obtain some of these
data, a contract was awarded to the
Goodyear Aerospace Corp. in January
1964 for a technical feasibility study.

Slide rules and computers said the
system was technically sound. More
research was needed to be reasonably
sure that balloon logging could be
economically sound. In February 1964,
Goodyear was asked for a logistic
study to determine economic feasibility of the new system. Again, the idea
looked sound.

Land managers, too, were excited
by the prospect of getting at locked-up
timber in difficult-access areas and developing logging methods less objectionable to conservationists. Faye
Stewart of the Bohemia Lumber Co.,
Culp Creek, Oreg., proposed a cooperative program to carry out the
balloon logging concept.

After encouraging trials with prototype balloons only 75,000 cubic feet in
volume, plans were made for a logging
operation on the Willamette National
Forest in Oregon using a 150,000-
cubic-foot-capacity balloon. Bohemia
Lumber Co. provided the crew,
ground equipment, and a Goodyear
balloon; the Forest Service arranged a
special tract of timber on Deception
Creek and had research engineers on
hand to assist in evaluating the operation. Logging began in June 1966.

Balloon logging is rapidly approaching commercial reality. This system,
along with other aerial concepts now
being researched by the Forest Service,
will help capture nearly a billion
board feet per year of allowable cut in
Pacific Northwest and Alaska timberlands that cannot be logged conventionally. It is estimated these aerial
systems will reduce access road mileage
on national forest lands alone by
11,000 miles in the harvesting of
Douglas-fir—with an anticipated saving of over $335 million.

Riffle Sifter for Alaska Salmon Gold

HERBERT J. SHIELDS

....

Some of the richest acreage on our national forests is not in trees, but in gravel beds where five species of Pacific salmon return to spawn. A relatively few acres of spawning riffles on streams along the Alaskan coast produced around 56 million salmon taken by fishermen in 1965, with a value of over $116 million.

Although normally every acre will produce over half a million youngsters, or "fry," clean gravel on the streambed can increase survival to over 2 million. Here lies a potential with which fishery biologists hope not only to continue this self-renewing resource, but to increase the yield.

P. D. Hanson, regional forester (now retired) for the Forest Service's Alaska Region, approached equipment developers in 1963 with a request to: "Develop a means of flushing the fine (silt) materials from the streambed of salmon spawning streams. . . ." His keen foresight started an exciting unraveling of engineering and inventive skills which still continues.

To comprehend the overall problem, John Holland, a mechanical engineer with the Forest Service's Equipment Development Center, then at Arcadia, Calif., sought the advice of Sigurd Olson and Bill Sheridan of the Forest Service's Wildlife Management Branch in Juneau, Alaska. We were all in for an education on the salmon's fascinating life cycle.

Salmon are born in stream gravel beds which are known as "riffles" or areas where the stream current is fairly rapid and washes around and through the gravel bottom. Laid in the late summer and fall, the eggs incubate until early winter. They then hatch into "alevins," or small fish with the yolk sacs attached, and during the spring emerge from the gravel as abou inch-long "fry."

Some species immediately migrate to the sea, and others remain in fresh water up to a year or more before they head out to sea to mature in salt water. Species vary, but after anywhere from 2 to 5 years, they begin the return to their exact stream and place of birth. Bill Sheridan relate stories of salmon finding and jumping walls of fish hatcheries to return to spawning areas. If they can't return to the area where they hatched, salmon may not spawn. Strangely, eggs can be moved to new locations, but once they are hatched, the navigational "fix" is permanent.

The fish stop feeding when they re enter fresh water, living on stored body fats as they fight their way upstream. Consequently, fish caught on their spawning run in the streams are no considered too palatable. They even change color, and some species become quite "blotchy" or highly colored in

∴   ∴   ∴

HERBERT J. SHIELDS *is an Engineer with the Forest Service's Equipment Development Center California.*

204

appearance and sometimes look downright unhealthy.

The female digs a nest, or "redd," on the gravel by hollowing out with her tail a crater-shaped pocket as much as 2 or 3 feet in diameter and up to 18 inches deep. Depending on the salmon species and size, up to 8,000 eggs are deposited in the redd, and simultaneously the male fertilizes them by covering them with a milky fluid called "milt." The eggs are covered with gravel; and, within the next few days, the parent fish die and the life cycle is now complete.

Clean gravel is necessary to enhance free circulation of water through the spawning beds to provide oxygen necessary for survival of eggs and fry and to wash away metabolic wastes. The lower the sediment content of the gravel, the better the circulation of water and the higher the survival of salmon embryos. Research in artificial spawning channels has shown this time and again. However, artificial channels are costly and difficult to maintain in Alaska.

An alternative is to develop a machine to clean sediment from natural salmon spawning beds. Also, when a spawning riffle becomes dirty or sedimented from logging, road construction, or landslips, the "Riffle Sifter" (this name for the machine has since stuck) could be used in order to remedy the damage.

So, we had the problem and need defined with a few other limitations peculiar to Alaskan operations such as:
• The gravel streambed should be disturbed as little as possible;
• The machine should be fully amphibious to permit crossing open water areas, mudflats, and rough terrain (there are usually no roads available near spawning streams); and
• Over 90 percent of the material under 1 millimeter (about ⅓₂-inch in diameter) should be removed from the gravel. Some material from 1 to 3 millimeters should be removed, leaving larger sizes undisturbed.

How do you go about starting work on a device for this job? Well, the first thing you can do is build a stream somewhere to use as a test bed. Since concern about conservation of wildlife is an easy emotion to arouse in scientists, it didn't take us long to talk the California Institute of Technology in Pasadena into letting us have access to their Keck Hydraulic Laboratory. Within this laboratory, we were able to set up an artificial stream where water flow and depth could be controlled. And best of all, it had glass walls so we could observe a cross section of the streamflow.

When Holland started bringing truckloads of dirty sand and gravel into the laboratory's previously clean hydraulic system, the professors did have some temporary misgivings about the operation. But they admired this direct approach to a hydraulic and mechanical problem, and were soon providing technical and moral support. By adding a winch-drawn cart to the top walls of the "flume," we were able to test various devices drawn through our streambed at controlled speeds.

Since the streambed was to be disturbed as little as possible, the first idea to try was a flushing bar pulled beneath the surface to boil the fines (silt materials) to the surface water where they could be collected through a hood. Dredge heads and screening and washing techniques used in mining operations were all examined as ideas and rejected because they disturb and completely replace the streambed. Fishery biologists are not yet ready to permit complete disruption of nature's spawning gravels since this may sacrifice other streambed arrangements built by nature over many years.

A T-bar arrangement appeared to show the most promise, with the T inverted and pulled along about 14 inches beneath the gravel surface. On the top surface of the bar, holes at various angles provided an upward water jet action toward the surface. A screened hood just beneath the water level sucked out the silt-laden water for pumping through a hose—and eventually to the streambank. The big

Second model of Riffle Sifter undergoes test trials in Alaskan salmon-spawning stream. Silt is cleaned from streambed to improve survival of salmon eggs.

unknown, of course, was: How tough were the Alaskan streambeds compared to our test channel?

Based upon Holland's testwork and many calculations, a crude design began to emerge. Keep the inverted T-bar flushing head and mount it in the center of a sturdy six-wheeled cart which could be winched along by cable from another small amphibious vehicle. This would eliminate the problem of driving wheels which might disturb the bottom, leave tracks, and, in deeper areas, float—thus losing traction entirely. If necessary, anchor the winching vehicle so as to provide a nonslip pull.

During the spring of 1964, engineers and technicians at the Equipment Development Center at Arcadia worked against time to assemble the first working model. It had to be tried out in Alaskan salmon streams no later than

the end of July to be ahead of the salmon runs or a year would be lost

This first trial gave us a lot of ideas and needs for correction. The machine was too small to clean the large areas required, it suffered damage from submerged boulders, and more power was needed. But there wa definite evidence of cleaning taking place—and the basic flushing principl appeared sound.

Richard Wilke, regional engineer o the Forest Service's Alaska Region agreed that we were on the righ track, but a much larger machine wa needed. It was decided to canvass in dustry for a heavy equipment manu facturer willing to contract and under take such a task. The following yea was spent presenting our case t interested companies and in turn eval uating proposals from them.

We were fortunate in eventuall

206

ettling on the Clark Development Division, Clark Equipment Co., Cassopolis, Mich. This group was headed by Cyril "Bruce" Rogers, an engineer with know-how in developing heavy equipment. It so happened Clark had a new concept for a pneumatic-tracked amphibious vehicle which appeared to fill the bill as a prime mover for the gravel-cleaning equipment carrier.

Clark felt some improvement could be made to the T-bar arrangement to reduce power requirements. So they built their own gravel bed and picked up where we left off. Eventually they conceived a clever vertical tooth with fan-shaped sprays acting as a water ladder to progressively lift the material upward while the teeth raked through the streambed. A collection hood would skid along the surface of the gravel and collect the silt-laden water for pumping through a nozzle 100 feet beyond the bank.

The machine also had its own winches, anchors at the end of the cables, and all the associated pumps, engines, and controls. The vehicle could "swim" and traverse any terrain we expected to encounter.

As finally constructed, the machine had five collection hoods with two teeth apiece which would cover a swath 10 feet wide.

When the machine finally arrived in Juneau in August 1966, many local folks thought the Forest Service was going in for gold dredging. This first summer was fraught with mechanical breakdowns and shortcomings in performance that prevented much actual progress in cleaning gravel. However, valuable experience was gained with on-the-spot environmental, transportation, and supply problems. We soon became adept in matching tidetables with work schedules.

During the winter of 1966 and early spring 1967, the machine was returned to Michigan and subjected to many changes in design. Trials in Missouri during May were more encouraging than ever, so we shipped the "Riffle Sifter" back to Juneau in July 1967.

Continued work during 1967 showed good progress and encouraging results, although salmon "runs" did not permit time for much experimentation or extensive cleaning. Improvements to the machine were made in the field, and it will be further developed. This working model "test bed" has provided many excellent ideas that can only lead to better performance.

Fisherman with a pair of salmon beauties.

Several complete streams will need to be cleaned to finally evaluate results. Cost studies alone show the work must continue. Based on a cost of cleaning of $2,000 per acre of gravel, the cleaned acre should, under ideal conditions, return over $131,000 worth of fish. But if it was left uncleaned, the acre would normally return only $26,000 worth.

This is a benefit ratio of 53 to 1 based on the original $2,000 investment for the first return 2 years after cleaning. If the effectiveness lasts several years, it could easily run more than 100 to 1.

Impressive as they are, figures don explain the emotion and the huma need to manage and make this natura resource more plentiful. We full expect to perfect the "Riffle Sifter to do the job or, eventually, to com up with an improved machine.

Just about everyone has enjoyed th taste of salmon, and many have ha the unforgettable thrill of landin these magnificent fighting fish by ro and reel. Since salmon is a self-pe petuating resource, enlightened mar agement and continued work of th kind will assure future generations bountiful supply.

Infrared Pinpoints Fires Through a Sea of Smoke

CRAIG C. CHANDLER

. . . .

It was already hot and dry in Santa Barbara that Tuesday morning in September as Forest Supervisor Bill Hansen drove in to his office. "Fire weather's still with us," he thought. "But we've made it all right through most of the summer, and an early October storm would save us for the entire year."

As manager of the 2-million acre Los Padres National Forest, Bill Hansen spends a lot of his time worrying about forest fires. The steep, brush-covered mountains of the Los Padres extend along the California coast from Monterey to Los Angeles. Roads are few and far between, and fires frequently move faster than the men and equipment sent to fight them. Some of the most costly and disastrous forest fires in the world have occurred here. Bill Hansen didn't know that another one would start that Tuesday afternoon.

It didn't sound like much at firs At 2:02 p.m., a fire was reported a the junction of Mountain Drive ar Coyote Road in the Santa Barbar foothills. As usual where fires start o the outskirts of town near the fore boundary, the city, the county, ar the Forest Service all sent firefightir equipment immediately. The actio was touch-and-go, for fire spreads fa in dry brush, but by 6 o'clock it looke like the men had won. Then came th wind: Strong out of the north and d enough to chap a man's lips within 1 minutes.

There was no chance of stopping i

∴   ∴   ∴

CRAIG C. CHANDLER is Assistant Director of Division of Forest Fire Research, Forest Servi. Before coming to Washington, he was in charge fire research programs in southern California. He a specialist in fire behavior prediction.

The problem: Where there's smoke there's fire, but how can you find out just where the fire is with all that smoke billowing up?

, shower of sparks blew across Coyote oad, and the whole area took off as a ngle sheet of flame—moving south-est, right into suburban Santa Bar-ara itself.

The next 24 hours followed the .assic pattern of southern California iburban firefighting. Put men and umper trucks in front of the fire to ive the houses. Use aircraft to drop hemicals and slow the fire down.

Build fireline on the flanks with bull-dozers and pray for the wind to quit.

By Thursday noon, the fire was 6 miles long and 3 miles deep. Scores of homes had burned, but many hun-dreds had been saved. And again, the men were gaining the upper hand. By careful backfiring along the roads, most of the open gaps along the 25 miles of fire perimeter were rapidly being closed. Shortly after noon, the wind died and the firefighters breathed a sigh of relief. But then the wind picked up again—this time from the southwest, blowing fire straight toward the Santa Barbara reservoir and the heart of the national forest. Now it was all Bill Hansen's fire.

Eighteen square miles of burning forest produces an awful lot of smoke: Enough to cover the State of Rhode Island in a blanket 160 feet thick every hour. When atmospheric conditions are right, the smoke hugs the ground. Airports close, drivers grope their way along mountain roads with headlights on full beam, birds roost at noon, and the all-pervading smell of smoke gives to even the most insensitive forest visitors a subconscious sense of terror.

But most important of all to the fire boss, visibility is reduced to near zero. From the air or from the ground, everything is smoke. Landmarks disappear. And like a well-trained raiding party in the jungle, the fire covers its tracks. No one can tell where it's been, where it is, or where it's going.

This is the situation that faced Bill Hansen on September 24, 1964, as he tried to plan control of the Coyote fire. The wind was blowing the smoke up the slopes of the Santa Ynez Mountains, and the marine inversion was holding the smoke low to the ground. Within half an hour, all the country from Big Pine Mountain, 20 miles north of the fire, to Ojai, 20 miles to the east, was smoked in solid.

The fire was down there, and it was moving—but where?

Fortunately, Bill Hansen wasn't the only man in the Forest Service who had worried about this problem. Stanley N. Hirsch is an electronic engineer at the Northern Forest Fire Laboratory at Missoula, Mont. Stan joined the Forest Service in 1961, after a 7-year stint as senior instrument engineer with General Electric. An avid hunter and ski enthusiast, as well as a superbly trained professional engineer, Hirsch is typical of the new breed of forest research men. Often—in fact usually—not professional for-

esters, they combine their scientifi skills with a personal desire to "hun fish, trap, and live in the woods." Th result has brought space-age technic talent to bear on some of man's olde and most primitive problems.

Stan Hirsch's first assignment wit the fire laboratory was to investigat new methods of detecting forest fire particularly lightning fires. Lightnin fires pose a specially nasty detectio problem. They often start in the bac country, far from roads, homes, an people. One dry storm may start hun dreds of fires. Typically, they don spread rapidly at first, but smolde away like little time bombs, each wit its fuse at a different setting. Whe the first few go off, they smoke up th countryside. The late exploders a hidden and grow unchecked until the are eventually discovered, often acc dentally by a fire crew traveling fight an earlier fire.

Stan Hirsch had an idea. Why n devise a system to detect the energ produced by the fire itself? Infrare or heat energy-detecting devices, ha proved very practical in military sy tems such as air-to-air missiles. The retically, an infrared sensor should capable of detecting something as h as a forest fire regardless of the optic visibility of the air between the instr ment and the fire. If the signals fro an infrared scanner were relayed to cathode ray tube, the result would a TV-type picture of the fire. Phot graphing the cathode ray tube with polaroid camera would produce permanent map of the burning area. sounded simple—and it worked.

But like most simple ideas, it took lot of work to make the fire mapper practical reality. Stan and his researc team had to find just the right wav length that would penetrate smok They had to devise a way to synchr nize the scanner with the motion of th airplane so as to get a clear pictur They had to build complicated ci cuits to keep the strong signal pr duced by a hot fire from overridi the weaker contrasts of the backgroun topography (have you ever seen

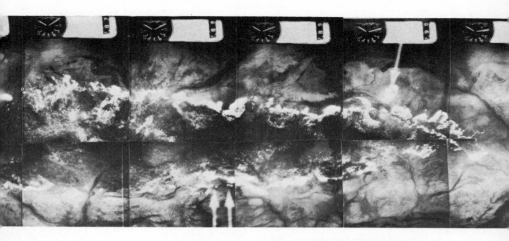

Infrared scanner in airplane made this map, *above,* at night through dense smoke of the Sundance Mountain fire, Kaniksu National Forest, Idaho. Arrows indicate spot fires outside the main fire perimeter. *Right,* fire information is transferred from the infrared imagery to a topographic map.

searchlight or other bright light during TV newscast black out your screen?).

Still, by late summer 1964—after 3 years of research and development—the infrared fire mapper was ready for field use. Under the code name Operation Fire Scan, a four-man technical team led by Hirsch waited for a chance to show their wares. They didn't have long to wait.

Bill Hansen had seen the technical reports about Operation Fire Scan. He phoned the regional fire dispatcher in San Francisco. Shortly before 4 p.m., the twin-engine Aero Commander with the Forest Service shield on its side landed at the Goleta Airport, 6 miles west of Santa Barbara and headquarters for the fire planning staff.

The briefing was short and to the point. "We're working blind up there," Hansen told Hirsch. "We've run out of roads and have to work the ridges. But the flanks are spreading faster than the crews can keep up. The last time we had a situation like this was in 1932 with the Matilija Canyon fire. That one went to a quarter million acres in 11 days. This one will do the same thing if we don't get on it fast. There are towns back there now that weren't there in '32.

"I've got to know where this fire is and I've got to know now! Can you get me a rough idea of the fire perimeter by 6 o'clock? By 2 a.m. I'll need enough detail about the exact location and rate of spread in the area east of the reservoir to plan the day shift strategy. We have to have the men on the line before daylight."

"It's going to be a long night," Hirsch advised his team when he returned to their plane. "So, let's get on with it."

Navigation without landmarks is ordinarily a tough job. With an infrared scanner on board, it's relatively easy. Bob Cook, the instrument technician, keeps the set adjusted for proper contrast. Bob Bjornsen, the photo interpreter, keeps one eye on the display tube and the other on a set of topographic maps. Eldon Down, the pilot, gets his headings over the intercom from Bjornsen. Hirsch sits by and waits for trouble.

Finding the back end of the fire was easy. Even though the ground had burned over 40 hours before, the earth was still warm enough to show up brightly on the scope. The ruins of an occasional house, still smoldering, stood out on the screen like bright green jewels.

"Try and follow the right flank," Hirsch told Bjornsen. "Bill's worried about the area east of the reservoir, and this way we can get a second look at it on the way back."

Trouble came within minutes after the plane turned north along the active fire flank. "I can't hold the contrast," Cook reported. "This fire's too hot. We're programed for temperatures up to 1,700° F., but those flames must be over 2,000° F."

"Just be glad you're not down there on the ground," Stan said mildly. "Take the plane up another 3,000 feet. Then we should get enough con-

trast along the edge of the screen t keep navigating."

In another few minutes he tried an other approach. "Turn the bias co rection all the way off. That will mak the interpretation job more difficul but it should take care of our contra problems." It did.

Bill Hansen got his intelligence by o'clock. On the east side of the rese voir, the fire had advanced 2 mil farther than anyone in headquarte had thought possible. On the west sid spot fires were springing up a quart mile ahead of the main blaze, makir direct attack impossible. Although th news was bad, it was the first soli information available. Now, the pla section could work with confidence.

The next 4 days and nights passe like a bad dream. The fire dictated th schedules, and time meant nothing the fire. Two a.m., 10 a.m., 4 p.m anytime, when normal intelligenc channels failed, Fire Scan was ther

Were there spot fires on the oth side of Hildreth Peak? Only infrare could tell. Had the fire crossed Mor Creek? Did the big bulldozer pil beside the fireline contain smolderir fuel that would blow across if the win rose? There were literally dozens questions which only Hirsch's cre could answer.

Finally, on the last day of Septem ber, it was over. Sixty-seven thousan acres had burned. One firefighter ha burned to death, 226 were injure One hundred and eighty-eight hous were burned or damaged by this 196 fire, and the total bill for costs an damages was nearly $25 million.

But, it could have been worse: Ha again as bad, like the Refugio fire 1955; or three times as bad, like th Matilija fire of 1932. As Stan Hirsc and his crew flew back to Missoul they had the satisfaction of knowir that their work had been instrument in helping to control the Coyote fir Not only had Stan Hirsch's idea pai for itself on the first real test, but nev again will a fire boss have to sta blindly into the smoke wonderir where his fire is and where it is goin

Saving the Water
Spent by Plants

PAUL E. WAGGONER *and* JAMES E. PALLAS, JR.

. . . .

Most of the water leaves our continent through microscopic pores in plants, not through faucets or drains or rivers. Ways are being sought to control this immense water loss through plants and thus to conserve our precious water resources.

Water is evaporated, or transpired, rapidly from plants because they are living wicks, reaching from moist recesses of the soil where the relative humidity normally exceeds 98 percent to the seeming desert of the air where humidity is low in the summer sun. To the eye or hand, the leaf seems a dry and ¬poor wick because most of its surface is covered by a waxy epidermis. Perforating this barrier and connecting the moist living interior to the dry air, however, are usually thousands of stomata or pores. For example, in the epidermis of a corn plant there are 40,000 pores per square inch. Although when open the pores occupy less than 1 percent of the leaf surface, they permit a canopy of leaves to evaporate about eight-tenths as much water as the equivalent surface of a lake.

The narrow axis of the elliptical opening is the most interesting dimension for it is variable, providing the plant with a means of regulating water loss. The stomata may close during droughts, sealing the interior from the outside air and conserving water in the plant's body. And every night the stomata in most plants close.

We would like to control the loss of water especially because only a small portion of water taken up by plant roots is incorporated into the plant body. Control methods seem obvious. First, a plug could be placed in the open stomata. Or natural closure of the stomata that ordinarily occurs at night or during drought might be managed when we want it. Before we undertake this management, we must, of course, understand why the holes are there and what the side effects will be if we close them.

Stomata serve two conflicting needs. On the one hand, the plant must conserve water and keep its interior moist enough for biochemical processes to run. On the other hand, plant metabolism demands the ready exchange of carbon dioxide for photosynthesis and oxygen for respiration. Stomata are a good compromise because they have variable resistance, opening and permitting free movement of gas during the day when much carbon dioxide is needed for photosynthesis, and closing at night when carbon dioxide is no longer needed. Further, air in the stoma has more nearly equal permeability to carbon

∴   ∴   ∴

PAUL E. WAGGONER *is Chief, Department of Soils and Climatology, Connecticut Agricultural Experiment Station, New Haven.*

JAMES E. PALLAS, JR., *is a Plant Physiologist, Southern Piedmont Conservation Research Center, Agricultural Research Service, Watkinsville, Ga. He took the photomicrograph illustrating this chapter.*

213

dioxide and water than would an unperforated membrane.

Other reasons for stomata can be mentioned, but appear less demanding. The sweeping up of nutrients in a stream of water might be a reason for rapid transpiration, but seems unimportant in nutrition because plants may be well fed in humid air where evaporation is slight. Since we ourselves require a constant body temperature and maintain it sometimes by sweating, we easily attribute a similar role of temperature regulation to the evaporation from plants. Beneath the desert sun where cooling is needed most, however, plants close their stomata and stop evaporation, showing that in some plants at least the needs of water conservation and not temperature regulation control evaporation. So, the cost of stomatal closure for the saving of water can be reckoned largely in terms of the increased obstacle to carbon dioxide.

The decrease in photosynthesis relative to water saving can be evaluated by examining obstacles to the diffusion of carbon dioxide and water. Carbon dioxide entering the plant and water leaving it must both pass through and encounter resistance in stomata and the air outside the leaf. Since air inside the leaf is nearly saturated with water, no other considerable resistances are encountered by water in its exit from the leaf. When carbon dioxide has passed through the stomata and entered the air among the cells in the leaf interior, it has not, however, completed its trip. It must next pass through the cell solution to the site of photosynthesis, encountering a third resistance. So, water and carbon dioxide both encounter two resistances, one in the air outside and the other in the stomata, but carbon dioxide encounters a third resistance.

Now suppose we modify one of the resistors, the stomatal, by shrinking the pore. This will change the sum of the two resistances encountered by the water more than it changes the sum of the three resistances encountered by the carbon dioxide. Just so, a change in stomatal resistance can decrease evaporation of water relatively more than it will decrease the uptake of carbon dioxide and growth. Needless to say, we must change the stomatal resistance without altering the interior of the plant.

However, we must also consider the effects of stomatal control from an economic standpoint. Exceptions can be conceived, but our argument says that whenever we decrease transpiration, we decrease photosynthesis. Since a pound of water is rarely worth a pound of soybeans, one may ask,

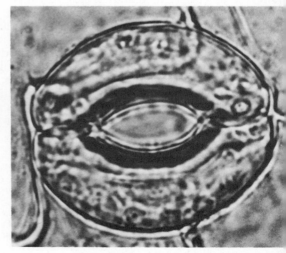

Bean stoma or microscopic pore, representative of most of the evergreen and deciduous plants. Open stoma is magnified 25,000 times.

214

"Under what conditions will transpiration suppressants be useful?" Suppressants might be useful when they:

• Reduce transpiration from a watershed to increase streamflow and water harvest.
• Prolong the availability of soil water where yield is not important, as in golf greens and lawns.
• Decrease evaporation until the plant has established its roots, after transplanting.
• Improve the efficiency of use of soil water in arid places where no irrigation is available.
• Increase or assure a yield by timely applications prior to important stages of growth that are extremely susceptible to drought, such as tasseling and silking in corn.
• Increase fruit quality by increasing plumpness or decreasing cracking by transpiration.
• Improve the quality of fruit, vegetables, or flowers during storage.
• Preserve Christmas trees and other ornamentals and decrease fire hazard.

Some of these techniques are being practiced on a limited scale, others are being investigated, and some have yet to receive attention. At any rate, many more uses will probably come.

The simplest way of increasing stomatal resistance is plugging the pore. Thus, nurserymen have long coated plants with wax to protect them from drying. Recently, several researchers have coated plants with plastic emulsions. Films permeable to carbon dioxide have been sought to permit photosynthesis while water is saved.

Unfortunately, plastics, like the epidermis of the plant, the cuticle of the insect, or our own skin, are much more permeable to water than to carbon dioxide; and the search for the ideal film has been difficult. In fact, materials tested up to this writing are so slowly permeable to carbon dioxide that photosynthesis in a well-coated leaf seems impossible. Coauthor Pallas found coatings harmful to plants. Yet, J. Gale of Israel has found that coated plants can sometimes grow well while water is conserved.

Perhaps an explanation of the sometimes encouraging results lies in partial, rather than complete, coating of the leaves. When needs for water conservation are great and for carbon dioxide are slight, some of the stomata may be completely closed to both gases with a saving of water and still an adequate supplying of carbon dioxide.

Encouraging stomata to close partially has, however, been the work the authors of this chapter and their colleagues have devoted themselves to. Physiologists had reported that growth regulators closed stomata. In 1961, however, Pallas found that in general, growth regulators—although capable of decreasing transpiration—most frequently caused unwanted side effects. It was indicated that compounds which are specific to stomatal operation were needed.

Also in 1961, Israel Zelitch of The Connecticut Agricultural Experiment Station discovered that enzyme inhibitors he was using in studying the metabolism of tobacco leaves narrowed their stomata without general toxicity to the leaves. Thus, great possibilities were opened, not only for studying the biochemistry of stomatal regulation, but for establishing the role of stomatal shrinking in the water cycle.

Two theories were current concerning stomatal regulation of evaporation from a single leaf. One said stomatal width would matter little so long as the pores were opened up the merest crack, while the other said that stomatal width would affect transpiration throughout the range of opening. M. G. Stalfelt's microscopic measurements of stomata indicated that widening stomata increased evaporation most when they were narrow, but widening always increased evaporation.

With the help of chemicals that would shrink stomata, this disagreement was quickly settled. The stomata of one tobacco leaf were narrowed by Zelitch and coauthor Waggoner with a spray of phenylmercuric acetate (PMA), while stomata of the other leaf were left untreated and open. When these two leaves were placed

Neutron soil moisture meter reveals that soil moisture was conserved after stomata of these 50-foot pines had been shrunk with a single treatment. Experiment was performed by Connecticut Agricultural Experiment Station.

in a chamber, the one with shrunken stomata lost considerably less water than the one with wider pores.

D. Shimshi found the same thing happened with maize. As predicted, photosynthesis decreased relatively less than evaporation. R. O. Slatyer of Australia obtained similar results when he sprayed cotton, but Pallas and Baker found that in the field, the transpiration and photosynthesis of cotton were equally curtailed. So, in isolated leaves at least, evaporation could be regulated through managing the stomata.

Evaporation from many plants in a pot could also be decreased. Thus, Pallas and D. C. Davenport in England found that a chemical which shrank stomata of grass also decreased transpiration. In 1962, in fact, H. Meusel had found that shrinking of

stomata on the Yale University golf course controlled wilting.

The next important step was into the world of crops growing in big fields. Within a large field of barley at the Rothamsted Experimental Station in England, two balances carried blocks of soil whose upper faces were flush with the adjacent field. Weight of these blocks indicated the loss of water from each was about the same. Then, in 1963, the leaves on one balance were treated by Waggoner, J. L. Monteith, and G. Szeicz, and the stomata shrunk for a few days. As long as the stomata were shrunken, the barley on that balance lost less water than the barley on the untreated balance. When the stomata of the treated plants again opened normally, the treatment was repeated with a similar effect.

These 12 to 33 percent changes in evaporation from a crop of barley bearing 6 acres of leaves per acre of land clearly showed that slight stomatal shrinkage in a field of cereal can materially change evaporation and the water cycle.

Much work must yet be done in stomatal regulating of evaporation in a crop. For example, J. M. Fulton of Canada treated potatoes in an experiment similar to the one in barley, but no detectable change in evaporation followed. Also, we still have little information on the effect upon growth of the crop following stomatal shrinkage.

Increasing water yield from a forest without injury to the trees is a problem important to our water resources, but one in which yields are less important. Can the water cycle of a full-grown forest be changed by merely shrinking microscopic stomata?

In 1964, the U.S. Forest Service Hydrologic Laboratory at Coweeta, N.C., and the Connecticut station joined in testing whether stomatal closure in a hardwood forest would increase the flow of the stream draining the watershed. Unfortunately, the experiment was unsuccessful, probably because the hardwood trees that clothe the hills of Coweeta bear stomata solely in the undersides of their leaves

216

where the helicopter could not deliver the stomata-closing material.

Pine needles, on the other hand, bear stomata on all surfaces, and pines were chosen for the next experiment. On June 1, 1966, Ben-Ami Bravdo, an Israeli scientist working at the Connecticut station, and Waggoner treated 50-foot, 30-year-old red pines in eastern Connecticut.

Stomata were shrunken for several weeks after treatment, and trunks of treated trees contracted less in the midday sun, indicating decreased demand for water. Between June 1 and October 1, about 20,000 gallons per acre less water was consumed by the plants with shrunken stomata than by the untreated plants. This was measured by frequent observation of soil moisture changes with the aid of a neutron moisture meter. It was as if 0.8 inch of rain had fallen on the treated tracts of the forest and missed the untreated ones.

The second year was much wetter than the first. Nevertheless, at least as much water was conserved in the soil in wet 1967 as in dry 1966.

Since the stomata of leaves are the pores through which most of the continent's water escapes, we have been encouraged by finding that small changes in these pores change the evaporation portion of the water cycle. We have also been encouraged to find that a little chemical per acre can assist the plant in managing its evaporation. Now we must learn when this managing can be done easily, efficiently, and safely.

For further reading:
Gale, J., and Hagan, R. M., "Plant Antitranspirants." Annual Review of Plant Physiology, Vol. 17, 1966.
Pallas, James E., Jr., "Mechanisms of Guard Cell Action." The Quarterly Review of Biology, Vol. 41, No. 4, 1966.
———— and Bertrand, A. R., "Chemical Sprays Reduce Water Loss by Plants." Crops & Soils, Vol. 17, No. 4, 1965.
Waggoner, Paul E., and Bravdo, Ben-Ami, "Stomata and the Hydrologic Cycle." Proceedings, National Academy of Sciences, Vol. 57, Washington, D.C., 1967.
———— and Zelitch, Israel, "Transpiration and the Stomata of Leaves." Science, Vol. 150, 1965.
Zelitch, Israel, "Biochemical Control of Stomatal Opening in Leaves." Proceedings, National Academy of Sciences, Vol. 47, 1961.

Preventing Fire From the Sky

J. S. BARROWS

Lightning flashed above the rugged northern Rocky Mountain forest country. Occasionally a searing white stroke—in stark contrast to its dark mother cloud—bored down the trunk of a tall conifer. A few seconds later, telltale smoke curled above the trees signaling the ignition of a lightning-caused forest fire.

Don Fuquay and Bob Baughman, atmospheric physicists of the Forest Service's Northern Forest Fire Laboratory, sat at the console of a lightning recording center. The scene was a trailer parked near the fire laboratory at the Missoula, Mont., airport. This was the nerve center for Project Skyfire—a research program aimed at the 10,000 or more lightning-caused fires which annually cause great costs and losses in American forests.

All around Fuquay and Baughman

∴   ∴   ∴

J. S. BARROWS is Director of Forest Fire Research for the Forest Service.

217

Lightning and a century plant.

in the trailer, instruments and recorders linked to a variety of sensors were measuring the characteristics of the lightning storm as it moved across the nearby mountains. Radios barked messages between the trailer and Skyfire aircraft flying near the thunderstorm clouds. Near the trailer two mobile radar antennas, one sweeping vertically and the other horizontally, were aiding in measurement of the storm. Fifteen miles away, on an 8,000-foot peak, a third radar was tracking lightning storms over a radius of 250 miles and transmitting the cloud imagery by microwave to readout scopes in the fire laboratory.

Suddenly, Fuquay and Baughman peered intensely at the instruments before them. Even before the thunderclap of a brightly dancing lightning stroke reached them, they knew that this violent discharge warranted special attention. The recorders showed it was no ordinary lightning stroke. Following the first cloud-to-ground discharge, an oscillograph recorded two typical return strokes, but these

218

were then followed by continuous charge transfer for the next 200 milliseconds. The continuing flow of current in the lightning channel was accompanied by brilliant luminosity.

This was the kind of lightning stroke that seems to stand and bore in determinedly at its ground target. Fuquay and Baughman knew from their lightning research results that this hybrid discharge was the type most likely to ignite forest fuels. Indeed, every documented lightning fire started in their experimental area was caused by this type of discharge.

Quickly, Don and Bob and their Skyfire research assistants, using data from a network of lightning sensor stations, plotted the location of the long continuing lightning strike. A radio message relayed the strike location to a Skyfire helicopter hovering near the storm. The job of the helicopter crew was to keep this spot under surveillance and determine whether or not the strike started a fire.

Within a few minutes, the helicopter reported that puffs of smoke were rising from the trees at the strike site. A fire suppression crew immediately was dispatched to the area. Accompanying this crew was Pete Taylor, Skyfire research forester. An expert in lightning damage, Taylor wanted to get to the site quickly so he could get firsthand information on the characteristics of the strike zone and the ignition features of the fire.

Research of lightning discharge characteristics is but one of many tasks being undertaken by Project Skyfire. Fuquay, Baughman, Taylor, and other members of the research team are developing basic knowledge and new technology for a variety of approaches which may provide better protection of forests from lightning fires. Other studies include the characteristics of storm systems, their potential to produce fire-igniting strikes, the physics of lightning generation, and systems for the remote sensing of lightning and the evaluation of lightning fire danger in forest regions.

One of the major goals of Project Skyfire is to determine whether or not lightning fires may be prevented through application of special weather modification techniques. All the studies of lightning and storm characteristics and the development of sensing systems are needed for support of the lightning prevention goal.

From the time of the pioneering discoveries by Schaefer and Langmuir in 1946 that clouds could be modified through introduction of ice-forming nuclei, the Forest Service has been interested in the possibility that such modification could change the electrical characteristics of thunderstorms. With this possibility in mind, Project Skyfire was organized in 1953 as part of the overall fire research program of the Forest Service. Throughout the history of the project, the research has benefited from the cooperation of many agencies and scientific groups including the National Science Foundation, U.S. Weather Bureau, Munitalp Foundation, President's Advisory Committee on Weather Control, National Park Service, General Electric Research Laboratories, Meteorology Research Inc., and several universities.

Prior to the formal organization of Project Skyfire, exploratory studies were made of thunderstorm conditions in the northern Rockies and lightning fire occurrence patterns. As early as 1949, the first attempt was made to seed thunderstorm clouds with dry ice. This historic cloud seeding attempt in which dry ice was dumped from the open door of a twin-engine aircraft flying at 25,000 feet demonstrated to the Forest Service fire researchers that weather modification was indeed a complicated, difficult, and even dangerous business. It stimulated the curiosity of everyone involved, and caused some people to think that we had become over impressed with the magic of Buck Rogers, but, most important of all, showed that lightning prevention research would require a long and carefully planned effort.

The first job of Project Skyfire was to gain basic information about mountain thunderstorms: When and where

219

do they form? How do they grow and move? How long do they last? How much lightning and rain do they produce? How many fires do they start? When and where are they most severe?

To help develop the answers to these questions, the Project Skyfire cloud and lightning survey was organized in 1953. This unique survey system has operated continuously during each forest fire season since that date. It utilizes a network of forest fire lookout stations in Oregon, Washington, Idaho, Montana, and Wyoming as observation points for clouds and lightning. The observers at these stations are given special training in order to enable them to observe and report on important features of clouds and lightning.

The Skyfire cloud and lightning survey was organized with the assistance of Vincent Schaefer, then director of research for the Munitalp Foundation, and Irving Langmuir, Nobel Prize scientist of the General Electric Research Laboratories. The Munitalp Founda-

tion, a nonprofit organization sponsoring basic research in meteorology aided the program by providing special equipment and funds. The special equipment included a mobile laboratory and time lapse motion picture cameras to use at fire lookout stations for recording cloud characteristics.

Fuquay, now the project leader of Project Skyfire, joined the program while working as a research fellow with the Munitalp Foundation and participated in the initial stages of the cloud and lightning survey. This research led to his development of a model of a mountain thunderstorm. It also provided the background for Fuquay to design initial research efforts to modify thunderstorms through cloud seeding.

By 1956, Skyfire was ready to initiate its first cloud seeding experiments. With the assistance of the President's Advisory Committee on Weather Control and other groups, the resources were assembled for a pioneering experiment. These included a mobile radar

Vincent Schaefer and Don Fuquay record data on clouds forming in mountains of the Lolo National Forest in Montana.

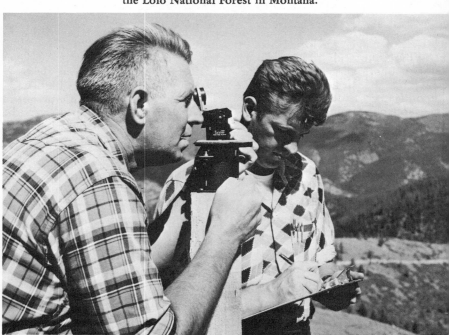

unit to help measure cloud systems, both airborne and ground-based silver iodide generators to seed clouds with ice-forming nuclei, and a cold box equipped airplane to trace the silver iodide plume dispersed by the generators.

The first cloud seedings were performed in the San Francisco peaks area of Arizona. Here, unique topography and atmospheric conditions provide an outdoor laboratory where relatively simple cumulus cloud systems form nearly every day during the late spring and summer. It is an ideal place to explore the phenomena that occur when supercooled water droplets in cumulus clouds are converted to ice crystals by silver iodide nuclei.

The Arizona operation was followed quickly by other pioneering seeding experiments performed during 1956 through 1959 in the intense thunderstorm region of the Bitterroot Mountains on the Idaho-Montana border. These experiments yielded a wealth of valuable information on both lightning storms and cloud seeding technology. Answers were starting to come on such questions as: What happens to silver iodide crystals dispensed by airborne and ground-based generators? What are the physical effects of ice-forming nuclei on cumulus clouds? Are changes in physical behavior of clouds likely to produce changes in lightning? Complete answers were not obtained to any of these questions, but the trends of the results gave encouragement to the Skyfire staff and demonstrated that good approaches were being made to the big question: Can lightning be prevented by cloud seeding?

The early field experiments also demonstrated that many special tools and techniques were required for lightning suppression research. These included efficient, safe, high-output silver iodide generators and techniques for their effective use on aircraft flying in the vicinity of convective cloud systems. Better methods were needed for measuring lightning discharges including identification of cloud-to-cloud and cloud-to-ground discharges and recording of their time duration, intensity, luminosity, and location.

From the beginning of the Skyfire program, Fuquay and his staff have devoted much effort to developing these essential tools and techniques.

By 1960, Skyfire had progressed far enough in development of basic knowledge, tools, and techniques to initiate a field experiment designed to yield specific data on lightning suppression. This experiment was started in a forest area near Missoula with the assistance of the National Science Foundation and the U.S. Weather Bureau. It is designed to yield statistical and physical data of lightning characteristics from both seeded and not-seeded cloud systems. Its primary goal is to test lightning suppression from clouds heavily seeded by Skyfire ram-jet silver iodide generators operated under the techniques developed through several years of experience with mountain thunderstorms.

Each day during the forest fire season, the Skyfire research team performs a variety of operations required by the lightning suppression experiment. Early in the morning, a fire weather forecaster of the U.S. Weather Bureau, Missoula airport station, predicts whether or not lightning will occur in the experimental area. If lightning is forecast, a "go day" is declared and preparations begin immediately for experimental operations.

The first step is to determine whether or not to seed the clouds in the experimental area. This is done by drawing a series of random numbers. If the numbers call for seeding, preparations are started immediately for operation of aircraft and silver iodide generators. On the next lightning day seeding is not performed. This randomization procedure provides a series of seeded and not-seeded storms to test lightning suppression results.

Fuquay, Baughman, Taylor, and their research assistants are old hands at seeding mountain thunderstorms. Each member of the staff has a definite job to do. One group operates the lightning measurement system—radar,

221

sensor stations, recorders, and radios at the control center. Another services the ground-based and airborne silver iodide generators. Pilots take their airplanes to the loading ramp at the fire laboratory where generators are attached to bomb shackles under each wing. The generators which burn silver iodide in an acetone solution are remotely controlled by the pilot. After the plane is airborne, he can ignite the generator with the touch of a button.

On a typical "go day," the seeding aircraft takes off from the Missoula airport as soon as clouds start to form. Each airplane has a Skyfire observer aboard in addition to the pilot. Both men need strong stomachs because the air is almost always turbulent around thunderstorms. Two seeding aircraft continuously seed the cloud system. A third seeding aircraft is used as a replacement as soon as one of the airborne units requires refueling of the silver iodide generators. In addition, a fourth aircraft or helicopter may be used for special cloud measurements and lightning fire observations.

The seeding aircraft fly a straight course just below the cloud bases. Bright orange flames flare from the exhaust of the ram-jet silver iodide generators under the wings. The generators emit millions of submicroscopic ice-forming nuclei which are carried by convective currents into the clouds. Each nuclei has the potential of converting a supercooled water droplet to an ice crystal when cloud temperatures are $-4°$ C. or colder. In seeding aimed at lightning suppression, the objective is to convert supercooled water droplets to ice crystals on a massive scale. The weather modification researchers describe this as massive glaciation.

Both field and laboratory experiments have shown the relationships of ice crystals to the lightning process. In a laboratory cloud chamber, Fuquay has shown that ice crystals reduce the sparking potential of air across a gap by 35 to 40 percent. The Skyfire field experiments show one-third less cloud-to-ground lightning from seeded clouds.

Seeding aircraft, flying straight course just below cloud bases, emits millions of ice-forming nuclei that are carried by convective currents into the clouds. Silver iodide generators are shackled to wings.

These results are encouraging. But many questions remain. One of these is whether or not seeding will reduce the number of hybrid strokes with long continuing flow of current. These are the strokes most likely to ignite forest fires. If they can be prevented, Project Skyfire may make a tremendous contribution to the protection of American forests. A large-scale experiment aimed at this question and at the effects of seeding an entire storm system is now being planned. The results already achieved by the Skyfire research program offer much hope that the future experiments will yield additional definitive answers to important questions about lightning and the prevention of lightning fires.

The importance of developing knowledge and technology for the prevention of lightning fires was vividly demonstrated by the critical 1967 forest fire season. Some of the worst forest fire

222

conflagrations of recent memory occurred in the Northwest and northern Rockies. Most of these fires were started by dry lightning storms. They destroyed valuable natural resources, burned homes and ranches, ravaged watersheds, curtailed forest industries, and killed people. They required the greatest massing of firefighting equipment and manpower in modern times. Two of these lightning-caused forest fires cost more to control than any in Forest Service history. The now infamous Sundance fire in northern Idaho traveled violently across 22 miles of heavily forested mountains in 12 hours, leaving a path of destruction.

Fuquay and his associates were at the scene of the disastrous 1967 lightning fires. They were constantly wondering whether or not these fires could have been prevented had Skyfire lightning suppression technology been advanced to an operational stage. No amount of conjecture will answer this question. But the answer can conceivably come from the future Skyfire research program.

Renovating Big-Game Ranges

KENNETH W. PARKER *and* JAMES P. BLAISDELL

. . . .

Those old "happy hunting grounds" of a great army of American sportsmen are being restored in the West. In years past, vast areas have been seriously overused by domestic livestock or big-game animals or both. The plants which provided the best forage have been destroyed in the process. This problem is especially acute during severe winters with deep snow when the herds of deer and elk cannot find enough food, and so many animals starve to death.

Fortunately, this problem is being vigorously attacked, and much progress has already been made from Arizona to Montana and from California to the Dakotas. A man with a "green thumb," A. Perry Plummer, a dedicated Forest Service scientist, is one of several who are uncovering the knowhow for successfully restoring valuable food and cover plants, both for domestic and wild animals. His work is on intermountain rangelands.

Thousands of acres of big-game winter range have already been improved. But, much remains to be done, both by researchers and land administrators. Millions of acres in the West need renovation. Of course, there is a large backlog of information on seeding of ranges with grasses, developed by research since the turn of the century by the State agricultural experiment stations and the U.S. Department of Agriculture. But, this article is mainly the story of restoration of ranges with shrubs, often referred to as "browse," on which comparatively little research has been done.

Wildlife is a vital part of the American heritage. It always has been an important wild land resource. Wild animals were an important source of food and clothing for the Indians and then for the white pioneers. Later, hunting and fishing developed into

∴   ∴   ∴

KENNETH W. PARKER *is Director of Range Management and Wildlife Habitat Research, Forest Service, Washington, D.C.*

JAMES P. BLAISDELL *is Assistant Director, Intermountain Forest and Range Experiment Station, Forest Service, Ogden, Utah.*

Plentiful, palatable shrubs on winter range are essential to producing healthy animals like this mule deer buck, *right*. In the West, elk summer on high mountain meadows, as in the Montana scene *below*.

popular outdoor sports for Americans.

Wild animals add a great deal of interest and beauty to our landscape. A herd of antelope on grassy plains; deer, elk, or bear in a forest setting; a flight of migrating geese overhead; or the song of an unseen thrush can greatly enhance an outdoor experience. More and more people are learning to appreciate the spiritual exhilaration and beauty which the land provides, with its grass, shrubs, trees, and wildlife. Range (or habitat)—which provides food, cover (protection from enemies and from bad weather), and water—is the key to wildlife abundance.

In the western mountains, deer and elk follow the snowline. As snow melts and retreats up the mountainside and plant growth begins in the spring, big-game herds migrate to the higher elevation summer ranges. With the first heavy snowfalls, these herds start their return trek to the lower elevations to spend the winter.

Summer ranges, with some exceptions, are in good condition and provide an ideal home for big game. Many of them are also grazed by domestic livestock. In contrast, the many winter ranges at lower elevations are badly deteriorated.

Browse is the "fountain of life" for big game on most winter ranges. But over many of these vast areas, disturbance by wildlife, cultivation and abandonment, attacks by insects and disease, and overuse by big game and livestock have practically eliminated many desirable species. Some 50 million acres in the 11 Western States are in unsatisfactory condition for wintering big game or for grazing by livestock. Furthermore, deteriorated winter ranges increase erosion, and muddied streams mar the natural beauty of the landscape.

These ranges occupy an area about the size of the States of Virginia and Kentucky. To restore them to their full productivity is a challenge of nationwide importance.

Plummer's research, a cooperative effort with the Utah Department of Fish and Game, has been aimed at finding suitable food and cover plants and learning how to establish them in the difficult environments typical of deer winter ranges. This information is urgently needed by land managers for successful renovation of intermountain big-game ranges.

The importance of good winter range in maintaining healthy, productive game herds has been demonstrated repeatedly in years of heavy snow and severe cold. In Utah, for example, during the severe winter of 1948–49, State and Federal wildlife scientists made careful observations on deer survival. On the "poor-condition" ranges, where the supply of browse was inadequate, deer losses were heavy—up to 42 percent of some herds—whereas loss of animals on ranges in good condition was 9.5 percent—this is only slightly higher than losses during moderate winters.

Since these foothill and mountain lands throughout the West are also a very important source of forage for domestic sheep and cattle, careful range management is necessary to provide for sustained production of both livestock and big game. A brief review of past deer-livestock management in Utah can help show us how some problems can arise, how teamwork in research can help solve them, and why further research is necessary in order to develop principles for intelligent land management throughout the West and elsewhere.

As early as 1890, suitable grazing areas in Utah were exploited by severe and unrestricted free use by domestic livestock. Deterioration continued, particularly on mountain rangelands, and within 30 years, the number of big-game animals reached an alltime low. Unregulated hunting, of course, contributed to this loss.

In 1897, the first Federal forest reserves in Utah, known since 1907 as national forests, were established. Under administration of the Forest Service, grazing by domestic livestock was gradually brought under improved management. The hunting of

WINTER MORTALITY OF MULE DEER IN UTAH
IN RELATION TO RANGE CONDITION

GOOD CONDITION

Total Browse
57.2 Pounds per Deer Day

9.5 Percent Winter Loss

FAIR CONDITION

Total Browse
12.5 Pounds per Deer Day

26 Percent Winter Loss

POOR CONDITION

Total Browse
9.4 Pounds per Deer Day

42 Percent Winter Loss

deer, elk, antelope, and bighorn sheep was prohibited by the State from 1908 to 1913. Then in 1914, and until 1934, the hunting of buck deer only was permitted.

Continued heavy grazing by domestic livestock on the lower elevation winter ranges ever since pioneer days has favored the increase of certain woody plant species such as juniper (sometimes called cedar although not a true cedar), big sagebrush, and rabbitbrush. Increase in these woody plants, although they had little value for livestock, may actually have benefited game on the limited winter ranges. Along with restricted hunting and the severe control of predatory animals, this permitted an excessive buildup in deer numbers.

The high populations, reached about 1942, seriously damaged essential deer winter ranges by destroying both forage and the ground cover of vegetation and litter which protects soil from accelerated erosion.

Both game and land managers had been deeply concerned about these deteriorating ranges for some time. In addition to the Forest Service and the Utah Department of Fish and Game, the Bureau of Sport Fisheries and Wildlife of the Department of the Interior and Utah State University finally undertook a combined research attack upon the problem.

The first research was to find what encouraged overpopulations and how to achieve best-sized herds through increased efficiency in harvesting the annual increase by hunting. Game-livestock relations also received early study. Recent studies have emphasized direct habitat improvement through research in reestablishing shrubs and other good food and cover plants.

Juniper-pinyon vegetation provides much of the deer winter range, particularly in Utah where it covers about a fourth of the State's area. Most pinyon-juniper sites are harsh environments in which to establish more desirable vegetation. Winters are cold. Annual precipitation averages only 10 to 15 inches. Elevations vary from 3,500 to 7,000 feet. Soils are often rocky, shallow, and of low fertility. At a typical site in Ephraim Canyon, Sanpete

County, where much of his work has been centered, Plummer described the problems to a group of visitors with these words:

"Note this closed stand of juniper-pinyon woodland. The valuable herbs and shrubs have been lost, and with them has gone the value of the land for grazing. Much of this loss of forage results from invasion by trees from outside the areas they originally occupied; but a great deal of this forage loss also results from the increased number of trees within the original boundaries of this plant community. This site is typical of the lower edge of the juniper-pinyon type, where stands have thickened from probably 50 trees per acre to some 250 to 300 per acre during the past 70 to 80 years. Closed stands of these trees may support as few as 200 trees per acre or as many as 1,500.

"Note the characteristic large barren areas between trees and clusters of trees. At this site, about half the land area is barren openings. These give rise to immediate runoff and erosion during high-intensity summer storms. Surface soil in these openings is permeated by millions of tree rootlets that efficiently take up the moisture and the nutrients. The skeleton remains of shrubs and grasses you see are mute evidence of the former abundance of forage. Important plants in the understory were antelope bitterbrush, four-wing saltbush, big sagebrush, black sagebrush, Brigham tea, bluebunch wheatgrass, and Indian ricegrass. Removal of the juniper and pinyon is necessary for successful reestablishment of such desirable species."

The cooperative research program at Ephraim has been aimed mainly at finding desirable grasses, forbs (broad-leaved herbs), and shrubs suitable for restoring deteriorated winter ranges; determining planting requirements for individual species; and developing methods for seeding and planting, including elimination of the competition caused by unwanted vegetation.

Ideal big-game habitat and hunting grounds in northern New Mexico.

227

Plummer, with the help of Stephen B. Monsen and Donald R. Christensen, two scientists from the Utah Department of Fish and Game, has screened hundreds of species and strains of forage plants—both natives and exotics. These were first evaluated in small "nursery" plantings on a favorable site just above the juniper-pinyon belt in Ephraim Canyon and then in a more severe site some 1,500 feet below. The best performers were later planted in larger range and pilot test areas. There they could be planted alone or in mixtures through methods that have been found workable for the particular site.

One typical example of deer-range restoration is a 600-acre tract in the foothills above Manti, Utah. This land, which formerly supported about 400 juniper and pinyon trees per acre, was chained twice and seeded by airplane between chainings in order to assure covering of the seed. ("Chaining" is a method of uprooting trees or brush wherein a heavy anchor chain or cable, about 200 feet in length, is hitched between two crawler type tractors and dragged over the area.)

The seed mixture, applied at the rate of 12.5 pounds per acre, included three wheatgrasses (crested, intermediate, and pubescent), smooth brome, Russian wildrye, ladak and nomad alfalfa, yellow sweetclover, rubber rabbitbrush, antelope bitterbrush, four-wing saltbush, and big sagebrush. The cost was about $12 per acre—divided equally between treatment and seed.

This range, which had supplied scarcely any forage plants before treatment, produced 1,600 pounds of herbage per acre in 1964. During the winter and spring of 1965–66, the area supported about 60 deer-days of grazing per acre, compared with 6 days before treatment. Habitat values have also been improved for other wildlife, particularly upland game birds. It is estimated that 3 acres can now support one cow for a month without loss of deer habitat values, and the fish and game department

plans to allow grazing by cattle in the spring, as on similar restored areas.

Terrain of this area is fairly steep, with an average slope of about 25 percent. Before treatment, it was a flood-producing area. Runoff water from high-intensity summer storms had damaged considerable property in Manti. Since restoration, there has been no runoff; former gully bottoms are stable and are supporting well-established vegetation.

For many years, planting or seeding desirable grasses, forbs, and especially shrubs was considered impractical. Application of Plummer's research findings in Utah during the past decade has dramatically shown that rehabilitation of big-game winter habitat is both feasible and practical. To date, more than 80,000 acres of deteriorated big-game winter range in Utah have been successfully restored.

As in other States, Utah has the responsibility for game management: Establishment of length of hunting season, number and sex of animals that can be taken by hunters, and other regulations. Utah has been one of the most progressive in setting up sensible regulations aimed at maintaining healthy, productive deer herds. Some biologists claim that deer numbers now exceed those of pioneer days. But Plummer is skeptical of the accuracy of that statement and prefers to assert merely that "deer numbers are sufficient for some of the best hunting in the world!"

Although shrub improvement has never received serious recognition in the past, Perry Plummer strongly believes that selection and breeding promise much for the future. Casual observations indicate that shrubs vary greatly in such traits as resistance to fire and disease, drought tolerance, growth rate, and palatability. Systematic selection for desirable characteristics could allow rapid progress.

His exploratory trials have shown that artificial hybridization can readily be effected between species within oak and saltbush complexes.

Species like Gardner saltbush and

shadscale have been used successfully to pollinate bushes of four-wing saltbush. More than 300 hybrid seedlings have been produced from these crosses and are awaiting maturity for further evaluation. This is all new research which may ultimately provide shrubs for soil stabilization on disturbed areas, beautification of the landscape, screening and cover on recreational areas, and the restoration of big-game winter ranges.

The Snail, the Mermaid, and the Flea Beetle

ROBERT D. BLACKBURN and LLOYD A. ANDRES

. . . .

A fisherman's frustration trying to retrieve a lure through a heavy growth of weeds, or the look of disgust on a boating enthusiast's face as he untangles a mass of weeds from the fouled propeller of his outboard, best illustrate the problem of waterweeds.

Helping to solve this problem is an unlikely trio consisting of a snail, a flea beetle, and a manatee—a blubbery sea cow once believed to be a mermaid. But first of all, here is some background.

Aquatic weeds interfere with agriculture, navigation, transportation, recreation, and flood control. They pose health problems by serving as host sites for disease-carrying organisms. Water skiers and swimmers have drowned in lakes when entangled in dense weed growths.

Millions of dollars are spent annually to control waterweeds in the United States. Chemical and mechanical means of control are often successful, but must be repeated frequently. Biological control, which uses living organisms to destroy pests, may be the economical way to overcome the problem. This method has proved most popular against aquatic weeds of foreign origin which flourish in this country free of natural enemies.

Nature's weapons to maintain the balance of nature between aquatic plants include plant-feeding insects, diseases, fish, snails, and manatees. The role of each varies with the particular problem. Specialists often seek out these organisms in the native home of the weed. Each is thoroughly investigated before introduction and cannot be released in the United States if it will attack any desirable species of our insects or plants.

Scientists can often select specific organisms suited to the weed problem and the degree of control desired. Those organisms that feed on a range of plants are especially useful where more than one weed is involved and open water is the desired result. On the other hand, a specific organism may be sought to remove a particular plant without further disturbing the balance of nature.

∴   ∴   ∴

ROBERT D. BLACKBURN is a Research Botanist, Aquatic Weed Investigations, Crops Research Division, Agricultural Research Service, Fort Lauderdale, Fla.

LLOYD A. ANDRES is a Leader, Biological Control of Weeds Investigations, Entomology Research Division, Agricultural Research Service, Albany, Calif.

229

In 1962, we teamed up at Fort Lauderdale, Fla., with a snail to control aquatic weeds. How fast is a "snail's pace"? This question was continually asked by fellow workers.

Biological control with the large fresh water snail, *Marisa cornuarietis* L. (hereafter referred to as marisa) was intriguing to the scientist. It was a dual-purpose biological agent. Marisa could control waterweeds and as a consequence reduce snail- and mosquito-borne diseases.

Marisa is native to the watersheds of the Magdalena and Orinoco Rivers in South America. It has been found in Puerto Rico and many other Caribbean Islands. In 1957, marisa was discovered in Coral Gables, Fla. It had been sold in the aquarium trade under the name "Colombian snail." Marisa's plant-eating habits became well known in the aquarium trade, and the snail was soon listed as an undesirable aquarium pest.

Adult marisa are mostly dark brown, with occasional three-planetary, thin, chocolate-colored stripes. Marisa reaches a maximum size of 2½ inches and is three-quarters of an inch thick. Shells vary considerably; thus, sexes cannot be differentiated upon the basis of shell characteristics.

Marisa eggs are laid in smooth, whitish, oblong, gelatinous masses. The masses usually contain 70 to 100 eggs and are attached to vegetation, concrete, rock, or wood surfaces. Average hatching time is 13 days.

The snail is exceptionally hardy. It can survive at temperatures of 48° to 110° F. It can tolerate highly polluted water and water with a salinity of 2,500 parts per million.

Marisa will not move out of water and is confined to this environment. If streams dry up, the snail survives by remaining tightly closed in its shell.

The U.S. Public Health Service in Puerto Rico found marisa can control other snails. Its indiscriminate feeding habits allow it to eat the eggs of disease-carrying snails. Marisa carries no disease of man and has actually been used as food in Puerto Rico.

At Fort Lauderdale, the war of snail versus aquatic weeds was waged in concrete tanks filled with various species of weeds. Snails put into the tanks fed vigorously on the submersed weeds: pondweed, southern naiad, coontail, elodea, and certain species of algae. To our great surprise, marisa ate all the submersed weeds in 10 weeks. We suddenly realized that the snail did not eat at a "snail's pace."

The snails fed on the roots of water-hyacinth and waterlettuce, but would not move out of the water to consume above-water leaves. However, they ate up the leaves of the floating weed, salvinia, which could be devoured without emerging from the water.

Immediately after introducing the snails into the tanks, we observed eggs attached to the aquatic vegetation. When the snails were removed later from both series of tanks, the population had increased five to seven times.

Major disadvantage of marisa is it may feed on rice, water cress, and waterchestnuts. This would restrict its use in some areas.

We stocked marisa in three small ponds near Fort Lauderdale in 1965 at rates of 8,000 snails per acre. One year later the ponds were free of submersed weeds and remained clean during 1966. Birds, rats, and certain fishes fed on the snails. However, predation did not prevent the snail from controlling weeds.

Snail populations appear to fluctuate with the weed population in a closed body of water. Snails survived in ponds free of submersed weeds by feeding on the algae that are attached to rocks and soil.

Stocking of snails into small lakes may need to be done before the weeds become extremely dense. If the weed population is dense, a combination of chemical and biological control may be needed for satisfactory control. Several aquatic herbicides are not toxic to the snail; however, water containing low rates of copper sulfate and insecticides will kill it. It should not be stocked into waters containing any of these chemicals.

Research initiated in 1967 under direction of Agricultural Research Service scientists at Fort Lauderdale will determine if the snails can be produced in numbers sufficient for large stocking programs. We feel a "marisa factory" is the main objective of this research program.

In contrast to the indiscriminate feeding of marisa is the fastidious taste of a flea beetle, *Agasicles* n. sp. The beetle is the entomologist's answer to the problem of controlling the imported alligatorweed (*Alternanthera philoxeroides*). In nature, this small beetle, which obtained its name by the way it hops, feeds only on alligatorweed and will starve in its absence, a fact uncovered through careful scientific sleuthing. It enabled the introduction of this insect to the United States with assurance that the insect would attack only its host plant.

Alligatorweed arrived in the United States via the gulf coast ballast dumps of old sailing ships. Freed from its natural enemies, it crowded out the native aquatic flora, eventually spreading from North Carolina to Texas. The Army Corps of Engineers, unable to keep all waterways open to navigation, called upon Agricultural Research Service scientists for help. Since the plant was introduced in this country from abroad and several successes had been recorded using insects to control similarly imported rangeweeds, the Entomology Research Division's special parasite introduction research unit was called in.

Entomologist George Vogt was directed to find the home of alligatorweed and determine what natural enemies could be used to control the plant in the United States, if such natural checks existed.

A search of the botanical literature and an examination of over 1,400 dried plant specimens indicated alligatorweed originated in the river courses and coastal regions from northern Argentina to the Guianas. Vogt concentrated his early exploratory efforts in Paraguay, southern Brazil, and northern Argentina, an area meteorologically similar to our gulf coast. Lagunilla, the common name for alligatorweed in South America, was found over much of this area, but never in the luxuriant abundance with which it has flourished in the United States.

Over 30 species of insects were found affecting the weed. Massive attacks by the *Agasicles* beetle had forced the plant from its aquatic habitat and onto the shores in many areas. It was the first candidate for study.

Argentine agricultural officials provided laboratory space at the modern Instituto Nacional de Technologia Agropecuaria at Castelar (Buenos Aires) for testing the beetle. A study program was carried out by Donald Maddox, another Agricultural Research Service entomologist. Failure of the beetle to feed or develop on over 40 species of plants assured its safe introduction to this country.

The quarter-inch-long beetle is colorfully marked with black and yellow longitudinal stripes and is easily spotted on growing plant tips. Eggs are attached to the undersides of the leaves in symmetrical clusters. The dark-colored larvae begin feeding on the lower epidermis, but soon cut irregular holes through the leaves. The mature larvae enter the hollow stems to pupate. The entire life cycle requires approximately 25 days.

Adult feeding and egg laying are linked to alligatorweed by chemical stimulants, apparently peculiar to the plant. Pupation in the hollow stems of alligatorweed automatically eliminates plants of dissimilar structure as possible hosts for the beetle.

Some 260 beetles were placed on the Ortega River, Jacksonville, Fla., in April 1965. By November, the flea beetles were well established, feeding and laying eggs normally.

By the spring of 1966, the hundreds of beetles had multiplied to thousands. What was once a solid stand of alligatorweed began yellowing under the feeding onslaught of larvae and adult beetles. The leaves were cut from the stems. A second wave of the beetles

231

Flea beetle, *left,* and marisa, *right,* feeding on waterweeds. *Below,* a manatee, or sea cow.

stripped the young shoots put out by the floating mat. Finally, to everyone's surprise, sections of the mat began to sink and rot, leaving patches of open water. By November 1966, the entire area was free from floating alligatorweed, and the shore was lined with dead stems.

Floating mats had torn loose from the banks and drifted downriver, carrying the beetles to new weed sites.

A survey of Florida in 1967 indicated that almost all alligatorweed sites are now infested with the flea beetle. In some areas, they were so thick that adults crawled from the plants into the survey boat by the hundreds. A concentrated effort is continuing to collect and ship beetles to other States where the weed exists.

Despite the startling success in Florida, the flea beetle failed to damage alligatorweed on the National Wildlife and Game Refuge at Savannah, Ga. Entomologists feel other insects may be needed. They have already released a species of thrips and are studying a stem-feeding moth in Argentina.

The marisa snail and the flea beetle are small and effective, but consider the manatee: Five hundred to 2,000 pounds of plant-eating mammal! Aquatic plants not relished by her counterparts are considered a delicacy by the manatee.

This animal's history is lost in antiquity. It passed through a mythological era in which manatees were believed to be mermaids. Sailors long at sea fancied that this fishtail animal was a sea maiden, thus the name mermaid. They also are called sea cows. Scientists know very little about them.

The manatee has a small head and brain, almost hairless hide, a horizontally flattened tail or fluke, and subcutaneous blubber.

The number of young born in captivity is very small. Probably only one calf is born every 2 years. Many scientists still question the ability of the manatee to survive and reproduce in fresh water. Some have associated salt water with mating activity.

The manatee is near extinction.

Only a few thousand are believed to exist. Meat of the manatee is of high quality, which may explain its near extinction. It is protected by law in many countries.

Unofficial reports collected from all areas of the world indicate the manatee probably could clear some of the world's lakes, canals, and waterways of aquatic weeds. In British Guiana, two manatees 7.5 feet long cleaned a canal 22 feet wide and 4,800 feet long in 17 weeks. The manatee was so promising that 46 animals were collected and distributed in weed-infested canals in the country.

A 3-year study of manatees and their usefulness in controlling aquatic weeds was completed by Florida Atlantic University (FAU) of Boca Raton in 1966. The study was supported by the Central and Southern Florida Flood Control District (FCD).

FCD officials became extremely concerned with aquatic weeds when they noted the rapidly rising cost of weed control in the district. In 1968, this cost is budgeted for $275,000, and it is expected to be a half million dollars by 1970. FCD is supporting research to find more and less expensive methods of aquatic weed control.

FAU's study was conducted to determine how many weeds manatees can eat, to study their rate of reproduction, and to learn whether or not the beast can be employed practically and economically as a means of biological weed control.

This study was conducted under the leadership of Dr. P. L. Sguros. The Miami Seaquarium was employed by FCD to capture seven manatees used in the 3-year study. They weighed from 384 to 2,170 pounds, and their size was soon found to be a problem when moving them to test sites. There was no noticeable period of adaptation after the manatees were introduced into the sites. Feeding commenced immediately and appeared to be a continuous process.

Weeds in test areas were primarily submersed types (coontail, naiad, and bladderwort). Cattail, arrowhead,

Water hyacinths, a major waterway pest, clog a creek in the Ocala National Forest, Fla.

pickerelweed, and several species of aquatic grasses were also growing along the canal bank and in the water.

Sguros estimated that 5,000 pounds of manatee, the total weight of five, can eat the submersed weeds in a half mile section of canal in 3 weeks. An equivalent weight in manatees would clear the same canal of water-hyacinth in 8 weeks. Test sites were free from vegetation for 6 to 8 months after the manatees were removed.

Manatees remained in several test sites after the submersed and floating aquatic weeds were consumed. They then ate all bank vegetation extending into the water and grubbed the canal bottom for roots of the weeds whose upper parts they had already eaten.

The name "sea cow" became very meaningful during the study. A strong bovine resemblance was noted with regard to herbivorousness, herding instincts, and passivity.

Manatees cannot tolerate water temperatures below 65° F. Three test animals in the study died from respiratory infections associated with low water temperatures.

The manatee has no peer, based on current knowledge, as a harmless, rapid, economical, and otherwise feasible means of controlling obnoxious aquatic weeds.

Successful use of the manatee as a weed-controlling agent depends on additional knowledge to be applied in sea cow husbandry procedures.

Growing Nations
and World Trade

Short Wheats Stand Tall

LOUIS P. REITZ

. . . .

Short wheats have brought new hope to millions who depend upon this time-honored food grain.

The opportunity for increased production associated with this new plant type has had a worldwide impact upon wheat breeding, management, and production.

World War II was over. The Nation had performed valiantly in producing food to support the war and the peoples of ravished countries. But crop yields remained low. Additional use of fertilizer was one of the key yield stimulants. How could fertilizers be used to stimulate wheat yields in the United States and abroad? Fertilizer made the plants grow taller, but the plant's energy "went to straw"—not to grain. Their support structure collapsed, and yields were often depressed rather than stimulated.

S. C. Salmon, an Agricultural Research Service scientist helping Japan get back on her feet, observed in 1946 that Japanese farmers were growing a number of remarkably stiff, short-stemmed wheat varieties. These, when fertilized heavily, remained erect to maturity and gave excellent yields. Dr. Salmon first saw Norin 10 at the Morioka Branch Station in northern Honshu and tells about it this way:

"It had been seeded in rows approximately 20 inches apart in accord with the Japanese practice and on land that had been heavily fertilized and irrigated. In spite of these very favorable conditions for vegetative growth, the plants were only about 24 inches high, but stood erect. They produced so many stems and there were so many heads, a second look was necessary to verify the fact that the rows were 20 inches apart instead of the common 6 to 10 inches in the United States."

He brought 16 varieties of this plant type to the United States, and, through the Department's regular seed introduction and evaluation program, they were made available to breeders at seven locations in 1947–48. One called Norin 10 is the best known and most widely used in breeding programs. Orville A. Vogel, ARS wheat breeder in Washington State, was the first to recognize its worth and to use it in a breeding program.

Norin 10 was an odd dwarf. The stems were very short, scarcely half as tall as most of our varieties, but the heads where the grains form were normal in size. On such short stems the heads appeared large indeed. The plants had as many leaves as normal plants. The straw was very strong. Norin 10 was unsatisfactory for direct use on farms outside of Japan. However, successful use of it in crossbreeding work triggered a revolution in wheat culture which has reached clear around the earth.

The word "Norin" is an acronym made up of the first letter of each word in the romanized title of the Japanese Agricultural Experiment Station. The numerals are selection numbers; hence, we have Norin 10, Norin 33, etc.

∴   ∴   ∴

LOUIS P. REITZ is Leader of Wheat Investigations, Crops Research Division, Agricultural Research Service.

236

We have recently learned more about the pedigree of Norin 10 from Dr. Torao Gotoh, Ministry of Agriculture and Forestry, Japan. It includes two varieties introduced from the United States: Turkey Red and Fultz. The original cross was Fultz x Daruma which hybrid in turn was crossed to Turkey Red. Daruma means a kind of tumbler doll in Japan, and the name was applied to a group of several varieties native to the country. The final selection from the last cross was made at the Iwate-Ken local wheat-breeding station located in the northeast section of Japan. Norin 10 was registered in 1935.

Crossing this dwarf with the U.S. varieties posed problems. Many of the flowers were male sterile and crossed promiscuously with adjacent plants. Timing mechanism of the wheat sprout was triggered wrong; it began unfolding before it reached the surface of the warm loose soil of the Palouse area. Norin 10 seemed susceptible to all of our diseases. Years of intensive selection and development were needed. When at last the most serious problems were solved, a new variety, Gaines, a winter wheat, was developed which, in its habitat of the Northwest, has set world record yields—one of 209 bushels to the acre. Fertilizer could be applied, and the plants would remain erect.

Long before Gaines was born, news of the new short-strawed germ plasm reached Norman E. Borlaug, a Rockefeller Foundation research scientist in Mexico. He obtained some of the early crosses and breeding lines from Vogel in 1953. Crossing these lines with Mexican and Colombian wheats, he combined the required adaptation and disease resistance with the short straw. A series of spring wheat varieties were developed including Pitic 62, Penjamo 62, Sonora 63, Sonora 64, Lerma Rojo 64, and Mayo 64. A semidwarf durum variety, Oviachic 65, has been released.

Certain of these varieties and related ones from Colombia and Chile are also adapted to similar latitudinal zones in many countries. They are being used in Afghanistan, Bolivia, Paraguay, Guatemala, Ecuador, Peru, Tunisia, Libya, Sudan, Kenya, Rhodesia, Jordan, Pakistan, India, Turkey, Israel, Nepal, and the United States. Perhaps 14 million acres were seeded to the Mexican wheats in the 1967–68 crop year. They are furnishing breeding stock to many countries to develop varieties more perfectly adapted to local needs. Improvement programs

Norman E. Borlaug recording the vigor and stage of growth of wheat in his breeding plot.

237

in some countries have reached a point where Mexico is now receiving new varieties from them. If current plans succeed, Pakistan, for example, will be self-sufficient in wheat production by 1970. Vast potentialities are available to those countries that wish to capitalize on short wheats.

Gaines and a similar improved variety called Nugaines, both bred by Vogel, produce straw as much as 18 inches shorter than standard varieties in the Pacific Northwest. In low rainfall areas, the difference may be only 4 inches. The grain yield records made by these two wheats have broken all those previously established; hence, to exceed 100 bushels to the acre is commonplace in Washington, Oregon, and Idaho where the varieties are best adapted. About 2¼ million acres were seeded to these varieties in the United States for harvest in 1968.

Vogel finds semidwarf varieties use nutrients and moisture more efficiently than other wheats. Applications of nitrogen fertilizer 25 percent higher than normally used give good results. He says they have a higher yield potential because they respond to higher moisture and nutrient situations, and they produce more seeds per plant than other varieties. He is not sure whether this is because more stems are formed or because more seeds are in each head. Several plant characters need to be in balance.

When one looks at a field of Gaines, the crop appears thick on the ground, and the heads are heavy with grain. Even longtime wheatgrowers are surprised by the outpouring of grain from the combine when Gaines wheat is being threshed.

Gaines and—to a lesser extent—Nugaines have been tested in all parts of the United States and in the major wheat areas of the world. They have limitations in many areas because they are winter wheats and may not head out unless the seedlings are subjected to a period of cool weather. They are late in maturity and suffer attacks from some diseases, insects, and severe winter cold. Even in their home terri-

tory, all is not always favorable. The thick canopy of growth creates a good environment in the field for development of rusts, mildew, leaf spots, and, worst of all, foot and root rots.

Vogel and his colleagues have taken up the challenge and are searching the world's wheats for resistant kinds to use in stabilizing the new level of productiveness found in the semidwarf wheats. Until they succeed in their breeding work, or find some other means of control, producers will not consistently realize from their efforts the maximum potential in the semidwarfs.

It took 20 years for Borlaug and his colleagues to do the impossible. Re-

First step in crossbreeding to develop a new strain of wheat. The three tiny anthers or pollen sacks are removed from the wheat flower with tweezers before the pollen matures.

sults of the research done by this Mexico-U.S. team enabled Mexican farmers to treble their country's average wheat yield and boost their total tonnage sixfold. Mexico became self-sufficient in wheat production. The separate factors making this happen were rust-resisting new varieties including semidwarfs, new land brought into productivity under irrigation, vastly extended use of fertilizer, weed and insect control, timely tillage, and proper seeding methods. The most important factor was the will of the research team and cooperating farmers.

Within the 20-year period, more than 30 new varieties were bred and released to Mexican farmers. Three phases can be seen here on variety development:

• Early success in stem and stripe rust control in more or less traditional types of varieties. This "control" was and continues to be a tenuous matter because rust races may change in an area. In Mexico, a change in stem rust races occurred six times between 1943 and 1965, and each required new varieties with the necessary resistance.

• Shorter, stiffer-strawed wheats based upon minor genetic factors accumulated from many sources to reduce the straw length was the second phase of development.

• Semidwarfs based on Norin 10 which were both shorter stemmed and more responsive to chemical fertilizer than any varieties ever observed before was the third and climactic phase. Three years after semidwarfs were widely distributed, 95 percent of the acreage in Mexico was seeded to them.

Among the semidwarfs, and some other wheats also, it was discovered that an important new dimension had been obtained. Some of these varieties were very widely adapted. They grew well in Mexico where days were about 2 hours long year around; they also grew well where days were 15 hours long. No wheat grows well in the humid tropics; however, the Mexican and Colombian wheats have turned in superb performances around the world in the drier and irrigated portions of the equatorial latitudes to about 40° N. and 40° S. These wheats have little or no frost hardiness so they cannot be safely used as a fall-seeded crop where winterkilling is a factor as, for example, in Kansas or Virginia.

What of other areas in the United States? Semidwarf germ plasm has been included in wheat breeding projects in all parts of the United States. Arizona workers developed the semidwarf Maricopa variety for the irrigated areas of the State. In New York, workers at Cornell developed a short-straw white winter wheat called Yorkstar. In North Carolina, Blueboy, a soft red winter wheat variety, was bred. Utilizing a Korean short parent, Seu Seun 27, Texas workers developed Sturdy, a semidwarf hard red winter wheat for use in the irrigated and high rainfall area. Semidwarf durum wheats are being experimented with in North Dakota. Semidwarfs have been tried in other States, but they have been found deficient in several vital properties including hardiness, disease resistance, or grain quality.

It is incorrect to imply that the Japan-Korean germ plasm is the only source of shorter, stiffer straw. Monon, Lee, Wells, Parker, and Ramona 50 are improved short wheats that have been developed, respectively, in Indiana, Minnesota, North Dakota, Kansas, and California.

And perhaps nowhere in the world have stiff, short-strawed wheats been developed which surpass the Italian wheats. Some of these, incidentally, have Japanese wheats in their ancestry.

The short wheats from Vogel's and Borlaug's breeding programs did something to people that was perhaps more important than mere development of plant forms: They challenged men to hope for and achieve new plateaus of food production. The specter of hunger was dimmed yet a little while. They showed that entrenched conservatism can be swept away, that people do change, and that war, pestilence, famine, and disease are not man's only recourse to bringing food production and population into balance.

239

Putting More Go-Go in Cargo—
Containers and World Trade

WILLIAM C. CROW *

. . . .

Ships are taking to the highway, trucks are sprouting wings, and railroads are crossing the oceans in a transportation revolution that is sweeping the world. It's called containerization.

In this dazzling new technique, products are moved from origin to destination—from Illinois to France, California to Hawaii, Ottawa to Saigon—in containers about the size of a truck trailer. The container may move first by truck, then by rail to a port where it is lifted onto a ship. At a foreign port, it is lifted off the ship and placed on wheels to go by rail or truck to the distributing warehouse. Sometimes the containers move by airplane, too.

So, a container is in effect a ship's hold, a truck trailer, a railroad boxcar, and even an airplane fuselage. Traditional differences between land, sea, and air carriers cancel out in a highly integrated operation.

Cost savings are so impressive that U.S. and foreign port cities are hastily revamping their facilities in a race for the lion's share of container shipping. Total investment in containerships in the near future is expected to reach $1 billion. Some Japanese shippers estimate that by 1970 half their cargoes will be containerized.

Possibilities in this cargo revolution read like science fiction. Future containerships may travel at speeds of 30 knots or more or about 35 miles per hour in your family car. Hydrofoil containerships may scorch the waves with speeds up to 50 miles an hour. Helicopters or other air vehicles will lift the containers from flatcars, ships, or airplanes and transport them to container yards, warehouses, or even to retail stores.

Through rates will be common. Customs and immigration procedures will be simplified. Movement of containers will be governed by computers.

Present-day containers are usually 8 feet wide, 8 feet high, and mostly from 20 to 40 feet long. Many are refrigerated and maintain an optimum temperature and humidity for the products they carry. They may be filled with packages of fruit, poultry, vegetables, meat, or any other commodity. At the point of production, the container is filled and the door locked. From that point on, the individual packages are not handled.

Advantages are many. One study estimates shipping cost savings of 38 percent. Stevedoring costs are reduced 82 percent, loss and damage claims 75 percent, and ship operating costs by 35 percent.

Containers weighing up to 30 tons can be loaded or discharged with gantry cranes from a containership at rates as high as 20 to 30 containers per hour with fewer men than previously

∴　∴　∴

WILLIAM C. CROW *is Director of the Transportation and Facilities Research Division, Agricultural Research Service.*

240

handled only 10 tons an hour. A vessel may need to spend only a day in port instead of 5 to 7.

Some vessels carry floating containers—or lighters—which can be loaded and discharged directly into the water.

Since containers are sealed by the shipper after loading, pilferage and damage are virtually eliminated. Correct temperature in the container can be maintained throughout the journey by plugging the equipment into an electric current. And because packages are not handled individually, they can be made of less expensive materials.

A fully loaded container was sent from Illinois to France in less than 10 days. The same shipment by conventional equipment takes weeks or sometimes months.

Until 1965, only two steamship lines could claim they were handling and transporting major volumes of containerized cargo. In 2 years since then, 70 full or partial containerships were in service under the U.S. flag, and orders for more such vessels were piling up.

Upon this development rests the hope of moving more products from U.S. farms and factories to world markets and of rejuvenating the U.S. merchant marine.

At the beginning of this revolution, U.S. Department of Agriculture transport researchers began to put containers to use in opening up foreign markets for farm and food products. In 1965 these men in cooperation with shippers, a railroad, and a steamship line made a containerized shipment of grapefruit from Florida to a wholesaler in Basel, Switzerland. The fruit arrived in less time, in better condition, and at lower cost than by conventional methods. The reaction of the Swiss buyer was "How can I get regular delivery of this quality product?"

Many other containerized shipments have been made since to test equipment, costs, and service. Fresh orange juice moved to Germany in bottles with hardly a broken bit of glass. Regular commercial movements followed.

Meat moved from Texas to Hamburg; poultry from Iowa and Virginia to Germany, Italy, and Greece; peaches from South Carolina to London; and mixed vegetables from Belle Glade, Fla., to West Berlin. Refrigerated cargoes and canned goods are moving from the west coast to Europe.

Most food moved between the mainland United States and Hawaii and Puerto Rico goes by containership. This method is also used for transportation between the west coast and Alaska and for intercoastal movement. The military uses refrigerated containerized service to Okinawa.

In April 1966, the Military Traffic Management and Terminal Service shipped a wide range of products out of the New York area in 283 containers. By December, the figure was up to 1,070. It is estimated that 50 percent of the freight MTMTS controls could move in this way. By November 1966, four emergency hospitals had been shipped in containers from Ottawa, Canada, to Saigon.

More than 50 railroads in the United States offer container service. Forty firms—mostly steamship lines—offer such service to and from 150 ports of the world. Some 35 airlines haul containers. From the United States containers go to Europe, Latin America, Africa, Oceania, the Near East and the Far East.

In June 1965, more than 20,000 containers were in marine service. In less than a year and a half the number doubled, and it is expected to reach half a million by 1975. U.S. railroads use 32,000 flat cars in piggyback-container service.

Containerships need special port facilities. They operate best from berths with wide aprons that provide easy access to the ship's side. For each ship's berth at least 10 to 12 acres of land is required for assembling containers to be shipped and space for those being unloaded. The most advanced terminals are equipped with shore-based cranes for loading and unloading containers, but many containerships have their own cranes so they can operate in ports without shore-based cranes.

The port of New York has taken the lead in getting ready to meet the requirements of this transportation revolution and is already recognized as the "Container Capital of the World." The Port of New York Authority, a corporate body established by compact between the States of New York and New Jersey, has embarked on a construction program which will produce 37 containership berths on a 900-acre site. Twelve of these are already in operation. The city of New York has announced plans for similar undertakings.

While New York is conceded the No. 1 position for North Atlantic container shipping, the race is on between Baltimore and the Norfolk area for the No. 2 spot. Other Atlantic coast facilities for handling containerships are in operation or soon will be at Wilmington and Morehead City, N.C.; Savannah, Ga.; Charleston, S.C.; and Jacksonville and Miami, Fla. On the west coast they are operating at the California ports of San Francisco, Oakland, Stockton, and Long Beach and also at Portland and Seattle. The gulf coast ports of Mobile, Ala., New Orleans, La., and Houston and Galveston, Tex., are expected to construct such terminals.

Other countries also are moving rapidly into this new form of transportation. The ports of England, Germany, the Netherlands, Scandinavia, Belgium, and France are preparing for container shipping.

Japan has announced a $400 million program for 34 containerships and terminal facilities and a program to purchase 50,000 containers. Australia has decided to introduce containerization on a national scale.

Containerized ocean transport has come a long way since the spring of 1956 when what is now Sea-Land Service carried 60 truck trailers on a trial run from New York to Houston and since August 1958 when the Matson Navigation Co. introduced containerized service to Hawaii. These pioneers have extended their service to Europe and the Far East, and the idea has excited the imagination of the shipping world.

Billions of dollars are being invested in containers, containerships, and port facilities. Yet many problems must be solved before the full potential of this development can be achieved. And these solutions must come fast to avoid costly mistakes.

Benefits of containerization flow largely from having an integrated transportation system. The containers must be handled by rail, truck, ship, and air; by many companies; through many countries; and they must transport a wide range of commodities. Getting agreement and coordinated action from all the firms and organizations that comprise the system is a herculean task.

First, agreement on the sizes of containers is imperative. These boxes must have universal interchange. They must stack, fasten together, fit onto trucks and railcars, go through tunnels, meet highway requirements, fit into planes, be lifted on and off ships by the same cranes, and hold quantities economical to transport. They must maintain the correct temperatures and humidity to prevent spoilage of the contents, be secure against water damage, and meet a host of other requirements. Finding the facts on each of these aspects is a big job. Reaching a consensus seems almost impossible.

For maximum use shippers must be able to get containers when they need them. This requires a large supply and competent management or containers will be in the wrong place at the wrong time. Common ownership and management of the supply may be the answer with appropriate rental charges for their use, but such an approach raises still other questions. Computers might help keep up with their whereabouts and plan their distribution. Idle time and empty backhauls must be avoided, of course.

Proper stowing of products in a container is important. The maximum quantity should go in the cube to save

From Florida citrus grove to Germany by piggyback—three-page photo story of a containerized test shipment. *Right,* grapefruit is picked in grove at Clermont, Fla. *Lower left,* USDA representatives explain how electric fan in the container door will ventilate grapefruit during trip. *Lower right,* fruit is loaded in container on truck at Lakeland, Fla., packing plant.

In Fort Pierce, Fla., container of grape-fruit is loaded on flatcar, *above,* for rail trip to New York. Taken across the Atlantic on United States Lines ship, container is offloaded in Antwerp, *below,* and put on a Belgian tractor trailer, *right.*

European press turns out in snowstorm to examine grapefruit when the container reaches Frankfurt, Germany, *left*. Grapefruit arrives at the Hertie Department Store near Munich, Germany, *below*, in time to be featured during special sale of U.S. products.

transportation cost, but some commodities require air circulation. Palletizing packages inside containers reduces handling costs, but wastes some space. Stowing by amateurs can lead to large product losses.

Costs of terminal facilities with all their land, cranes and other expensive equipment, and the need for quick turnaround time for ships will tend to create a concentration of movement at a few large ports. A properly designed and located containership terminal can handle 500,000 long tons annually per ship berth. To achieve optimum volume at a port without increasing the total transportation cost for the entire journey is a hairy problem to be worked out.

Regular and dependable service is essential. Coordination of movement of a container handled by several carriers requires accurate scheduling of arrivals and departures. When receivers in a foreign country cannot get dependable and regular deliveries, they find it difficult to meet demands of their customers. If the service is too undependable, they will have to find other sources of supply.

Institutional barriers must be reduced and compliance with regulations simplified. Varying inspection requirements, commodity standards, health laws, tariffs and customs regulations, restrictions on weight and size of vehicles, and a host of other regulations of transportation and commerce may be burdensome. Without some international cooperation on such problems, delays will be encountered and the flow of commerce impeded. Through service, through rates, and

through responsibility are also among the essential requirements.

A major problem in foreign commerce is paperwork. President Johnson said that "We have mounted a sizable Government-industry program to expand exports, yet we allow a mountain of redtape paperwork to negate our efforts." The National Committee on International Trade Documentation estimates at $5 billion the annual cost of paperwork related to our international trade. This documentation must be simplified.

Many obstacles to be overcome in containerization are physical and economic, but the greatest is that of getting people to work together. Success in overcoming the obstacles can save billions of dollars and facilitate the exchange of surplus products of one country for those needed from another. More hungry people can be fed. Food deterioration and spoilage can be reduced, and the general world standard of living raised.

Transportation research people in the U.S. Department of Agriculture are helping in many ways to solve the problems of containerization. For instance, they are working with shippers and transportation companies to improve equipment. From this research has come:

• Equipment to maintain uniform temperature throughout the journey;
• Better insulation for refrigerated containers;
• Development of a forced air circulating system so as to provide uniform temperature throughout the load;
• Evaluation of newer refrigerants such as liquid nitrogen;

• Development of a multipurpose van container in which products in one part of the container can be maintained at low temperature while the products in another part of the same container can be maintained at a higher temperature;

• A new type of vent plug that will let air in and keep water out;

• A thermal rating system for the containers.

Researchers are studying sizes of cartons or packages used in this country and comparing them with standards required in other countries. They are developing packages suitable for foreign shipment in containers.

Conversion systems have been developed so the same vehicle can be used for refrigerated or for nonrefrigerated products; for packaged goods in one direction and for liquid or bulk commodities in another. Better loading patterns have been developed. Quality of many products has been checked on arrival at foreign markets so any off-quality may be detected and corrective action taken.

Test shipments are organized with the cooperation of shippers, truckers, railroads, airlines, ocean carriers, and foreign receivers. Thus the performance of equipment, handling methods, and packages is checked. And changes are recommended to cut costs, speed up handling, expand the service, and maintain quality.

These USDA researchers are working with all groups involved to get regular and dependable service through ports that can move our farm and food products. They are serving on industry and government committees to establish standards for containers and devices needed to handle them, to simplify paperwork, and to get international standards for package sizes. Theirs is a concerted effort to streamline the physical handling of products between our farms and all possible markets at home and abroad.

A decade ago containerization was only a dream. By April 1965, a containerized shipment of 36,500 pounds of packaged meat moved directly from a packing plant in Fremont, Nebr., to a supermarket in Honolulu. In March 1965, Southern Railway containers loaded with grapefruit were moved through the streets of Paris and over the highways of Germany.

One enterprising man in Africa handled meat in a container cooled with liquid nitrogen from a livestock-producing area to city consumers hundreds of miles away, moving it over roads and on a riverboat. In this way storage, refrigeration, and two methods of transportation were combined to do the job in a developing country—and at a profit.

On the horizon is an international container system that could move from 50 to 75 percent of ocean commerce, if it is properly nourished and developed.

Fully automated container trains, shorter than the usual freight train, are envisioned. These trains will bypass classification yards and speed directly to major distribution points and ports. All major world ports, and many small ones, will have container yards.

To conserve land, many of the larger yards will stack containers instead of spreading out. In these yards containers will move automatically into and out of storage and on and off flatcars, containerships, trucks, and planes at the push of a button.

Specially designed containerships with space for 1,200 containers will be fully automated. According to one study they will be able to operate at 39 percent capacity with rates 25 to 35 percent below present Atlantic rates.

Many containers will bypass conventional warehouses and may even be used as small warehouses or become a detachable part of warehousing and handling facilities.

When these things happen we really will have an efficient, low cost, fast, and safe system of transportation so essential to the tremendous era of world trade which lies on the horizon. To bring this about requires ingenuity, hard work, and the cooperation of many groups in many lands. But the payoff will be the enrichment of life for people throughout the world.

Will Cows on Synthetic Diets Help End World Protein Hunger?

ARTTURI I. VIRTANEN

. . . .

In the developed countries, a great part of protein in food comes from milk, dairy products, and meat which contain all of the amino acids needed by the body in order to synthesize its proteins.

In developing countries overcrowded with people, the protein of cereals— poor in some essential amino acids— is almost the sole source of protein. General malnutrition is mainly due to this, because with the deficiency of even a single essential amino acid the body cannot synthesize all its necessary proteins. Yet despite the great value of milk and meat as a source of protein, it has lately been questioned whether animal production should be emphasized for future food needs since animals are too inefficient in converting feed to food.

Milk production has the highest efficiency in regard both to feed and protein. Theoretically, the cow should be the domestic animal best adapted to live in the world of the future. And new experiments with synthetic feeds seem to increase the cow's capabilities most dramatically.

The unique digestive tract of cows and most other ruminants has a large stomach, called the rumen, at the beginning of the tract. In the rumen, the feed is digested by the numerous microbes there.

Carbohydrates form the most important energy source of cows. Feed carbohydrates are fermented mostly to volatile fatty acids, which are transferred into the blood. Simultaneously, protein is formed in the rapidly dividing and growing microbial cells from the nitrogen compounds in the feed. When the microbial cells in the flow of rumen contents reach the fourth chamber of the digestive system and the small intestine, the cells are digested, and their proteins are split to amino acids. These are absorbed into the bloodstream and are used for protein synthesis as in other mammals.

Many ruminal bacteria grow well with ammonium salts as the sole source of nitrogen. But to what extent this happens in the cow's rumen has been obscure. Urea is a cheap synthetic chemical today and a common nitrogen ingredient of fertilizer. The nitrogen in this compound is readily converted to ammonia by bacteria, of which there are great numbers in the cow's rumen.

Many feeding experiments in different countries with urea have led to the conclusion that only a small part— maybe 15 to 20 percent—of the protein requirement of milk cows can be replaced by urea. High protein content in feed has therefore seemed necessary for milk production.

In the spring of 1958, I arranged an

∴   ∴   ∴

Nobel Prizewinner ARTTURI I. VIRTANEN *is Director of the Biochemical Research Institute, Helsinki, Finland. He received the Nobel Prize for chemistry in 1945 for developing a way to increase the nutrient value of stored livestock feed.*

experiment where a cow on normal feed was fed ammonium nitrogen in which a part of the usual elementary nitrogen of atomic weight 14 was replaced with the uncommon nitrogen of atomic weight 15, a heavier form of nitrogen which can be readily detected by physical analysis of any compound containing it. Since all amino acids contain nitrogen and all proteins are made up of amino acids, this test for heavy nitrogen enables one to decide if the nitrogen of an ammonia molecule ends up in a specific amino acid or protein. In this experiment, the amino acids of the cow's milk proteins contained heavy nitrogen, thus showing that dietary ammonia can be converted in part to the amino acids and proteins in milk.

Our body requires eight essential amino acids in our diet; if any one of these is missing or present in an inadequate amount, we develop malnutrition. Animals, including the cow, likewise require eight to 10 preformed amino acids in their diets. The experiments to be described below show that the cow under proper dietary control and with the help of micro-organisms in her stomach can synthesize to some degree all her essential amino acids.

This experiment showed definitely that ammonium nitrogen had been utilized for synthesis of all the components of milk protein. The experiment was repeated several times with the same result. Amino acids of the milk proteins contained heavy nitrogen to a considerable extent in as little as 3 hours after feeding the heavy nitrogen. Of the amino acids of the milk proteins, essential histidine picked up the heavy nitrogen most slowly. It is thus possible that histidine formed a bottleneck in protein synthesis.

When at the beginning of the 1960's we started to investigate whether the normal flavor substances of milk are formed within the cow's organism or whether they are due to the feed, it was important to try to produce milk on the simplest feed containing as few flavor substances as possible. The planned feeding consisted of 55 percent purified starch, about 25 percent wood cellulose, and about 20 percent granulated sugar, with urea and a little ammonium sulfate and phosphate as the sole source of nitrogen.

Besides organic matter, a cow's feed must contain all the 16 mineral elements known to be necessary for normal health. These include appreciable amounts of iron, calcium, potassium, and sodium, plus traces of many other inorganic substances. In a purified synthetic diet, these are ordinarily supplied as a mixture of salts, called a salt mixture. These feedstuffs were given mainly as briquettes. As fat, a small amount of vegetable oil was used. Of the vitamins, A and D were given as synthetic preparations.

The feeding experiments were started in the autumn of 1961 with one cow, and new cows have been included since 1962. All the test cows were Ayrshires, with an average weight of about 1,000 pounds.

On a protein-free synthetic feed, the cows produced 4,400 to 6,000 pounds standard milk per year (standard milk = 4.0 percent fat, 3.2 percent protein, and 4.9 percent sugar) during the first 2 years, when the amount of urea fed was relatively low, at the most 1 pound per day. As it was observed during the experiments that there was no danger to the cow's health even when feeding a greater amount of urea, the dose of urea was raised gradually so the ration of urea plus ammonium salts corresponded in the autumn of 1966 to 1½ pounds of urea per day.

The increased urea had a favorable effect on milk yield, and the highest amount of urea enhanced the milk's protein content. Annual yield of the test cow Metta (born 1955, calved six times on normal feed, twice on experimental feed) in 1964–65 was 9,297 pounds standard milk on an energy basis; during 1966–67, her yield was 9,060 pounds.

The test cow Jairu, born during 1961, produced in a year (1965–66) 8,448 pounds.

Thus, it was demonstrated for the

cows are transferred to synthetic feed. Protozoa (microscopic single cell animals) generally disappear entirely or decrease enormously, while the number of bacteria rises manyfold.

This leads to a better use of ammonium nitrogen for the synthesis of bacterial protein.

Milk produced on synthetic, protein-free feed is called in our laboratory zero milk (0-milk). Composition of 0-milk is very similar to that of milk rich in fat and protein produced on normal feed. Average fat content of 0-milk has varied from 4.5 to 6.3 percent (with normal feed, it is 3.6 to 4.7 percent) and the protein content from 3.8 to 4.3 percent (normal feed: 3.2 to 3.9 percent). Only the sugar (lactose) content of 0-milk has been somewhat lower than normal milk, from 4.4 to 4.7 percent (with normal feed, it is 4.8 to 5.1 percent).

Amino acid composition of the total protein of 0-milk is so similar to milk produced on normal feed that no real differences have been found. Individual milk proteins are similar in 0-milk and normal milk.

On the basis of taste tests, the flavor of 0-milk is very similar to that of normal milk. Chemical analysis of flavor substances has confirmed re-

Proud mother at Beltsville, Md., *above,* has something besides her calf for USDA researchers to brag about. This Angus cow ate only synthetic feed in the 3 years since she was weaned. Her calf is normal. *Below right,* Animal Husbandman Robert B. Oltjen squeezes handful of the synthetic feed through his fingers. These photos deal with some of the same subject area, but are unrelated to Dr. Virtanen's work in Finland.

first time that the cow is able to achieve a moderately high milk yield without any protein, using urea and ammonium salts as the sole source of nitrogen. This surprising result opened new views about the cow's ability as a producer of protein.

Adaptation of cows to the test feed is best achieved by gradually removing normal feed and adding test feed in corresponding amounts during about 2 months before calving. The cows were fed twice a day. Cows with a high milk production eat their large feed rations intermittently, with some rest periods, and thus they themselves regulate the intake of urea.

Estrus of the test cows has been regular, but the cows with the highest milk production needed a bull's services many times before they became pregnant. The long lactation period and high milk production per lactation resulted from this situation.

Great changes occur in the microbial population of the rumen content when

sults of the taste tests. Normal flavor substances of milk are thus formed in the cow's organism and are not due to the feed used. This does not mean that some flavor substances of plants could not pass into milk in trace amounts, inadequate to produce a flavor effect in milk. Only plant substances with a strong repulsive odor are known to cause off-flavors in milk observable in taste tests.

The content of water-soluble vitamins in 0-milk is approximately at the same level as that of normal milk. Thus, the vitamins seem to be formed to a sufficient extent by the rumen bacteria. Vitamin A- and D-content in the 0-milk depends on how much of these vitamins is given to the cows.

Composition of the fat of the 0-milk depends on the quantity and quality of the fat fed. When about 5 ounces of vegetable oils are included per day, composition of the fat of 0-milk has corresponded approximately to the fat of milk produced on normal feed. Further increase of vegetable oil in the feed causes a decrease in the fat content of 0-milk.

Results obtained on a protein-free synthetic feed have given impetus for a study of how great an amount of urea can be used in dairy rations containing normal feed low in protein. For 2 years, we performed such experiments with six cows. In the results so far, one cow (Lila) which calved for the first time has produced 10,743 pounds of standard milk per year on a feed containing potatoes, dried sugar beet pulp, and hydrolyzed hemicellulose from wood as energy nutrition.

The annual milk yield is about 11,905 pounds of standard milk after the second calving.

Two other cows (Kelo and Lelo), which had calved once before transfer to the test feed, have produced 11,466 and 11,905 pounds of standard milk per year. Their feed contained dried sugar beet pulp, crushed oats, barley, and hydrolyzed hemicellulose—a waste product of the wood industry.

Annual milk yield of three other cows on a feed containing more digestible true protein and correspondingly less urea has remained below that of the three cows mentioned first. Cereals (crushed oats and barley) and sugars as the sole source of carbohydrate seem less suitable for milk production.

Feeding experiments with only a few cows do not, of course, give results from which firm conclusions can be drawn. They will, however, give some guidance. On this basis, it can be concluded that the annual yield of more than 8,800 pounds of standard milk achieved on a protein-free synthetic feed can be raised to 11,000 to 12,000 pounds by using common feed poor in protein. It is still unclear whether the increase in milk production is due to the digestible true protein contained in the feed used or to other types of feed components stimulating bacterial growth and promoting feed intake.

Our results show that the proteins have lost their dominant position in the feeding of milking cows, even at a fairly high level of milk production. Thus, new possibilities for milk production have opened even in areas where common feed, especially grass, cannot be cultivated. By this I mean tropical regions in particular, where the greatest part of mankind lives and where long dry periods prevent cultivation of grass. In these regions, it is possible to produce harvests of plants rich in starch and sugar but poor in protein, which can be used for feeding milk cows when supplemented with large amounts of urea. In regions rich in forests, wood hemicellulose can be used in cattle feeding along with urea.

In general, the demonstration that protein can be replaced by urea to the extent of 60 to 80 and even 100 percent in the feed of dairy cattle extends the possibilities for milk production all over the world.

This research was financed in part by a grant made by the Agricultural Research Service, U.S. Department of Agriculture.

251

Dwarf Rice—a Giant in Tropical Asia

ROBERT F. CHANDLER, JR.

. . . .

Rice is an ancient crop, its cultivation dating back more than 4,000 years. But the most significant rice improvement of all time took place during the past 5 years in tropical Asia. And this breakthrough may influence the well-being of mankind throughout the rice-growing world, especially the tropics.

Locale of our story is the Philippines, at the International Rice Research Institute, established and supported by the Ford and Rockefeller Foundations. Let me give you some background first.

When modern methods of rice production are applied to tropical rice, results are discouraging. Use of adequate fertilizer—especially nitrogen—and adoption of good weed, insect, and water control practices cause these tropical rice varieties to grow excessively tall, to produce extra-long, drooping leaves, and to lodge or fall over. The stark facts of the case are that the average rice yield in Southeast Asia is only about 1,400 pounds an acre, compared with Japan's average of 4,400 pounds.

From evidence accumulated in Japan, Taiwan, the United States, and elsewhere, we know a key factor in obtaining high yields is that the rice plant must remain erect until harvest. Indeed, there is a direct relationship between grain yield and the number of days before harvest that a rice plant lodges. The earlier the lodging, the lower the yield.

This knowledge led plant breeders at the International Rice Research Institute to seek to develop short and stiff-strawed varieties, with relatively narrow, upright leaves—plants that would resist lodging even when heavily fertilized and intensely managed.

To do this, good men were needed and luckily were at hand. The Institute's first plant breeder was Dr. Peter R. Jennings, who had served as a rice specialist in the Rockefeller Foundation's Colombian Agricultural Program. Dr. T. T. Chang, formerly with the Joint Commission for Rural Reconstruction in Taiwan, became the Institute's geneticist. And Henry M. Beachell, who for over 30 years had served the U.S. Department of Agriculture as a rice breeder at the Texas Rice-Pasture Experiment Station in Beaumont, came to play a vital role in developing the new varieties. A consultant to the Institute for 1 month in 1962, when the breeding program was being mapped out, Beachell permanently joined the Institute in 1963.

Chang, especially familiar with the rice improvement program in Taiwan, suggested that several semidwarf *indica* varieties from Taiwan might be excellent sources of short stature. Accordingly, three varieties, Dee-geo-woo-

∴ ∴ ∴

ROBERT F. CHANDLER, JR., *is Director of the International Rice Research Institute in the Philippines. Before joining the Rockefeller Foundation in 1954, he was President of the University of New Hampshire.*

gen, I-geo-tze, and Taichung (native) 1, were used extensively to develop short, stiff-strawed varieties. They were crossed with such tall, vigorous, heavy-tillering (able to produce many stems on a single plant), disease-resistant tropical varieties as Peta and Sigadis from Indonesia, H-4 from Ceylon, and BPI-76 from the Philippines.

During 1962, Jennings and his colleagues made 38 crosses, 11 of them involving either Dee-geo-woo-gen or I-geo-tze as one of the parents. Other crosses were largely between tall tropical *indica* varieties and the so-called Ponlai varieties from Taiwan, which are actually *japonica* varieties developed for the tropics and subtropics.

Several crosses made in 1962 were successful; others were soon discarded because of such inferior characteristics as disease susceptibility and poor plant type. The eighth cross, however, proved exceptional. From it came a variety, now named IR8, which has opened new vistas to rice yields and has given added hope for food sufficiency to the vast number of Asians who are dependent upon rice for their staple food.

This dramatically different rice plant was obtained by crossing Peta, a tall Indonesian variety that has disease resistance, heavy-tillering ability, seedling vigor, and seed dormancy, with Dee-geo-woo-gen, a short-statured Chinese variety. Of about 10,000 plants grown in each of the second and third generations, only a few hundred were retained for further testing. In the fourth generation, plant No. 3 in row 288 was among those selected out and was appropriately designated IR8-288-3.

After further purification in the fifth and sixth generations, IR8-288-3 was planted in its first yield trial. This was in March 1965, less than 3 years from the date the cross was made. In July, t surprisingly produced a computed yield of about 6,000 pounds an acre. In the cloudy monsoon season in the humid tropics when plant performance s seriously limited by insufficient solar radiation, a yield of that magnitude is excellent. Later, we found that in the dry season and under high-level management, this strain could produce over 9,000 pounds an acre and would regularly yield between 6,000 and 8,000 pounds.

Moreover, we soon learned that high yield records for the new variety were being established not only in the Philippines and Southeast Asia, but in Latin America and Africa as well. Widespread adoption of this promising new rice plant seemed assured. In recognition of its general acceptance, the International Rice Research Institute, in November 1966, announced that henceforth IR8-288-3 would be known simply as IR8.

How can a new rice variety, tailored to predetermined specifications, be created so quickly? Fortunately, the short stature of Dee-geo-woo-gen is simply inherited and can easily be incorporated into the progeny of any cross. More specifically, in this Chinese variety shortness is a simple recessive characteristic. Thus, in accordance with Mendelian laws of heredity, in the second generation, one-fourth of the plants were short and three-fourths were tall. Very quickly, therefore, a large population of short plants was obtained, from which the IR8 variety could be selected.

The importance of Dee-geo-woo-gen (and of the other Chinese dwarf varieties) is comparable with that of the introduction into the United States after World War II of the Japanese wheat variety, Norin 10. That out of Asia came the dwarfing genes which drastically changed the yield potential of the world's two most important food grains is a dramatic coincidence.

Although we don't know the absolute origin of Dee-geo-woo-gen, we assume the original variety was brought to Taiwan from mainland China before the Japanese occupation. There is no clue to whether the short-stature mutation occurred in China or Taiwan. Probably, it appeared as a natural mutation and was selected by some enterprising Chinese or Taiwanese

Mexican research student demonstrates a cross-pollination method to officials from India visiting the International Rice Research Institute.

farmer before the turn of the century. (Dee-geo-woo-gen translates to "short legged, brown tipped," and is the sort of local descriptive name commonly used by Chinese farmers.)

If this variety was so outstanding, why had it not been used before? First of all, in Taiwan the Japanese—who preferred *japonica* rice to *indica*—concentrated their breeding efforts on development of the Ponlai types. Secondly, such low amounts of nitrogen were applied to farmers' fields and experimental plots that yields from Dee-geo-woo-gen were never exceptionally high. Happily, though, the Taiwan Agricultural Research Institute in Taipei kept the variety in its collection for many years and thus saved it for our use today. And the Chinese were the first to use it, Dee-geo-woo-gen being one of the parents of Taichung (native) 1, the first improved local variety in Taiwan.

With these genetic developments, there now are available types of rice that not only have a higher yield potential than ever before, but which respond positively to the improved cultural practices man can furnish. The IR8 variety shows a dramatic and continuous yield response to fertiliza-

tion with nitrogen, even up to a total of 120 pounds of nitrogen per acre. Tall, tropical varieties, on the other hand, respond only to about the first 30 pounds of nitrogen, while higher amounts cause decreases in yield. This is mainly why fertilizers have not been widely used on rice in the tropics, and yields remained so low.

In contrast, IR8—which has been tried extensively on all important experimental fields in Southeast Asia—nowhere has failed to establish new yield records, usually about double those attained before. Where 4,000 pounds per acre used to be considered an exceptional rice yield, it now takes 8,000 to arouse much notice.

To make possible such dramatic increases in yield, breeders shortened the plant from the traditional height of about 180 centimeters to an astonishingly low height of 100 centimeters (39 in.). They made the leaves short and upright, so water would run off quickly and sunlight would penetrate to the lower leaves. They retained the high tillering capacity of the tall tropical varieties, insuring that many panicles (heads of grain) would be formed on each of the plants.

Still not content, the breeders introduced into the short upright plants sufficient disease resistance to enable them to compete well with other varieties. They produced varieties with not only short straw but stiff straw, accomplishing this by selecting plants with thick stems and with leaf sheaths well wrapped around the stem.

The plants, therefore, were doubly protected against the ravages of heavy rains and winds, common hazards in the tropics.

Because of their short upright structure, the new varieties make such efficient use of energy from the sun that significantly more photosynthesis occurs between flowering and harvest (a period of only 30 days in the tropics), thereby greatly adding to grain yield. In the process of drastically changing the architecture of the rice plant, the grain-straw ratio has been increased from about 0.6 to 1.2. This means more than half the dry matter is in the form of grain. Lastly, the new varieties are earlier maturing and photoperiod insensitive, thus making it possible to plant them at any time in the tropics and, where year-round irrigation is available, to plant as many as three crops annually. Photoperiod insensitive means they flower in a given number of days after planting, regardless of the length of day and hence the latitude at which grown.

As soon as IR8 was discovered among the many thousands of genetic lines at the Institute, seed was sent to other countries for testing. In every tropical area where it was planted, the variety has shown exceptional promise. In the Philippines, in July 1966, almost every blade of IR8 was grown on experimental fields of the Institute or the adjacent College of Agriculture of the University of the Philippines. A year later to the month, it was estimated 100,000 acres were planted to the variety. It is believed that in India, over a million acres had been planted to IR8 by mid-1968. In Malaysia, the area planted was 30,000 acres in 1967. Pakistan, also, is moving ahead rapidly with the new variety. In all these countries, IR8—along with several similar new creations—is essentially doubling yields of farmers' fields.

How quickly Asia will become self-sufficient in rice remains to be seen, but the future looks brighter than ever before. Now at last the tropical rice farmer, too often struggling at a bare subsistence level, can apply fertilizers and insecticides with assurance that yield increases will more than offset costs. Although he may need twice as much money to grow the new variety, his income will at least triple.

Many agronomists estimate the average rice yield in Southeast Asia will double in the next 10 years. This 100 percent rise, formerly undreamed of, is imperative if food production is to keep pace with the population spiral.

In Asia, where rice is king, probably no single factor is more important in promoting peace and order than the rice supply. IR8 is the first giant step toward a full rice bowl for Asians.

Graph showing grain yield response to nitrogen of three typical tall, tropical rice varieties, and that of IR8, a new short, stiff-strawed variety. Data, obtained at Los Banos, the Philippines, represent average yields during the dry, sunny seasons of 1966 and 1967.

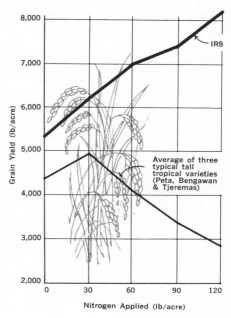

255

Self-Help Soybean Mill—
New Weapon Against Hunger

EDWARD L. GRIFFIN, JR., *and* DEAN H. MAYBERRY

. . . .

Hungry people can now help themselves to better food with a soybean flour mill designed to exploit primitive resources and modern scientific knowledge.

If a man can kindle fire and wield a stone axe, he can—if he will—boil soybeans and crank the mill equipment. He can make high-protein, high-energy soy flour to feed his family. His willpower—his desire—equals or perhaps even exceeds his muscle power as a design requirement of this self-help soy flour mill.

Self-help makes the difference between a hand and a handout—between a meal and knowing where the next one and the meals after it are coming from.

By "mill" we mean not only the equipment in the prototype, but also the concept of a series of specific steps. These steps can be applied with various equipment.

Just as an old recipe for rabbit stew begins, "First, catch your rabbit," so does the self-help mill concept demand the availability of soybeans.

Soybeans are grown in countries of Asia, Latin America, and Africa—where people are hungry. In some of the countries, soybean production is too small to feed many people, but does demonstrate that the acreage could be increased—across national boundaries as well as within them. In other countries, soybeans can be diverted from feeding livestock to the nourishing of children.

The mill was developed by Gus C. Mustakas and William J. Albrecht, Agricultural Research Service engineers at the Northern Utilization Research and Development Division, Peoria, Ill. It is only one result of research on using soybeans and other oilseeds for food in countries where people are hungry.

The Agency for International Development (AID) requested and financed this research. It called for development of vegetable protein foods, processing technology for developing countries, and the training of foreign technicians "so they can apply these processes in their homelands."

"Inadequate dietary protein is particularly serious with infants and preschool children, especially in tropical and subtropical areas," AID noted.

Food that would fit the need would have to be acceptable to people who need it and available at a price they could afford. It would provide protein, be free of toxic substances, and be easily transported and stored without refrigeration.

In many places where people are hungry, low-priced soy flour would do the job fine.

∴ ∴ ∴

EDWARD L. GRIFFIN, JR., *is Chief of the Engineering and Development Laboratory, Northern Utilization Research and Development Division, Agricultural Research Service, Peoria, Ill.*

DEAN H. MAYBERRY *is a Journalist in the Information Division, Agricultural Research Service, Peoria.*

The price of conventional soy flour, of course, includes cost of power, investment in machinery with precision pressure and temperature controls, wages for technicians skilled in operating this machinery, and costs of storage and transport.

Attacking these costs, Mustakas and Albrecht followed traditions of Yankee ingenuity and of helping others help themselves, at the same time applying modern engineering principles and chemical technology.

The mill they developed has flexibility in power sources, requires a low investment, and provides built-in, natural controls. Its only inflexible requirements not built in are human will—self-help—and, of course, soybeans.

Wages? These are food—high-protein food—satisfaction, hope, resolve, dignity, and all else that returns when a man feeds his family.

This project challenged Mustakas and Albrecht in their Peoria laboratory to specific action on man's eternal

USDA Engineer William J. Albrecht explains to international soybean conference delegates how the hulls are separated from the rest of the bean in the self-help mill.

problem of hunger and malnutrition. It called for soy flour mills "scaled to the economic capabilities and technical competence" of hungry people on three continents.

Mustakas, in early reports, zeroed in: "Need for protein is greatest among children . . . early death can result . . . (some) areas do not have electricity or other power sources . . . fuel may be scarce . . . people in villages lack technology . . . soybean flour can be used in gruels and beverages to provide protein for children.

"We must devise simple, uncomplicated equipment with which people in villages can make high-quality soy flour for their own use."

Equipment in the prototype mill would have to be hand operated and adaptable. Arms and backs in any village of any country can crack, dehull, and grind soybeans. Animals, wind, and running water can replace humans and be replaced by tractors, motors, and other machines as availability and ingenuity suggest.

But the prototype mill would be designed for resources man had from the beginning—muscles, survival instinct, intelligence.

"The limit on simplicity was only what would be helpful," in Albrecht's words. "There wouldn't be much point in telling people they could grind soybeans between two stones. Anybody would know that."

But few people would know about trypsin, an enzyme that digests protein. They wouldn't know that raw soybeans contain factors like trypsin inhibitor. (It must be deactivated or destroyed before the soy protein can give full value to man or animals.)

They wouldn't know the balance between just enough cooking to deactivate trypsin inhibitor and too much. (Excessive cooking wastes fuel and time and can reduce food value.) Few villagers would know how to use and maintain precision instruments and controls for processing soy flour with high pressure and temperature.

Villagers using the self-help mill

257

make soy flour that gives high protein value. They deactivate trypsin inhibitor without knowing it. Their "controls" are laws of nature put to work in Mustakas and Albrecht's design.

In the mill, soybeans are soaked, boiled, dried, cracked, winnowed, and ground. The technique is described in detail in "Full-Fat Soy Flour by a Simple Process for Villagers," ARS–71–34.

Equipment for the first two steps includes soaking and cooking pots and sacks in which beans are suspended in the pots. Cracker, winnower, and grinder in the prototype mill were bought from a Japanese company for about $125. They are cranked by hand and can be adapted to some other source of power.

Soaking takes 4 to 6 hours. It assures that a short boiling deactivates trypsin inhibitor. It saves fuel.

Soaked beans are boiled 10 to 15 minutes, depending upon altitude. They reach a maximum temperature that is the boiling point of water. This control and the brief cooking prevent damage to the protein.

Cooked beans are spread in the sun to dry. Dried beans are cracked, dehulled, and ground to flour.

Mustakas and Albrecht suggest that villagers use hulls as part of the cooking fuel. Hulls are the only part of the bean not converted to food in the self-help mill.

With hand-operated equipment, six men can make enough soy flour in 8 hours to provide more than half the protein needed daily by 1,600 adults.

Most people get some protein in their food. Soy flour will supplement that, not replace it.

Villagers in places with names like Pernambuco, Brazil, and Litowa, Tanzania, are getting instructions on the self-help mill.

In Rio de Janeiro, Mustakas trained a group of staff members at the National Children's Bureau, Brazilian Ministry of Health. Dr. Victor de Lamare, director general of the Children's Bureau, requested the training program to introduce the self-help mill in Brazil and promote soy flour in food. He learned about the mill at an International Conference on Soybean Protein Foods at Peoria.

His staff members are training people who will take the training to villagers in northeastern States like Pernambuco, Paraiba, and Rio Grande do Norte. Most of Brazil's problems of malnutrition occur in sugarcane areas of the northeast.

In one plan for interior villages, soy flour made in self-help mills will be sold at a low price to mothers. They will make bakery products for home use and for sale to the federally sponsored school lunch program.

The United Nations Children's Fund (UNICEF) is authorizing self-help mills in five States: Pernambuco, Paraiba, Piaui, Ceara, and São Paulo.

In Africa, the self-help mill focuses three lines of effort—private, industrial, and USDA—on hunger.

Catherine M. Powers of Stormville, N.Y., is a volunteer teacher for Africa sponsored by Phillips Brooks House, Cambridge, Mass. She learned self-help milling at the Peoria laboratory before she left for Africa late in 1967. The Monsanto Co., St. Louis, Mo., sponsored her training and furnished a mill for one small African village.

The mill is a new tool in a self-help program already working in 4-year-old Litowa and 12 other new villages. The Ruvuma Development Association, organized by people living in the 13 villages, has programs to increase soybean production and introduce the beans into foods. Small crops of soybeans are grown in the region, but not for food, and the native diet is low in protein.

Hsi Lin Chen in Taiwan and Dionisio T. Salon in the Philippines are applying soy processing principles learned in training on self-help milling and other soybean technology at the Peoria laboratory. Their training was sponsored by UNICEF.

In other parts of the world, UNICEF, AID, and the Agricultural Research Service are distributing copies of self-help milling instructions.

For Better Living

Off Limits, Mr. Termite

HARMON R. JOHNSTON

. . . .

To a termite, your house is just a restaurant. But if you don't want him eating there (and bringing his relatives), you can keep him out.

That, in brief, is the message that U.S. Department of Agriculture scientists specializing in termite research would like to get to the American public. They hope the public listens, because termite damage annually costs U.S. homeowners almost half a billion dollars. This is only the cash outlay. The emotional shock is harder to calculate. But if you think it's small, then you have never had termites in your own home.

Contrary to what many people appear to believe, a termite invasion is not something that just happens. It's a consequence of oversight or carelessness by homeowners and builders. Research in parts of the country where termite populations are extremely heavy has developed simple, inexpensive methods by which attacks can be prevented.

Control of going infestations is also possible, though more difficult and expensive than prevention.

These statements apply to the native subterranean termites found throughout the continental United States. They probably also apply to the Formosan subterranean termite, which has recently been found in parts of some southern coastal cities.

Termites are social insects like bees and ants, living in well-organized colonies established and centered around a queen and her mate. The queen's chief function is to lay eggs. Termites of a worker caste, white in color, tend the eggs and young and go forth to find food. Other termites form a soldier caste; they are white also, but have larger heads than the workers. In the spring, young queen and king termites—brown or black in color—fly from the nest and enter the ground to mate and start new colonies.

The colonies are underground because the soil provides moisture the termites need to sustain life. A worker dining on a tasty door frame, for example, may make several trips below ground daily, both to bring food to the colony and to replenish its own moisture supply. If its retreat to earth is cut off, it will die. In brief, termites only go into wooden structures to eat. They can't move in and set up housekeeping there unless they find a supply of water, as from a plumbing leak in a wall. Almost every termite infestation begins with a colony based in the soil. If you have a way of keeping the pests underground, you don't have to worry about them.

Of course, a termite can't damage wood that has been properly pressure-impregnated with a chemical like creosote or pentachlorophenol. But to build an entire house of treated wood is expensive. Buying such wood just for foundation members is advisable in regions where termites are plentiful, but the insects may bridge over treated wood to get to unprotected parts.

∴   ∴   ∴

HARMON R. JOHNSTON *is Principal Entomologist, Southern Forest Experiment Station, Forest Service. Since 1954, he has been in charge of the Wood Products Insects Laboratory at Gulfport, Miss.*

Besides, protection is needed for houses already built of untreated wood.

A control method suggested by early termite researchers was to treat the soil under and around buildings with chemicals that are capable of repelling or killing termites seeking to pass through. Before 1945, though, there were no chemicals satisfactory for the purpose. Sodium arsenite was known to stop termites, but it is highly toxic to all forms of plant and animal life. Less dangerous chemicals had been tried, but gave only a few years' protection.

Still, the idea continued to look promising. With the development of new chemicals during and just after World War II, USDA scientists decided to give it another try. The task was assigned to a team of entomologists stationed at Gulfport, Miss. The Department of Defense aided these studies, since it wanted a way of keeping termites out of military supplies stored on the ground in tropic and subtropic parts of the world—wooden ammunition boxes, for example.

As a first step, the Gulfport researchers went to a pine forest north of town and set up a testing ground. The site was ideal from a termite's viewpoint. The soil was light and sandy, rainfall was abundant, and the climate was warm and humid. There was a heavy population of termites living on fallen limbs and dead trees, but ever hungry for other items of cellulose.

Between 1944 and 1952, the Gulfport scientists put in tests of 25 chemicals. They included repeat tests on the better of the older chemicals, and they added new chemicals—including the chlorinated hydrocarbons such as DDT or chlordane—as fast as they became available. Most chemicals were tested at several concentrations and rates of application and in both oil solutions and water emulsions. It was—and still is—one of the biggest ventures of the sort ever undertaken anywhere. There was an extension in a jungle in the Panama Canal Zone.

One of the first results was an improved method of testing. Heretofore the so-called stake test had been commonly used. For this test the researcher excavated about 2 cubic feet of soil, mixed the soil with chemical, and then put it back. Finally, he drove an untreated pine stake 12 inches into the treated soil. The method, while time consuming, simulated treatment of soil around foundation posts and walls.

The Defense Department wanted a chemical treatment that could be applied just by putting insecticide on the surface of the soil. To test such treatments the ground-board method was devised. In it, chemical is sprinkled on the surface of a 17-inch square of soil; after it sinks in, a pine board is laid flat on the soil surface. A termite must cross or penetrate the treated soil to get to the board. This method has given accurate results and has been adopted as a standard test.

Before long, it became clear that some of the chemicals were capable of stopping termites. After 5 years, several were still giving complete protection and were tentatively recommended to the Defense Department and the public.

The tests were continued, and today, after 18 years, a 1 percent water emulsion of chlordane is still giving 100 percent protection where it was applied at the rate of 1 pint per square foot of soil surface. At the same rate of application, 0.5 percent water emulsions of aldrin, dieldrin, and heptachlor are still good after more than 15 years. How much longer will they last? No one can say, but the trials will go on until the termites get through.

Oil solutions of these chemicals have done well too, but oil adds to the cost and damages vegetation.

The four leading chemicals have also given excellent protection in thousands of applications under concrete house slabs and around the foundations of buildings. Furthermore, they halt established infestations in buildings. They are the primary chemicals in use by the pest control industry and State and Federal agencies. They are more effective and much cheaper than the chemicals formerly used.

Detailed instructions for preventing and controlling termite infestations are available from USDA in Home and Garden Bulletin 64. However, some general principles may be worth repeating here.

At least in the southern part of the country, householders should remember one thing: If a termite can get into a house, it will get in.

A few precautions in building or maintaining a house will reduce the number of entry points. Wood should be kept out of contact with the ground. For either slab or raised houses, the outside gradeline should be at least 6 inches below all exterior woodwork. The site should be sloped to drain away from the house.

Slab-on-ground construction is susceptible to termite attack, and infestations are difficult to control. Among slabs, the monolithic type is best, because the floor and footings are poured in one operation, and there are no joints to permit entry. Before any slab is poured, the ground under it should be treated with one of the four chemicals mentioned above. These chemicals are sold as concentrated solutions which can be diluted with water.

Although professional pest control operators can offer expert termite control service, the houseowner can do the job himself if he is careful to observe all safety precautions. The chemicals used must be kept from contact with the skin; if some is spilled on the skin accidentally, the affected area should be washed off immediately. If applying a chemical in a confined area, the houseowner should be sure to provide adequate ventilation or use a respirator. It is important that the applicator avoid breathing in excessive amounts of the chemical.

In raised houses, girders and beams should be at least 12 inches above the ground. Solid concrete makes the best foundations, but well-pointed brick is satisfactory. Hollow blocks should not be used unless capped with a minimum of 4 inches of reinforced poured concrete. Householders should inspect the

Severe termite damage in this home could have been prevented by treating soil around the foundations with an insecticide.

foundations at least once a year for mud tubes of termites.

Practically no U.S. research has yet been completed dealing with the Formosan termite, discovered in 1966 in some southern port cities. Experience with related species encountered in the Canal Zone tests suggests the chemicals recommended above will be effective, but that the concentrations would have to be doubled. The Department of Defense has reported that a 2 percent water emulsion of chlordane has been effective on the Formosan termite in Guam.

As of January 1, 1968, no chemical has been registered for use specifically against the Formosan termite.

The researchers at Gulfport are looking for still better soil chemicals, and they are also studying the life history and habits of termites, both domestic and Formosan. They hope to find biological controls, such as diseases. Possibly they can discover an attractant that can be used as bait. Perhaps they can find a weak point in the insect's life cycle.

Right now, though, chemically treating the soil under and around foundations is the best method of preventing or controlling attacks in buildings. If architects, builders, and homeowners would insist on such treatment, then we could truly say, "Off limits, Mr. Termite."

For further reading:

St. George, R. A., Johnston, Harmon R., and Kowal, R. J., *Subterranean Termites, Their Prevention and Control in Buildings*. Home and Garden Bulletin 64, U.S. Department of Agriculture, Washington, D.C. 20250, 1963.

WURLAN—*Wool Fabric for Modern Living*

ELEANOR C. TAYLOR

. . . .

When you describe something as "all wool and a yard wide" you mean it is genuine, good, desirable. Wool fabrics have long been the standard of excellence, and they still are, but they have also been called a luxury. Frequently, however, it is not the cost, but the upkeep which has labeled them so.

Now chemical modification treatments of wool fibers are changing this picture. Wool treated by these processes can be machine washed and, after tumble drying, the garments need only a light pressing, so drycleaning costs can be eliminated. On the horizon are wool fabrics that need no ironing, and have excellent soil resistance.

Between 1960 and 1966, wool machine-washable children's clothes, men's shirts, robes, blankets, socks, housecoats, sweaters, and women's dresses appeared in stores all over the country. Fabrics treated by one of the processes, called the WURLAN process, were adopted by more than 100 apparel manufacturers. They sell the WURLAN-treated products under many trade names.

∴   ∴   ∴

ELEANOR C. TAYLOR *was formerly an Assistant to the Director of the Western Utilization Research and Development Division, Agricultural Research Service, Albany, Calif. She is now with the Public Information Office, Fort Ord, Calif.*

263

Alanna Crimmins, Miss Wool of America, 1967, admires WURLAN-treated fabrics displayed by Dr. Harold P. Lundgren.

Manufacturers of synthetics were spending hundreds of millions of dollars on research and promotion, and customers were delighted with many features of the new fabrics made of synthetics—especially their easy care features. But wool remained the standard of excellence because of its durability, comfort, excellent tailoring qualities, and elegance for stylish clothing. Perhaps the market could be recaptured if wool could compete with synthetics on the basis of easy and inexpensive maintenance.

Representatives of the wool-producing industry appealed to the U.S. Department of Agriculture, and USDA responded by starting a vigorous research program. Since the late 1950's, the Wool and Mohair Laboratory under the direction of Dr. Harold P. Lundgren at Albany, Calif., has been grinding out one discovery or development after the other, all leading to better knowledge of the wool fiber and better quality in wool products.

The laboratory is part of the Western Utilization Research and Development Division of USDA's Agricultural Research Service. And all discoveries are available without fee to the U.S. textile mills.

When the research program started, the most urgent need was to eliminate shrinkage of wool during washing. A logical approach was first to find out why wool shrinks, then to learn how to prevent the shrinkage. Proceeding in that direction, the scientists undertook studies of what the wool fiber is composed of, how it is put together, and how it behaves under different environmental conditions. Sophisticated modern analytical instruments and techniques were available, and they were applied to answering these questions. The objective was to learn how to design and produce, in a highly scientific manner, the desired fabric qualities. Fortunately, wool is a protein substance that lends itself readily to chemical modification, so it should be possible to tailor it chemically to meet the requirements of the mills and the consumers.

How did it come about that so many companies all used a single process? No one of these companies invented the WURLAN process nor did any single individual. No nationwide publicity campaign launched the WURLAN fabrics—the usual procedure with a new product. Who, then, did invent WURLAN, and how did it spread so rapidly through industry?

The answer lies in team research conducted by a public agency for the benefit of consumers and in response to the needs of an important segment of our economy.

In the late 1930's, textile manufacturers began to shift over from using natural fibers (especially wool and cotton) to using the new synthetic fibers. By the late 1950's, wool consumption had decreased slightly, while consumption of synthetics had increased eightfold. This change was a serious threat to our domestic wool producers. They realized that something had to be done quickly or they would be out of business.

The fact that the surface of the wool fiber is covered with overlapping scales all pointing in one direction was a clue to shrinkage. When the wool fiber is wet it softens. As the fibers slide along each other, they tangle together and are held that way, probably by the scales. This is called "felting." If the scales could be smoothed off or a coating applied to cover them, the fibers might slide back to their original positions. Various coatings had, at times, been applied to wool fibers, but they left the fabric harsh and boardy. The need was for a coating that did not change the soft resiliency of the fibers, and one that would stick on through wear and washing.

Polymer chemists in the wool research group suggested that interfacial polymerization (IFP), a chemical principle which was then fairly new, might be applicable. A process employing the IFP principle was devised. Essentially this consisted of bringing together two chemicals in solutions that do not mix, but the chemicals react at the interface of the solutions to form a polymer, a compound having characteristics which are different from the starting materials.

The fiber chemistry team experimented with the many chemicals that can be used for this reaction. They found that when wool fibers were coated with one chemical and then dipped in another, the polymer formed on the wool fiber. The result was that the scales were covered over with an extremely thin layer of a nylonlike material—the experiments were successful. This procedure was the first practical application of the new IFP principle.

Next step was to develop methods to perform the process on a commercial scale. The pilot-scale textile mill at the Albany laboratory enabled development work to go forward at a rapid pace. Since many pairs of chemicals polymerize interfacially, a choice had to be made on the basis of cost, ease of handling in the process, and effectiveness of the treatment. The concentrations of chemicals in solutions, temperatures, immersion times, and many other variables were studied.

Results were most encouraging. The treating procedure turned out to be relatively simple. It could proceed at room temperature, no heat curing of the treated fabric was required, and the wool needed no pretreatment. Fortunately, some of the most effective chemicals were economically feasible.

Excellent resistance to felting shrinkage was achieved with relatively low polymer uptake—an advantage because of cost. Also, a heavy coating might change the texture and softness of the fabric. Although the coating is ultrathin, it survives through repeated launderings.

This new process was named WUR-LAN, a word coined from the initials of the *W*estern *U*tilization *R*esearch and Development Division combined with "lan" from the Latin word "lana" for wool.

Samples of treated fabric were sent to commercial textile mills for evaluation, and interest was immediate.

In WURLAN process, an ultrathin coating of a nylonlike material is grafted around each individual fiber in the wool fabric.

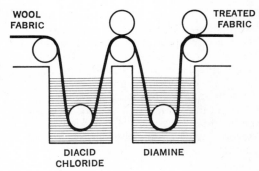

WOOL FABRIC

TREATED FABRIC

DIACID CHLORIDE

DIAMINE

When several companies arranged to run plant-scale tests, Willie Fong and other members of the team who had played prime roles in pilot-scale development went into the mills to work directly with the engineers and operators. These trials, conducted in cooperation with industry, demonstrated that the treatment can go on in a completely satisfactory manner under mill conditions. Effective and uniform treatment was possible in continuous runs. The process could be integrated into the conventional wet-finishing routine; and the solutions were adequately stable to meet processing requirements. The process was ready for commercialization.

During this research and development sequence, testing and evaluation were important to every step. Had the fabric been damaged by the treatment? Did it retain its softness, resiliency, moisture-absorbing ability? Could it be dyed satisfactorily? Could it survive repeated washings and wear? Many tests were made by using sensitive complicated instruments, and some new instruments were devised. Members of the laboratory staff subjected the experimental garments to practical wear tests. They wore treated shirts, trousers, and socks under prescribed conditions and with a specified laundering schedule until the garments wore out.

Results of the testing showed that the WURLAN treatment not only reduced shrinkage to a minimum, but it had some bonus features. The treated fabrics had better abrasion resistance and resistance to forming small balls of fibers (pills) than did untreated wool fabrics, they were stronger, and they were somewhat more resistant to certain kinds of soiling. Treated goods could be steam pressed or dry pressed. Durable pleats and creases could be set into the treated goods by usual commercial techniques.

Over the years, many other shrink-resist treatments have been tried and several are in use. The earlier treatments weakened the fabrics or made them stiff and harsh. The WURLAN

process was the pioneer in what are called "additive finishes." Since its development, other additive finishes have been developed in laboratories around the world, but WURLAN is still one of the best. In 1967, the German Wool Research Institute conducted an international competition for fabrics treated for shrink resistance. Wool fabrics with WURLAN processing placed first and were the only ones passing their most severe shrinkage test.

But good as WURLAN is, there is still room for improvement. New, cheaper chemicals have been found, and the processing methods are being improved.

A technique for applying the WURLAN treatment to wool top—as opposed to fabrics—has been developed. ("Top" is the assemblage of wool fibers from which worsted yarn is spun.) This technique allows the manufacture of machine-washable knitted goods,

A USDA Chemist, Richard O'Connell, doubles as a "guinea pig" in the wear tests of WURLAN-treated socks, shirt, and slacks.

which were very difficult to treat in finished form because they became distorted.

Need to press treated wool garments after laundering will soon be a thing of the past. True no-iron fabrics made from blends of the treated wool and modified cellulosic fibers are already on the market. The cellulosic component of these blends contributes its excellent no-ironing effect, while the wool gives the fabric esthetic values, wrinkle resistance, warmth, and resiliency. All-wool fabrics which require no ironing are now a major subject of research.

Cheap and long-lasting finishes to make wool fabrics oil repellent and water repellent may soon be available. New fluorine compounds discovered by Dr. Allen G. Pittman at the Albany laboratory confer repellency to oil, water, and the soils carried by oil and water. Several new families of fluoro chemicals have been prepared, and some of the most promising of these should be far more economical to make and use than any related materials now known.

Goal of the staff at the Wool and Mohair Laboratory is to find a single treatment which gives multipurpose benefits to wool. But even without a one-shot process, these various new treatments for wool are widening the scope of use for this elegant fabric. With soil resistance and wrinkle resistance, machine washability, and longer wear life, even children's clothes and apparel in delicate pastel colors are practical. We can have our luxury and afford to maintain it, too.

Frozen Foods— New Techniques

J. G. WOODROOF

. . . .

From field to dinner table, frozen foods have won a place for themselves. Farmers grow varieties of plants just for freezing. Equipment has been developed exclusively for harvesting, handling, processing, storing, and hauling frozen foods. Eating establishments routinely use hundreds of frozen food items. The housewife uses frozen foods in most of her meals.

One of the secrets in frozen food quality is quick freezing. The trend in preparing, storing, and using frozen foods has been to use lower and lower temperatures. This increases the rate of freezing, reduces labor costs, better retains the quality of food, and adds certain conveniences to using.

Before 1928, meats, fish, strawberries from the Northwest, and a few other foods were bulk "sharp frozen." The washed and graded products were packed in barrels or other large containers and placed at 0° F. until they froze. This kept them from spoiling and preserved the "freshness" fairly well—that is, better than heat-processed foods and those that laid on the fresh produce counter for several days. From many hours to a week was required for the foods to freeze solid.

∴ ∴ ∴

J. G. WOODROOF was formerly Chairman, Division of Food Science, University of Georgia, and has spent more than 20 years studying frozen foods. He is now Professor Emeritus.

267

Much of the processing took place after the product was thawed.

"Quick freezing" was applied to products frozen in a half hour or less and was begun about 1929. This required smaller containers and closer contact of the food with the refrigerant. For quick freezing, foods were prepared for the table, frying pan, or broiler before being packaged. This eliminated waste and added maximum convenience.

The most commonly used quick-freezing method is by placing filled consumer-size containers of food between metal plates at $-40°$ F. Freezing begins almost immediately and is complete in an hour.

A second way is by placing consumer-size containers of food on trays and subjecting them to a blast of air at $0°$ to $-40°$ F. About twice as long is required to freeze packages by air-blast as on cold plates, yet the difference in quality of product frozen by the two methods is not great.

In the homefreezer, prepackaged foods are quick frozen on cold plates in the freezing compartment and in cold air in the storage compartment. Here again, the difference in quality is negligible for either method.

A third way of quick freezing is spreading such products as peas, beans, berries, diced carrots, and shrimp on a wire mesh belt and slowly moving them through a freezing tunnel at about $-40°$ F. The individually frozen product is scraped off the belt and packaged in bulk or in consumer-size containers.

An improvement of "belt freezing" is "fluidized freezing" in which a current of cold air is passed upward through the metal belt, lifting the product off the belt, and causing it to tumble and freeze in air. This not only produces quick freezing, but prevents the individual pieces from sticking together and allows each piece to freeze equally from all sides. Freezing is so quick there is little drying.

Cryogenic freezing is freezing with liquid nitrogen ($-320°$ F.), liquid or solid carbon dioxide ("dry ice" at $-109°$ F.), liquid air, or other low-temperature refrigerants. These refrigerants have been used for holding

Cream cheese cakes, *left,* move from bakery oven toward blast freezer where they are frozen within minutes to "stop the clock" at the peak of freshness and flavor. *Right,* housewife selects frozen concentrated orange juice at a market.

and shipping frozen foods in a limited way since about 1928, though the product seldom reached the refrigerant temperature.

However, about 1960 commercial installations for cryogenic freezing became available. And since 1965, fleets of trailers on the highways, "piggyback trailers" on railway flatcars, and insulated railway cars have been equipped with liquid nitrogen facilities. Operational installations tripled in each succeeding year.

Increased experience, widening availability of liquid nitrogen and carbon dioxide, rapidly dwindling costs, and more stringent laws regulating the temperature of frozen foods favor cryogenic freezing. Besides freezing foods rapidly, it quickly reduces the temperature of entire loads of foods while in transit.

Freezing foods very quickly has several advantages qualitywise. Succulent vegetables like green beans, asparagus, and okra, and fruits with delicate texture like whole strawberries and sliced pineapples and peaches, have much firmer texture with greatly reduced leakage of juices when frozen very rapidly. Freezing by cryogenics produces qualities in most frozen foods that are closer to the fresh state than any other process now being used commercially. This applies to the appearance, color, and palatability of these foods. Nitrogen is inert and does not react with the product or with its constituents.

These advantages make it practical to freeze many products previously considered unsuitable for freezing. Products that are or may be frozen by this method include such hitherto unlikely candidates as whole peeled bananas, avocados, pineapples, fresh mushrooms, green peppers, onion rings, watermelon, and tomatoes as well as a wider variety of seafoods including lobster, scallops, flounder fillets, and raw and cooked shrimp. One plant in Florida froze more than 5 million pounds of shrimp with liquid nitrogen in 1966 and an even larger quantity in 1967.

Shrinkage during freezing by cryogenics may be under 1 percent, less than with any other freezing method.

The cost of freezing with liquid nitrogen or carbon dioxide is initially 3 to 5 cents per pound, which is high compared with 1 cent for sharp freezing. But an advantage is being able to save a shipment from possible total loss while in transit.

With cryogenics, freezing may be complete or just "case frozen" (freezing the outside very quickly and allowing the inside to freeze more slowly). Complete freezing, by reducing the temperature in the center of each piece to that of the freezing medium, is seldom accomplished. This is because more time would be required, no appreciable difference in quality would result, and the berries, peas, or other particles would likely break due to the sudden expansion of the centers.

Possibly the highest quality frozen produce is produced at the lowest cost by "case freezing" the outside of each piece with liquid nitrogen, and allowing the inside to freeze by a slower and cheaper method, such as fluidizing.

Liquid nitrogen systems have almost entirely eliminated potential hazards from mechanical failure in transportation. Special trailers are designed to handle four tanks of liquid nitrogen. These are serviced from 500-gallon supply stations across the Nation. This system provides delivery of frozen foods to any point in the country in the best condition at the lowest cost. In many cases, mechanical units on trailers supply the regular needs while liquid nitrogen is used for quick cooling purposes.

Some foods do not require instant freezing. The differences in quality due to method of freezing vary with the products.

For many, and perhaps most products, the physical differences between instant and slower frozen products is not markedly apparent.

In products such as candies, fruit cakes, precooked meats and vegetables, and prepared meals, the differences are virtually nonexistent. In candies, there are no cells to rupture, and in precooked products, the cells have already been altered by cooking. In fruit cakes, the high sugar concentration protects the tissues from damage.

One may not need to go to "instant" freezing to obtain all the quality improvement practical in the home or commercial operations. In most cases, an excellent product can be had by using a generally available freezing temperature ranging from $-10°$ to $-40°$ F. and giving more attention to other factors relating to quality.

Often more important than the method of freezing are factors like variety, maturity, method of preparation and packaging, and kind and shape of package.

One of the main reasons for freezing foods quickly is to minimize microbial spoilage. This is especially true with

Grapes on belt entering nitrogen freezer.

precooked foods that must pass through a warm zone between cooking and freezing. Fruits that are not heated may mold or otherwise deteriorate if freezing is delayed. Quick freezing is very important in preventing microbial spoilage of cooked foods like meat pies, fowl stuffing, and meat and vegetable dishes.

In freezing, the rate of heat removal is important, not the temperature of the freezing medium. Widely different rates of freezing may occur at a given temperature, depending upon whether the product is packaged or is loose, the density of the product, the rate of the airflow, and the amount of metal contact.

Because of the short harvesting season for peas, green beans, corn, lima beans, and diced carrots, large amounts of these vegetables are frozen loose and bulk packaged in portable bins (tote boxes) holding about 1,300 pounds. The bins are made of corrugated fiber or plywood boards and lined with polyethylene film sheets. They are placed close to the freezer, and the frozen vegetables travel directly from the freezer to the bins through 6- to 8-inch tubes. The plastic sheets are folded over the product, which is stored for later packaging into consumer-size packages. Some plants freeze up to 10,000 pounds of vegetables per hour, for holding in portable bins.

During the slack season, peas and green beans from the Northwest, corn from the Midwest, carrots from Texas, and lima beans from California can be packaged together. Strawberries, cherries, and raspberries are sometimes repackaged also.

Advantages of bulk freezing are:
• The products are hurriedly prepared and frozen at the peak of the season and stored for subsequent packaging.
• Packaging and labeling are done at slack seasons, thereby equalizing the labor load.
• Special packs of mixed vegetables or mixed fruits can be prepared throughout the year on demand.

• The transportation of bulk frozen products from one section of the country to another is cheaper and requires less space.

• The same grade of frozen products can be packed and distributed under separate labels.

A disadvantage in bulk freezing and storage is that double handling into and out of storage is required.

Low labor and costs are provided by frozen prepared entrees packed in 12- by 20-inch disposable aluminum steam-table pans. Each pan holds 18 pounds of food. Shipped two pans per carton, they are the same size as conventional steamtable pans and can be set right on the serving line. Entrees include chicken fricassee, turkey a la king, sliced turkey and gravy, sirloin tips and gravy, individual meat loaves, beef stew, sliced beef and gravy, and spaghetti sauce with meat.

In a few hours, one or two persons can prepare and set up for serving enough food for hundreds of customers. Small freezers with as little as 6 cubic feet of storage space and requiring floorspace of 27 by 27 inches are available in stainless steel, maple-top, or undercounter models. They operate on 115 volts, but have no moving parts.

More than 2,000 frozen food items are on the market, and they are increasing constantly. Where formerly each kind of vegetable, fruit, meat, or fish was frozen separately, they are now cooked and combined into many dishes, dinners, or trays. There seems no end to the possible combinations of frozen foods.

Some of the frozen prepared dishes that have recently appeared on the market are crabsticks, cocktail deviled crabs, deviled crabs, fried clams, fried soft-shell clams, stuffed flounder, stuffed peppers, whipped sweetpotato casserole, apple crisp, 1-, 2-, and 5-pound packs of meat loaf, macaroni and cheese, oven-baked beans, barbecued beef, beef stew, sliced roast beef with gravy, Italian beef, sage dressing, meat ravioli, veal parmigiana, pork liver, chop suey, and chili con carne.

In addition, there are dozens of kinds of pies such as chicken, meat, turkey, cherry, apple, apricot, and others.

Containers for frozen foods must protect the product from drying out (freezer burn) and discoloring by oxidation. They must also be of suitable material for cooking and serving the food in the package. Most vegetables are frozen in boil-in bags that can be cooked and served directly from the bags. Meat pies, TV dinners, and casseroles are completely prepared, seasoned, and frozen in metal trays so they can be cooked and served from the freezing containers. Ease of cooking without waste, and convenience of serving without leftovers, is accomplished by innovations in frozen food containers.

Freezing methods and handling innovations now in the developmental stage include:

A tubular container with a tear thread which may also serve as a freezing and cooking utensil and a dish from which the cooked food can be eaten directly (U.S. Patent 3,301,687).

A two-stage process in which unfrozen food particles are tumbled with gaseous coolants along a spiral path to bring them to a predetermined subfreezing temperature (U.S. Patent 3,300,993).

Retail packages of frozen foodstuffs are sealed in an insulating container which remains unopened until moved to a dispensing station at the retail area (U.S. Patent 3,302,420).

A process for molding and freezing together irregularly shaped food items (U.S. Patent 3,300,994).

Freezing apparatus including an insulating cold treatment chamber in which a foodstuff may be subjected to either a rain of liquid nitrogen or total immersion (U.S. Patent 3,302,423).

A freezing process in which cold vapor evolved from liquid nitrogen is directed down an incline in heat exchange relationship to food items being conveyed up the incline. Liquid nitrogen is sprayed upon the cooled foods to partially freeze them (U.S. Patent 3,298,188).

Stop Crabgrass Troubles Before They Start

HAROLD D. KERR, FELIX V. JUSKA, *and* DAYTON L. KLINGMAN

Weed scientists know how to stop the growth cycle of crabgrass. Several herbicides have been discovered which will prevent its germination and growth, yet lawns all across the Nation still are infested with crabgrass. The information gap between research findings and consumer use of the results must be narrowed. Uniform verdant turf will beautify any landscape, but the villainous crabgrass must be arrested to attain this goal.

Heavy foot traffic, disease and insect damage, mechanical injury, and openings around flowerbeds favor invasion of lawns by crabgrass. When established, crabgrass—as the name implies—spreads by the prostrate stems which take root at the joints (nodes) and produces seed abundantly.

Crabgrass, like other annual grasses, could not persist from year to year if it did not produce seeds. A crabgrass plant starts from a seed and grows until it produces seed to complete its own annual life cycle—from seed to seed again. Stopping seed production or keeping the seed from producing a new plant to start the life cycle is the key to control of crabgrass.

Two common crabgrass species are large crabgrass, *Digitaria sanguinalis* (L.) Scop., and smooth crabgrass, *D. ischaemum* (Schreb.) Muhl. These are somewhat similar, but smooth crabgrass is not so coarse and robust, does not have hair on the leaves and sheaths, and may be more purplish or bluish in color.

Warm temperature and plentiful soil moisture are necessary for germination of crabgrass seeds. The soil temperature will be higher on a bare surface, on the south slope where the sun shines more directly on the soil, and on the south sides of buildings. Germination is rapid in hot and humid weather when daytime temperatures are 80° F. and above. Unfortunately, all seeds do not germinate at the same time. Each succeeding hot rainy spell causes additional seeds to germinate. Germination continues through the spring and summer.

Crabgrass grows with astonishing vigor. When young, it is distinguishable from lawn grasses by the coarse appearance of individual leaves and by its lighter green color. The well-established plants have many prostrate stems growing out radially from a common shoot base. These stems lie close to the ground, root at the joints, and thus escape the mower blade. Dense patches of crabgrass growing all summer can kill the lawn grasses.

The seedhead branches into three or more fingerlike divisions (rachises).

HAROLD D. KERR *is Assistant Professor of Agronomy, Department of Agronomy, University of Missouri.*

FELIX V. JUSKA *is a Research Agronomist, Crops Research Division, Agricultural Research Service.*

DAYTON L. KLINGMAN *is an Agronomist with the Crops Research Division.*

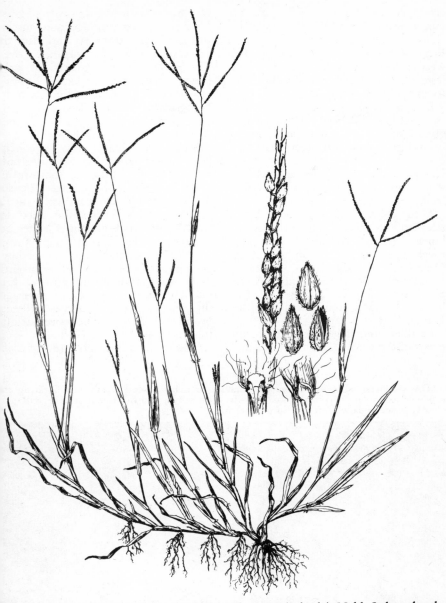

Side view of smooth crabgrass, *Digitaria ischaemum* (Schreb.) Muhl. It has sheaths with a purplish color, light hairs only near collar of leaf, and it roots at the joints of the prostrate stems.

in which many seeds, oriented on one side of each rachis, are produced. Seeds one-sixteenth to one-eighth of an inch long mature and begin to fall to the soil soon after the seedhead develops. As crabgrass matures, it becomes tougher and stemmy and may take on a purple color contrasting sharply with the other grasses. The first frost kills crabgrass, leaving an unsightly brown, dead area wherever it has been growing.

Use of scientifically proven principles of turf grass management will reduce crabgrass infestations. Crabgrass occurs year after year because these principles of lawn care are not followed. Proper management helps control weeds; however, once a lawn is infested, herbicides are needed in order to control the weeds.

Be sure to plant your new lawn at the right time. Seeding cool-season grasses in the fall allows them to develop into a good turf before the crabgrass season arrives the next spring. Choose grasses that are adapted to your area and climate when establishing a lawn.

Many seed mixtures contain unadapted or undesirable species for lawns. Mixtures containing bentgrass, ryegrass, redtop, and timothy will not produce a desirable lawn. Kentucky bluegrass alone or in mixtures with fine-leaved fescues makes the best lawn in the cool, humid regions of the United States.

Fertilize your lawn according to the needs of the grass. High rates of nitrogen promote succulent growth of grass. Succulent grass is much more susceptible to fungus diseases; and after the grass dies, crabgrass can take over. Too much nitrogen makes the grass leaves grow fast at the expense of root growth. This weakens the lawn for crabgrass infestation. Too little fertilizer results in thin lawns which soon become infested by crabgrass.

Proper watering of your lawn helps keep out crabgrass. Do not water until signs of slight wilting or footprinting appear. Then water to wet the soil 6 inches deep. Do not water again until the grass shows the need for water. About 600 gallons of water per 1,000 square feet falls in 1 inch of rain.

Wetting only the surface of the lawn encourages crabgrass and is of little value to the desirable grasses. Frequent, skimpy watering encourages shallow rooting and increases disease problems which may be more harmful than no water.

Close mowing will not prevent crab-

USDA seed specialist makes purity analysis of a lawn seed mixture, separating the kinds of grass seeds from the weed seeds, crop seeds, and inert matter. He will also check to see if label information is accurate.

grass from producing seeds, but it does weaken the lawn to crabgrass invasion. Mow Kentucky bluegrass and mixtures of Kentucky bluegrass and fine-leaved fescue lawns at a height of about 2 inches. Close mowing in hot weather will weaken and may kill cool-season grasses. Mow frequently enough so that only one-half or less of the leaf blade is removed at one mowing. Leave the clippings on the lawn unless the growth is excessive. Lawn grasses mowed at a height of 2 inches shade the soil and help prevent crabgrass germination. Warm-season grasses such as bermudagrass and zoysia species should be mowed at a height of 1 inch or less. Their dense growth does not favor crabgrass.

Diseases may become a problem even in a perfectly managed lawn. Learn to diagnose disease problems and apply the proper fungicides. It is usually necessary to use disease control methods before or at the time major injury symptoms appear in the lawn. If left uncontrolled, diseases will open spaces in the lawn making it easy for crabgrass to grow.

Many kinds of insects damage lawn grasses. Some insect grubs feed on the roots of grass. Other insects feed on the leaves and stems of the grass or suck the juices from the plant. When insect injury starts, apply the proper insecticides to save your lawn.

Remember that a thick turf will deter crabgrass.

Stop crabgrass before it starts. Several herbicides will selectively control crabgrass in turf. Control is simpler and most reliable by use of pre-emergence herbicides. These are herbicides which prevent the germinating crabgrass plants from becoming established in the lawn.

A good time to apply the pre-emergence herbicide is when the flowers of the forsythias, *Forsythia suspensa* (Thunb.) Vahl. and *F. ovata* Nakai, start falling off the plants. An exact calendar date cannot be given as the correct time to apply preemergence herbicides. Concurrent warm temperature and plenty of moisture in the soil are needed before crabgrass will germinate. At 40° N. latitude, crabgrass may start germinating from late April to mid-May. It germinates later farther north or at higher elevations at a given latitude.

Herbicides are sold in granular and liquid formulations with the amount to be applied listed on the label for a definite area of lawn. No complicated calculations are needed to determine how much to use. Our advice is to read the label completely before using any herbicide. The granular or dry formulations are easy to apply. All effective preemergence herbicides control crabgrass if applied in either granular or liquid formulations.

By stopping crabgrass early in the year as the seeds germinate, the home-owner avoids having to reseed patches in the lawn that would occur if large widely spread plants were killed later. Treatments applied late in the year might allow some seed production, and then treatment the next year would be necessary.

Common name	Full chemical name	A trade name product
benefin	N-butyl-N-ethyl-*alpha, alpha, alpha*-trifluoro-2,6-dinitro-*p*-toluidine.	Balan.
bensulide	0,0-diisopropyl phosphorodithioate S-ester with N-(2-mercaptoethyl) benzenesulfonamide.	Betasan.
DCPA	dimethyl tetrachloroterephthalate	Dacthal.
DSMA	disodium methanearsonate	Ansar 184.
MSMA	monosodium methanearsonate	Ansar 170L.
siduron	1-(2-methylcyclohexyl)-3-phenylurea	Tupersan.
terbutol	2,6-di-*tert*-butyl-*p*-tolyl methylcarbamate	Azak.

Mention of only one trade named product for each herbicide does not imply endorsement by the U.S. Department of Agriculture of that product over other products containing the same herbicide as the active ingredient.

Benefin, bensulide, DCPA, siduron, and terbutol are herbicides suitable for controlling crabgrass as it germinates. Labels on the packages give the proper doses to be used.

The label precautions should be strictly followed in overseeding lawns after treatment with herbicides. Usually, lawns treated in the spring should not be overseeded until autumn. Reseeding is possible soon after treatment with siduron, but toxic residues of the other preemergence herbicides will injure seedling lawn grasses.

Siduron is a unique herbicide for crabgrass control because it will not injure Kentucky bluegrass, red fescue, and several other grasses regardless of the application time.

In fact, siduron and bluegrass or fescue seeds may be mixed together and spread at the same time.

It is possible to stop crabgrass after it has become established in lawns. Seed production is prevented, and a crabgrass problem may not develop the next year, if all of the crabgrass is controlled before the seedheads appear. Crabgrass intermixed with the desirable lawn grasses is difficult to remove by pulling. Less effort and time are required if postemergence sprays of MSMA or DSMA are used, and lawn damage from pulling this weed pest is avoided.

These postemergence sprays may cause some discoloration of the lawn grass leaves. Mowing removes this discoloration, but should be delayed 3 or more days after treatment.

MSMA or DSMA performs best when the crabgrass is growing fast, and the air temperature is above 75° F. The lawn may be overseeded in the fall after MSMA or DSMA has been used for the postemergence control of crabgrass.

For further reading:

U.S. Department of Agriculture, *Better Lawns.* Home and Garden Bulletin 51, Washington, D.C. 20250, 1966.
———— *Lawn Diseases—How to Control Them.* Home and Garden Bulletin 61, Washington, D.C. 20250, 1967.
———— *Lawn Insects—How to Control Them.* Home and Garden Bulletin 53, Washington, D.C. 20250, 1966.
———— *Lawn Weed Control With Herbicides.* Home and Garden Bulletin 123, Washington, D.C. 20250, 1967.

An All-Purpose Potato

AUGUST E. KEHR

. . . .

Some like it hot,
Some like it cold,
Some like it as a chip,
Bright as gold.
It may be baked,
It may be fried,
It may be mashed,
Or even be dried.

The "some" may mean an average American housewife, a teenager in any movie theater, a chef in the Swank-Ritz, an Ibo in Nigeria, or perhaps the local breadman in his delivery truck.

"It" can mean only the all-purpose potato variety, Kennebec. Because of its adaptability, it is grown widely in all of the continental United States. Likewise because of its versatility, it is marketed fresh, frozen, dehydrated, and processed. As paraphrased, the variety is baked, panfried, french fried, boiled, mashed, chipped, and even used as starch in bread or pancakes.

Varieties such as the Kennebec de-

Average Total Potato Production and Yields, Selected Years 1930–65

	Total Acres Harvested	Yield Per Acre Harvested	Total Production
	1,000 Acres	Cwt.	1,000 Cwt.
1930	3, 189	65. 7	206, 290
1940	2, 832	79. 9	226, 152
1950	1, 698	152. 6	259, 112
1960	1, 397	184. 3	257, 435
1965	1, 403	206. 0	288, 927

veloped by Dr. R. V. Akeley and his coworkers at Beltsville, Md., have enabled the potatogrower to lower his costs of production. This is because planting, cultivating, harvesting, and similar costs per acre are not much different for a crop that results in 400 hundredweight per acre from one that yields only 200 hundredweight.

The success story in higher yields of potatoes by the American farmer is perhaps unparalleled in all history. Yields have doubled every 10 years for the last 30 years. The American potatogrower today grows about 50 percent more potatoes on only 44 percent of the land area used in 1930. The yield trends are still upward.

Shifts in the geographical areas of production, shifts to fewer and larger farms, marked changes in mechanization and crop utilization, and improved cultural methods have all contributed to the intensification in production and increased yields per acre.

The exact birth date of a potato variety cannot be accurately established. However, the Kennebec story began in the winter of 1940 when cross No. B70 was made in the greenhouses of the Plant Industry Station at Beltsville, Md. In the pedigree were famous names such as Earlaine, Katahdin, Chippewa, and an introduction from Germany. A population of several hundred marble-sized seedling tubers were grown and sent to Presque Isle, Maine, in May 1941 for further growth and increase.

∴   ∴   ∴

AUGUST E. KEHR is Chief, Vegetables and Ornamentals Research Branch, Agricultural Research Service.

From this large group only seven were saved on the basis of their superior horticultural characters and reaction to various diseases. The fifth one chosen from among these survivors was designated B70–5. B70–5 had passed its first crucial test and had risen along with its close competitors from anonymity to become known by a number. The date was now September 1941.

Now began 7 years of grueling tests. The neophyte, B70–5, was subjected to all kinds of field performance tests by Akeley and his coworkers, Geneticist Dr. F. J. Stevenson and Plant Pathologist E. S. Schultz. These men rigidly compared B70–5 to the best varieties known anywhere in this country and in many foreign countries. They compared it to the highest yielding varieties they had developed up to that time. They determined its dry matter content, its yield of U.S. No. 1 tubers, its resistance to the serious potato diseases, including resistance to late blight, mild mosaic, and net necrosis. Cooperators in New York, New Hampshire, Pennsylvania, Florida, California, South Carolina, and Hawaii were among the many who, like Akeley, tried hard to find a weakness in the selection.

B70–5 passed all these tests with flying colors. It continued to prove it was a vigorous and fast-growing, main season variety at all locations. It outyielded Green Mountain, Katahdin, Chippewa, Sebago, and all its near relatives. It averaged nearly as high in dry matter as Green Mountain. It was judged as very good to excellent for either baking or boiling by a relatively large number of people who tested it for cooking quality. It became

277

a standard of excellence for its chipping quality.

In disease tests, it resisted late blight, the disastrous disease which caused the famous Irish famines a century previous. Even leaf roll disease caused little damage to the tubers—it showed no net necrosis as compared to nearly 40 percent for Green Mountain. After 7 years and an estimated 150 tests, the selection B70–5 was finally declared superior and eligible for a name. Dr. E. V. Hardenburg, Cornell University, aptly summarized it as follows: "It appears to have everything to commend it, including yield, marketability, blight resistance, internal quality, and maturity." It had merited its name Kennebec, after a well-known river in Maine.

Despite its relative youth—it is not yet 20 years old—the variety represents about 14 percent of the total

Kennebec potato, *upper left,* brings savings for consumers and profits for growers. *Below,* scores of dehydrated, canned, and frozen potato products are available.

potatoes grown today. It is surpassed only by Katahdin—its grandparent—and by Russet Burbank, a variety nearly a century old. Each year it moves closer and closer to the coveted top rating spot, especially replacing Katahdin.

How can you distinguish the Kennebec variety from others similar to it? This is not always easy, even for its originators. The growing plant has large leaves and a few white flowers per stem. Kennebec tubers are oblong and medium thick with distinctly shallow eyes. The skin is very smooth and creamy buff colored.

Akeley and his coworkers in developing Kennebec have put money into the pockets of potatogrowers, potato shippers, potato processors, and potato marketers. At the same time, the consumers of 1968 have to dig less deeply into their pockets to eat better potatoes and potato products than in 1948. But what happens in 1978 or even the year 2000?

Already there are new potatoes being developed that far surpass Kennebec in yielding potential, disease resistance, and quality. There are lines resistant to every major potato disease and to many insect pests and nematodes. Nematodes are small wormlike pests that injure plant roots and cause lowered yields or even plant death. The all-purpose Kennebec of today will most certainly be replaced by a still more superior potato of tomorrow. The future holds great promise for potato growers, shippers, processors, and the potato consumers as the result of Akeley's work of today.

Flame-Retardant Fabrics Safeguard Your Life

GEORGE L. DRAKE, JR., *and* LEON H. CHANCE

. . . .

One afternoon in 1951, a young scientist sat on a stool in a laboratory surrounded by an intricate setup of flasks and beakers. This young man was Wilson A. Reeves, one of the chemists employed by the U.S. Department of Agriculture's Southern Regional Research Laboratory in New Orleans. He was gazing intently at the gurgling solutions, bubbling gases, and wispy vapors issuing from the strange-looking vessels that were separated from him by a safety shield. Little did he suspect that at this very moment he was on his way to the discovery of THPC, a chemical which is now used all over the world as a flame retardant for clothing.

Why the safety shield? Wilson had reason to suspect that almost anything could happen to his chemical reaction—the bubbling gas was phosphine, a vapor that catches fire immediately when exposed to air and is quite toxic when inhaled. He was also using two other noxious chemicals, formaldehyde, often used for preserving biological specimens, and hydrochloric

∴   ∴   ∴

GEORGE L. DRAKE, JR., *is Chemist in charge of the Special Finishes Investigations at the Southern Utilization Research and Development Division, Agricultural Research Service, New Orleans.*

LEON H. CHANCE *is a Senior Research Chemist of the same group.*

Treating children's clothing with flame-retardant chemicals may avert a tragedy. Dresses of these dolls were touched simultaneously with lighted candles on the birthday cakes. Untreated dress, *left,* burst into flame. But the dress treated with a flame retardant did not ignite.

acid, a very corrosive liquid. You may ask what this young chemist could hope to gain by mixing such an explosive combination of chemicals. Oddly enough, this chemical magic produced a compound which, instead of being dangerous and harmful, would greatly benefit man by making textiles resistant to burning.

Why do we need flame-retardant fabrics? Listen to these true stories and you will understand. Early one morning, the peace and quiet of a home was shattered by the terrified screams of two young children. Their mother rushed to the bathroom, where she gasped in horror to see her two daughters engulfed in flames. She tried desperately to beat out the flames with her bare hands, but to no avail. The girls, aged 8 and 3, clothed in flannelette nightgowns, had been standing near an open gas heater in the bathroom when the tragedy struck. During the awful months that followed, the little girls' lives were a nightmare of pain, treatment, and plastic surgery, to say nothing of the anxiety and agony suffered by the parents. The costly operations brought financial disaster, but far worse was the emotional stress from which the family will never be able to recover.

But homes aren't the only places where flame-retardant fabrics could save lives. A plane suddenly bursts into flame; the pilot opens the hatch, ejects, and pulls the ripcord. The parachute pack cover flies off the chute, as it should, but the pilot continues to fall rapidly toward earth. He waits for the parachute to open, but nothing happens. In desperation, he tries to find the trouble. He plummets to his death.

The following questions are asked at the inquest. What was actually the cause of death? Was it fire? Was it the failure of the parachute cover or failure of the parachute itself? Here are the answers. Nylon, which is used in parachutes, melts easily at a rather low temperature. The flames from the plane had melted the nylon parachute so that it would not open after the parachute pack cover had been ejected. A flame-resistant cover with the additional property of relatively low heat transfer would have insulated the nylon parachute from the heat, prevented its melting, and thus saved the life of the pilot.

In 1951, as Wilson Reeves worked in his laboratory, tragedies such as these were repeated over and over again in homes, hospitals, and on the battlefield. What were some of the problems that had to be solved before the situation could be changed?

The first problem was solved relatively easily, but only after considerable embarrassment and discomfort to Wilson. During the early stages of the laboratory development of THPC (tetrakis (hydroxymethyl) phosphomium chloride), there was a very unpleasant odor problem. This odor not only permeated the laboratory in which he worked, but also saturated his clothing. He was unpopular with his fellow workers and equally unpopular at home. Wilson's wife, Happy, insisted that he change to fresh clothing in the garage before she would

allow him to enter their home. Then it was discovered that impurities in the THPC were causing the bad odor; finally, a way to remove them was found, and the problem was solved. These little problems are what make research so challenging.

A big problem was the need of a manufacturer. The small quantities of THPC made in a research laboratory were totally inadequate since millions of yards of fabric had to be made flame resistant. An extensive search began to find a company to make THPC. Then a small company in Niagara Falls, N.Y., the Oldbury Electro-Chemical Co., agreed to begin production. Phosphine, needed in the manufacture, was one of the waste byproducts of this company. Now, they had a new use for their byproduct, and we had a source of supply for our new flame-retardant chemical.

At this point in the development of flame-resistant materials, things moved rapidly. In the United States, our military recognized the potential of this finish and financially supported further research. Cooperation was also given by the National Cotton Council of America. Many companies also became interested in this new treatment that would make cotton durably flame resistant. Trial runs were made in textile mills throughout this country and shortly afterward in foreign countries, too. In England, for example, the Proban Co., Ltd., was formed specifically for the application of the THPC flame-retardant finish to cotton fabric.

But success in the laboratory doesn't always mean immediate success on a larger scale. In the beginning, it was not a simple matter to apply this finish in a textile mill. The first fabrics produced were stiff and tore easily. The process had worked very well in the pilot plant at the Southern Regional Research Laboratory. So why, then, didn't it work in some of the textile mills? Frequent visits were necessary to find out. In one mill that had obtained poor results, the culprit was a little dipper that was used to measure 2 pounds, but actually measured 2 quarts. This simple—but not so little— error had so altered the formulation that the fabric wasn't properly treated. Another little thing that meant serious mill trouble was water.

Alkalinity of the water used in making the treating solutions affected the finish. It's really hard to believe that changes as simple as these could cause such a tremendous difference in the final product.

Eventually, however, the finish was improved so that it could be used on some apparel fabrics to impart flame resistance while maintaining many desirable properties of the untreated fabric. Flight suits, work clothing, industrial uniforms, and similar garments could now be made from the new flame-retardant fabrics. And, they were comfortable to wear—certainly not stiffened so that they would stand by themselves, as had many previous flame-retardant garments. Ultimately, the protection of these garments treated with THPC would be offered to people all over the world.

You're probably wondering just how these garments protect their wearers.

Fabrics treated with THPC have an outstanding characteristic: When they are held in a flame, they form a tough black char which still retains the fiber structure and has some strength. This char is crucial. It not only protects, but insulates. But the fabric is important, too. Cotton appears to be one of the few fabrics that forms a flexible char after being treated with THPC. Even applying a blowtorch to the char of cotton fabrics will only cause the char to glow, but will not penetrate its protection.

The steel mills use a test for flame-retardant fabrics that illustrates this protection. A small frame is inclined at a 75° angle to the ground and is covered with the flame-retardant fabric. Beneath the fabric is placed a polyethylene film which reacts similarly to human skin. A small ladle of molten steel is then poured onto the fabric. It is then observed whether the slag adheres to the fabric or runs off, whether the fabric has burned or been badly damaged, and to what extent the polyethylene film has been affected.

The ultimate test, of course, is what

Mannequins are exposed to gasoline fire. Obviously, one on the right is wearing flame-retardant coveralls.

happens when human flesh, not polyethylene film, is beneath the treated material. In industrial accidents, two men clothed in flame-retardant clothing and thermal underwear were exposed to high temperatures. One was splashed with molten steel from a ladle, and the other's back was engulfed in flames erupting from a furnace. Although their clothing was a total loss, their skin was not burned at all. Needless to say, these men were badly frightened, but they were able to return to work almost immediately. By wearing flame-retardant clothing, they remained two living workers instead of becoming two charred bodies.

Protective clothing is also obviously a necessity for firefighters. The District of Columbia Fire Department developed and uses new turnout coats and trousers made from flame-retardant fabrics. According to Battalion Chief Morris H. Clarke, property officer of the D.C. Fire Department, the reaction of the personnel now wearing these protective garments has been favorable. In one case, a fireman returned from a fire with the back of his coat badly charred, but didn't even know that he had been touched by flames. Can you imagine what would have happened if the coat had not been treated?

Who would have thought that Wilson Reeves, sitting on that little stool, watching the bubbles in his reaction flask, could have paved the way for these outstanding developments? Today, he has been internationally honored for his achievement, but the battle is not yet over. The perfect finish has not been developed. Research *must* and *is* being continued at the Southern Regional Research Laboratory. Wilson Reeves and his coworkers are still researching out bits and pieces of information that can hasten attainment of the ideal flame-retardant finish.

Timing and Tailoring Flowering Plants

HENRY M. CATHEY

. . . .

Easter lilies always bloom at Eastertime, even though the dates for Easter may be weeks apart in consecutive years. Christmas has its red, white, and now, pink poinsettias of just the right height to glow and last for weeks on the coffee table in the living room. Thanksgiving with its traditional chrysanthemums now sees azaleas—red, pink, white, and variegated, as vivid and long lasting as those that bloom outside at another time of the year.

Spring flowering bulbs brighten winter's dull days and hint of spring. Hydrangeas and hyacinths compete with Sweetheart roses and pots of mums for Mother's Day. Throughout the year, florists offer us, as consumers, a wealth of flowers and green plants that were not available at any price only a few years ago. Whether it be that single carnation for the boy friend's boutonniere or a dozen long-stemmed "American Beauty" roses for that special anniversary, the florist seems always able to meet our request.

Timing the growth and flowering of ornamentals is an art and also a science. Of course, this is a vast country and somewhere some flowers are always in bloom. Modern air transport can whisk the plants and flowers anywhere they are ordered in a matter of hours. Many florists find it easier to buy their flowers than to grow their own. Even so, thousands of greenhouses throughout the country provide the "climates" necessary for flower production throughout the year.

We think of greenhouses as providing light and shelter for the plants in foul weather and fair. They also permit the florist to ply his art, to exhibit his green thumb, feeding, watering, pruning, fighting the bugs and diseases, coaxing his plants to bloom at the right times and in the right amounts. His task is easier because of the work of plant scientists around the country like Neil W. Stuart, veteran plant physiologist in the Ornamentals Investigations section of the U.S. Department of Agriculture. A plant physiologist studies how plants grow and how their growth can be regulated. He studies the effects of light, both kind and amount, the influence of temperature on growth and flowering, the various mineral nutrients, and the countless products the plants make in their own laboratories—their stems and leaves—that control their growth.

How does light affect plant growth and flowering? Garner and Allard, USDA plant scientists, discovered about 50 years ago that the lengths of the daylight period and of the night set the course for many kinds of plants and determine when they will flower. Thus, chrysanthemums and poinsettias, short day plants, flower in the late fall when the nights are longer than the days. About 25 years ago, USDA Scientists H. A. Borthwick, Sterling B. Hendricks, and the late Marion W.

∴   ∴   ∴

HENRY M. CATHEY *is Leader, Ornamentals Investigations, Crops Research Division, Agricultural Research Service.*

Parker found that if the night was interrupted with a short period of light, certain soybean plants failed to flower.

Stuart and his colleagues applied those results to chrysanthemums and found that these short day plants continued to grow even in the middle of winter provided they were lighted in the middle of the night. When the plants had made enough growth, the nightly interruptions were stopped, the plants budded and bloomed just as they would have done at their normal flowering time in the late fall. During the long days of summer, the process is reversed, and the plants are shaded with black cloth from early in the afternoon until the following morning, producing an 8- or 9-hour "day." Thus, exposed to an artificial short day (and a long night) at 60° F., the plants bud and bloom just as in the fall. Controlled day length and temperature are the basis for the commercial practice of flowering chrysanthemums throughout the year. Visitors to florist shops see and buy chrysanthemums of an excellent quality during any month of the year.

Storage temperature is the key to controlling the blooming of flower bulbs. Stuart, with colleagues Emsweller, Brierley, and Gill (in Tifton, Ga.), demonstrated that new crop Easter lily bulbs that were produced in the Gulf States could be flowered promptly if exposed to cool storage 45° to 50° F. for short periods of time.

For later blooming, longer storage at lower temperatures (31° to 35° F.) maintains dormancy, but results in the production of fewer leaves and flowers when the plants are forced. To overcome this difficulty, we sometimes plant the bulbs before they have been exposed to low temperature, allow them to root in the early fall, and sprout under the influence of cool night temperatures.

The resulting plants are usually short, leafy, and produce many flowers.

Latest development is the finding by a Florida grower that artificial light applied to the sprouting lilies hastens their flowering in the same way as

IRIS

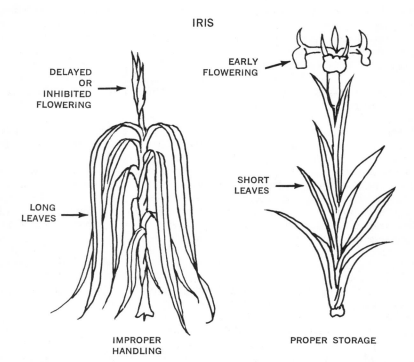

DELAYED OR INHIBITED FLOWERING →

EARLY FLOWERING →

SHORT LEAVES →

LONG LEAVES →

IMPROPER HANDLING

PROPER STORAGE

does exposure to cold storage. Final timing of the crop for Easter depends upon temperature manipulation in the greenhouses as well as good luck as far as the weather is concerned.

The bulbous iris story is an interesting one, if for no other reason than that we have developed a lively export business to Europe. Now, millions of blue Wedgewood iris bulbs that were grown in western Washington State flower in greenhouses on Guernsey of the Channel Islands and are the winter joy of many a housewife in London. These irises find their way to the Scandinavian countries, to Germany, and elsewhere in Western Europe.

Stuart and his colleague Charles J. Gould of the Western Washington Research and Extension Center, Puyallup, have grown and flowered iris for 20 years, learning how to treat them for dependable flowering at any time of the year. The prescription for success involves a series of temperature treatments aimed at making the iris feel that they have grown in their original homeland.

We harvest the bulbs in July when they have received a certain number of degree-days or heat units after June 20. Then, within 5 days, we "sweat" the bulbs at 90° F. for 10 days, following with 3 or 4 weeks at 65° F., and then with 6 weeks at 48° to 50° F. The bulbs can now be planted for early blooming in December, but if they are held for another week at 65° F. after the 50° F. treatment, the leaves will be shorter when the plants bloom than on similar plants without the 65° F. treatment. For a continuous season of bloom, the bulbs are "retarded"—held after harvest at 80° F. They remain dormant and can be kept in good condition for at least a year. They are activated at any time by exposure to 50° F. for several weeks followed by a few days at 65° F. (to shorten the leaves) before planting.

Tulips are typical of temperate regions. However, thanks to the work of Stuart, Gould, and Gill, they can be grown successfully in gardens of the Deep South. Again, the success treatment depends upon the right sequence

285

of temperatures. Without enough cold storage, the tulips produce undesirably short stems. Tulips that would flower "on the ground," if planted in Georgia or Florida without cold storage, will rival those grown in Northern States provided the dry bulbs have 8 weeks at 40° F. before they are planted in the garden. Longer storage at 40° F. produces abnormally long, thin stems and small flowers.

In contrast with the iris, any delay of more than a week between removing from storage and planting destroys the effect of the storage and is ruinous to the tulips. Cooperative studies with workers in the Netherlands confirmed our findings and are the basis for the Dutch "5° C." treatment used successfully in exporting their bulbs to other countries.

The third tool in the physiologist's bag of tricks, nutrition, is always with us. Plants grow and flower by virtue of the water and mineral elements they absorb. Equally important is the "invisible fertilizer," the carbon dioxide of the atmosphere which enters the green leaves and by the plant's own alchemy is converted to sugar, starch, and the materials for growth. Physiologists the world around have starved plants and fed them to excess, seeking the magic combination that would hasten growth and flowering over and above that obtained in the most fertile soil. In fact, soilless culture became a fad and remains a fascinating hobby for many amateur gardeners.

Perhaps some time in the future the size of the world's population will demand soilless culture production of food supplements. Similarly, enriching the earth's atmosphere with carbon dioxide to enhance growth is attracting world attention. The potential for greenhouses and field application is still to be determined.

Physiologists have known for years that while nutrition as well as light and temperature affect plant growth, the plants produce their own growth regulators. In roughly the last 30 years, we have seen the isolation or synthesis of

TULIPS

BULBS STORED
AT 50° F.

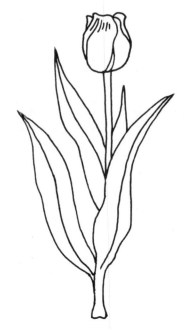

BULBS STORED
AT 40° F.

Plant Scientist Henry M. Cathey demonstrates effect of chemicals and day length on petunias. Petunia at left was given short days to make it late flowering and to produce a short plant. Petunia at center was given long days to make it early flowering and tall. Petunia at right was sprayed with growth retardant to make it short, and given long days to make it bloom early.

literally hundreds of chemicals which in some way affect growth of plants. First came the chemicals that stimulate production of roots on cuttings. They are widely used in plant propagation even though we do not know how they bring about their action. Certain of these root initiators turned out to be herbicides—weedkillers with such an amazing selectivity that they kill "weeds" and leave the desired crop plant unharmed.

Thanks to Japanese scientists, we were introduced to gibberellins. These compounds stimulate plant growth, stretch the stems, and cause bolting (flowering) of some biennial vegetable and flower crops without the customary exposure to low temperature.

"Retardant" chemicals which can cancel the stimulating effects of gibberellins have now appeared. Treated plants range from being slightly shorter with leaves closer together than the control plants to "miniplants" much reduced in size. We use these chemicals to prevent poinsettias from becoming "leggy." At certain times of year, they are useful in producing compact chrysanthemums. Commercial formulations of the retardants that produce these effects are now on the market, available at garden supply houses, and are used commercially.

Stuart and Cathey applied the retardants to many flowering and ornamental plants. Their effect on azaleas was dramatic; shoot growth stopped and flowerbuds appeared. Further trials showed that azaleas in growth would always form flowerbuds if sprayed with solutions of the retardants. After adequate bud development and suitable cool storage, the azaleas flowered as well in November, for example, as in May, thus permitting year-round flowering of this important pot plant. In the future, we can expect to see azaleas in bloom at the florist or nursery at many times during the year.

A recent development in the use of chemicals to "tailor" plants is the chemical pruning story. Chrysanthemums and azaleas must be "pinched" (pruned) once or more to induce development of additional shoots and to produce compact flowering plants. Such pinching is monotonous, time consuming, and costly. Furthermore, the results are only as good as the worker's conscience. In desperation, growers resort to mowing machines or shears which have no conscience but no discrimination either. We have looked for a chemical which would destroy only the shoot tip without affecting the rest of the plant.

As is so often the case, the application we wanted came from workers in other fields. T. C. Tso, a tobacco biochemist in USDA, observed that certain fatty acid esters prevented the growth of leafbuds when they were applied to tobacco plants whose tops

287

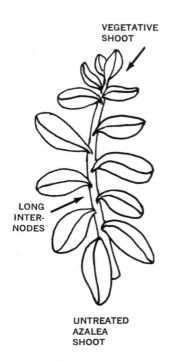

VEGETATIVE
SHOOT

LONG
INTER-
NODES

UNTREATED
AZALEA
SHOOT

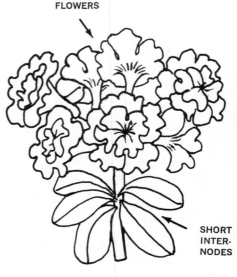

FLOWERS

SHORT
INTER-
NODES

AZALEA SHOOT
TREATED WITH
GROWTH
RETARDANT

had been removed. His objective was sucker control. While making other tests, the author found that spraying chrysanthemums with the emulsions used by Tso killed the growing points without injuring the leafbuds which later developed into normal shoots. The chemicals pinched or pruned the plants. We now know that some kinds of plants are not affected by the esters now available, while others, including azaleas, respond in the same manner as the chrysanthemum. Nurserymen and florists who grow azaleas are clamoring for the "chemical pruner" which is expected to be available for commercial use shortly.

Thus it is we see that Stuart and his coworkers at Beltsville and all over the country have contributed in some measure to improving commercial production of ornamental flowering plants. We have better plants and flowers, available over a longer portion of the year, produced with more assurance, and at less cost. Truly, beautification of America with decorative plants will take place both in and out of doors.

For further reading:

Alcorn, S. M., and Stuart, N. W., "Growth and Flowering Characteristics of Five Tulip Varieties in Southern Arizona." *Southern Florist and Nurseryman*, Vol. 72, 1959.

Cathey, Henry M., and others, "Chemical Pruning of Plants." *Science*, Vol. 156, 1966.

Gill, D. L., and others, "Some Effects of Bulb Storage Temperatures and Planting Conditions on Production of Tulip Flowers in the Greenhouse and Outside in Southern Georgia." *Proceedings, American Society for Horticultural Science*, Vol. 70, 1957.

———— and Stuart, N. W., *Effects of Photoperiod in the Field and Greenhouse on Forcing of Georgia Lily Bulbs.* (In press).

Stuart, N. W., "Chemical Pruning of Greenhouse Azaleas With Fatty Acid Esters." *Florists' Review*, Vol. 140, 1967.

———— "Effects of Temperature, Supplemental Light, and Type of Storage on Forcing of Easter and Other Lilies." *The Lily Yearbook*, Vol. 17, 1964.

———— "Initiation of Flower Buds in Rhododendron After Application of Growth Retardants." *Science*, Vol. 134, 1961.

———— "Iris Storage Treatments Control Forcing Rates." *Florists' Review*, Vol. 130, 1962.

———— "Present Methods of Handling Bulbs." *Easter Lilies*, New York State Flower Growers, Ithaca, N.Y., and Ohio State University, Columbus, Ohio, 1967.

288

A New Low-Fat Cheese

BYRON H. WEBB

Make a flavorful full-bodied cheese from the cow's milk protein which now supplements butterfat in all of our best cheese. This was the assignment received by two Agricultural Research Service scientists. Casein, our most highly nutritious protein and the principal protein of milk and all of the gourmet cheeses, had never been successfully molded into an edible cheese without its companion milk component, butterfat. The diet-conscious American public was becoming increasingly protein conscious and also was looking for low-fat foods. The two scientists, R. E. Hargrove and F. E. McDonough, realized that the source of flavor in our finest cheeses was the fat and the products derived from fat by the bacteria that develop cheese flavor. If flavor were proportional to fat content, who would eat a cheese without fat and flavor?

There are 400 varieties of cheese—one for every day in the year and some to spare. Why make another, especially since skim milk cheese is already manufactured? The answer is obvious to anyone who tries to bite into a flavorless, hard, rubberlike chunk of skim milk cheese which contains mostly protein with no fat and little water. This kind of product is made to be shredded for food manufacture. When dry, its protein, casein, is a horny, tough, brittle substance, a material from which plastics and fibers can be made. Moisture softens it to a rubbery mass. Too much water provides ideal conditions for spoilage. Clearly, here was a research problem needing the creative skills, imagination, and hard work of the milk technologist, microbiologist, and chemist.

Nutritionists' praise for cheese is based largely on its high content of milk protein—the best balanced natural protein we know. Cheese also is an important source of calcium. This essential mineral is held in the curd which is coagulated by rennet during the cheesemaking process. Other less important soluble salts such as sodium are drained off in the whey. Milk fat is regarded nutritionally as one of our finest fats.

Fat and water contribute flavor and a soft, pliable body to cheese. The low-fat cheese researcher must produce both flavor and an acceptable body without the fat. He must build water into the system as a readily available softening agent; but high water content permits an undesirable bacterial activity and it is conducive to poor keeping quality. The soft and mellow body of normal cheese is produced during ripening, a period of slow biochemical breakdown of fats and proteins. Here, the essential catalysts are the enzyme systems provided by continuous microbial activity.

The problem faced by Hargrove and McDonough was how to eliminate the fat from cheese, substituting for it water and protein. They must encourage bacterial breakdown to produce flavor and softness, but maintain suitable keeping quality.

∴ ∴ ∴

BYRON H. WEBB is Chief, Dairy Products Laboratory, Eastern Utilization Research and Development Division, Agricultural Research Service, Washington, D.C.

Cheese varieties.

Cheese is made in large vats holding thousands of pounds of milk to which acid-forming, flavor-producing, body-softening bacteria must be added to help rennet coagulate the milk. The curd that forms after a few hours is cut and heated. This cooking liberates whey from the shrinking curd just as water is pressed from a wet sponge. The firming curd is gathered together, salted, and placed in molds to cure 2 to 8 months, producing mellow, flavorful cheese. Research on cheese means trying, testing, failing, and starting anew, making hundreds of tests with thousands of pounds of milk. To save on time and materials, Hargrove and McDonough devised an experimental procedure to make batches of cheese with only 50 pounds of milk.

Cheddar cheese is made from milk containing 3.5 percent fat. The new skim milk cheeses were made from milks containing from 0.1 to 1 percent fat, and it was found that 0.7 of 1 percent was optimum under the researchers' experimental conditions. But to produce flavor, something unusual must be done. Could some kind of additive be used? Of many tried, none were judged fully acceptable. Perhaps the fat itself could be made to give up more than its usual amount of flavor. What about various pretreatments of the milk? Homogenization proved particularly effective in subdividing the fat, making it accessible to the fat-splitting enzymes in the milk. And this greatly improved the flavor in the cured cheese.

The puzzle of how to handle moisture had to be resolved. The more water incorporated in the cheese protein, the softer and more tender would be its body. But the superb ripening and keeping quality of commercial cheese derives from its delicate balance of water, salt, and bacterial food. These enable flavor-producing bacteria to grow, discouraging the spoilage

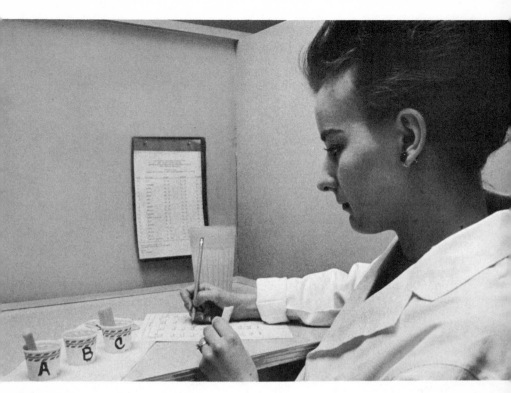

Trained taste panel evaluation, *above,* of EUDA cheese. *Left,* preparing for consumer acceptance test of the new cheese.

organisms. Hargrove and McDonough tried many moisture levels from the 38 percent of Cheddar cheese to the 70 percent of Schmierkäse, which actually liquefies in ripening. But high moisture leads to instability, and so Schmierkäse cheese quickly deteriorates in storage. Finally, using their new process, the researchers found the best moisture level to be 57 to 59 percent. They were now producing an attractive, new, and flavorful semisoft skim milk cheese in the laboratory.

At the Agricultural Research Center at Beltsville, a pilot plant team, H. E. Walter, A. M. Sadler, and W. A. Mattingly, was tooling up for the next step—experimental production in commercial-size equipment. Batches grew from 50 pounds of milk to 100 pounds and then 3,000 pounds.

But problems seemed to expand with the size of the batch. In the laboratory, the curd could be cooked and the whey drained in 5 minutes. Not so with commercial-size batches, where these steps took at least 30 minutes. During that time, excessive acid quickly developed in the curd. To control this, adjustment was made in the amount of bacterial starter added to the milk and in the rate of cooking and cooling the curd. Other adjustments were made, and finally a skim milk cheese comparable to the laboratory product was produced in the pilot plant. The Beltsville pilot plant would be capable of producing hundreds of pounds of low-fat cheese for consumer and market testing.

Next, the new cheese must have a name to identify it in the marketplace. The researchers thought of their product as "low-fat cheese" which indicated it contained less fat than ordinary cheese. Skim milk containing 0.6 or 0.7 percent fat was actually the raw material used in its manufacture. In consultation with the Food and Drug Administration, the product was classified as a "semisoft skim milk cheese." To identify the cheese for consumers, it was named EUDA (pronounced uda) for "Eastern Utilization—Department of Agriculture."

EUDA cheese contains only 6 percent fat compared to 33 percent for Cheddar. Its moisture and salt content is also higher than Cheddar. But of most significance is the protein content of EUDA cheese, which is 30 percent while that of Cheddar is 24 percent.

Here is a cheese of unusually high nutritive value with more protein on a pound-for-pound basis than any of the well-known cheeses. Even cottage cheese, the classic example of a high-protein product, contains less than 14 percent protein. The ratio between the two most important cheese components, fat and protein, is more favorable in skim milk cheese than in the other cheeses.

Analyses of Cheddar, Cottage, and EUDA Cheese

	Cheddar	Cottage (creamed)	EUDA
Fat %	33	4. 2	6
Moisture % . .	38	78. 3	56
Protein % . . .	24	13. 6	30
Salt %	1. 7	1. 0	2. 4
Calories per 100 g . .	398	106	185

EUDA cheese is mild, but attractive in flavor, although it does not have the well-ripened, full flavor of an aged Cheddar. The new cheese is semisoft, but because of its short period of ripening, its body is more pliable and less mellow than Cheddar. Flavor and body of EUDA cheese develop in a few weeks at refrigerator temperature (40° F.). Its shelf life under normal refrigeration is about 60 days, so that some control of distribution time will be necessary. EUDA cheese has four times the shelf life of cottage cheese, which is considered to be 15 days.

Spurred by consumer interest in cheese of low fat content, investigators in at least two of the State agricultural experiment stations recently have made excellent cheese containing about half the fat of the normal products. At the University of Minnesota Experiment Station, H. A. Morris and S. T. Coulter have produced Port du Salut, Brick, and Swiss cheeses containing 14 to 20 percent fat. Consumer acceptance of these has been excellent as judged by actual sales.

At Iowa State University, G. W. Reinbold and F. M. Madsen made Cheddar, Colby, and Swiss cheese containing one-half to two-thirds the fat content of the normal cheese. They found these to have very high consumer acceptance.

The technical problems of making cheese with less fat than that of normal cheese are being rapidly resolved. The American consumer will soon find in our markets cheese to suit any taste. Of special interest to weight watchers will be EUDA semisoft skim milk cheese which will keep fat intake low, but at the same time will satisfy a craving for good cheese.

Saving _Your_ Skin— Insect Repellants

JOHN A. FLUNO and DONALD E. WEIDHAAS

. . . .

When you fish or bathe at the beach without picking up any mosquito bites, or hike in woods and fields without acquiring ticks or chiggers, you should thank a small group of men who worked years and even offered their own skins as bait so you wouldn't be bitten.

To scientists of the Entomology Research Division, Agricultural Research Service, go many of the laurels for effective insect repellants and efficient insecticides which today can afford you this comfort.

For years you bought fragrant concoctions made of citronella or pennyroyal or peppermint oil and smeared yourself in the hope that mosquitoes would then leave you unbitten. If you didn't mind the pungent or minty smell and the mosquitoes weren't too plentiful, you may have been almost satisfied. Almost, but not quite, because these oils only worked for an hour or less. Besides, the mixtures were greasy on the skin.

Maybe somebody would have found a better repellant someday without urging. But the prod was applied

when citronella oil, best of the plant extract repellants, became scarce during World War II. Entomologists of the Agriculture Department began a broad screening program to find a substitute.

Chemists in the Entomology Research Division, in universities, and in private industry made thousands of new chemicals and sent them to the Division's entomologists for trial. These trials or screening tests soon showed several synthetic chemicals to be excellent in repelling mosquitoes. Those found safe included many in wide use today, dimethyl phthalate, ethylhexanediol, and dimethyl carbate, and others less often used.

Not only did these chemicals prevent

∴ ∴ ∴

JOHN A. FLUNO _is Assistant to the Chief, Insects Affecting Man and Animals Research Branch, Entomology Research Division, Agricultural Research Service._

DONALD E. WEIDHAAS _is a Research Entomologist in the same branch of the Entomology Research Division. He is stationed at its laboratory in Gainesville, Fla._

mosquito bites, but they also helped in preventing the bites of chiggers, fleas, and ticks.

But each was best against only one kind of pest. If you wanted to be protected against all four kinds of pests—mosquitoes, chiggers, fleas, and ticks—you had to use a mixture of several repellants. Besides, as with citronella, these repellants felt greasy on the skin. True, they lasted for hours, but Department scientists thought they could come up with a longer lasting material which might be even more effective than those found during the screening trials.

Entomologists reported to the chemists all of their test results with thousands of materials. The chemists studied these results and carefully noted the molecular structure of chemicals that showed repellancy. They saw that those chemicals termed diols and cyclic amides often had repellent action.

Then the chemists were able to make refined guesses about what made a chemical compound repellent to mos-quitoes. They planned the molecular structure of some entirely new chemicals, explored ways of making them, and went into their laboratories to work. They made 33 new chemicals, purified them, and sent them to the entomologists who were waiting with their hungry insects.

The men who rear the thousands of hungry mosquitoes needed for screening tests brought in the bloodthirsty insects. The mosquitoes were tested and found to be hungry enough. First or "screening" tests were made with the new chemical applied to a section of a stocking slipped over the arm. If the mosquitoes do not bite during a 1-minute period, the scientist pulls the treated stocking off and hangs it safely away for another day.

Several of the brand new chemicals were good, but one was outstanding. This one passed all the preliminary tests with mosquitoes when the repellant was applied to stockings. Cooperating scientists of the Army tested the new chemical and reported it safe

Mosquitoes feed on untreated portion of man's arm, stay clear of part above dark stripe treated with insect repellant.

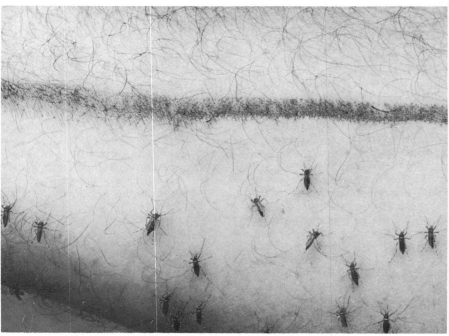

for tests on the skin of the Department volunteers. At this point the thorough testing began.

The new chemical was found to give long-lasting protection. Even when diluted to half strength with alcohol, it protected against mosquitoes for over 4 hours. No test was ever completed with the new repellant at full strength; the men were too sleepy after staying awake for about 20 hours of testing the only time this was tried.

Best of all, the new compound also repelled ticks, chiggers, and fleas. Diluted with alcohol, it lost its greasy feeling, and it was removed less easily by the effects of sweating and the rubbing of clothing than other repellants. The full chemical name of the outstanding material was N,N-diethyl-*meta*-toluamide.

By agreement, to make it easier to remember and identify on a label, the name was shortened to "deet."

Repellants are very nice when you need them and can conveniently use them. Nevertheless, they may leave something to be desired. If you miss a spot, the mosquitoes will quickly find the untreated bit of skin and bite. If you bathe or swim, you will need to dry off and apply more repellant if you plan to stay on the beach. Most persons would rather avoid any beach where repellants are necessary and bathe instead where mosquitoes are controlled. And, there are ways to control the mosquitoes and make repellants unnecessary.

At first, the alternatives for mosquito control were either very slow methods like ditch-digging or filling or using one of two insecticides, fuel oil or paris green. Besides being slow, with the possible beneficial results too far removed in time from the efforts spent, ditching and filling were criticized for damaging the natural habitats of our wildlife.

Oil had to be applied as often as once a week and as much as 15 gallons an acre were often needed. Anyone who saw what this did to duck feathers was outraged. And it did little good to point out that for some unknown reasons the oil sometimes did not spread properly, and that wind and wave piled it up along the shore.

Of course, paris green was not so bad. But people just naturally did not care too much for the idea, since paris green is part arsenic. Somehow, there was very little comfort in the statement that only about a pound per acre was needed.

Then, at the same time that Agriculture Department scientists began their efforts to find a new and better repellant, during World War II, other scientists working in the same laboratories set out to find better ways to kill mosquitoes. At first, their goals were not very clear. They hoped to find one or more chemicals that might kill mosquitoes at dilutions of about 100 parts of insecticide per million parts of water. They easily found many that killed at dilutions of 10 parts and even 1 part per million. There were in fact a few compounds that killed all the mosquitoes at dilutions of 1 part per hundred million.

Two of these amazingly efficient chemicals were not really new at all. One had been made for the first time in 1874 by a Swiss student as part of his university work. The other had been made in 1825 by none other than Michael Faraday, the British scientist who discovered the principles on which modern-day electric motors are built as well as the process by which silver plating is done. The first of the "new chemicals" is now known as DDT; the second is lindane or BHC (benzene hexachloride).

Thanks to these two insecticides and their efficient control of malaria mosquitoes, body lice, and other insects that attacked our troops, World War II was the first major war in which fewer men died from disease during the war than from bullets. And, thanks to these two chemicals, especially the DDT, civilian agencies also became interested in mosquito control.

If, in their readiness to control mosquitoes with the new tools, laymen rushed in where scientists might have feared to tread, should we blame them from our position of hindsight? The amounts of the newer materials needed were so infinitesimal compared to the old oil and paris green. Why, we are *not* now discussing 15 gallons or even 1 pound per acre, we are talking about one-tenth or two-tenths of a pound per acre. In more familiar terms, about 1½ to 3¼ ounces per acre.

But wait—just as over 50 years ago one kind of scale insect developed resistance to old-fashioned cyanide fumigation, some kinds of mosquitoes developed resistance to DDT. A bit of reflection and research showed that this was evolution in action, selection of those parts of the mosquito population which had defense mechanisms against DDT or lindane or whatever insecticide was used.

And—equally frightening—some of these new insecticides, including DDT, were awfully persistent. True, DDT and others broke down into relatively harmless chemicals, but they didn't disappear completely. DDT and its breakdown products began showing up all over the world. Of course, DDT was being used all over the world, saving millions of human lives that would otherwise be lost through malaria, plague, and typhus. But its very persistence frightened many persons.

Scientists of the Department have found, through cooperation with industry, many insecticides that can be used as substitutes for DDT. Some, called organophosphates because their structure includes and relies upon phosphorus, rather than chlorine, are in general less persistent than DDT and its relatives in the environment.

Looking at the Inside From the Outside

CALVIN GOLUMBIC

. . . .

Egg candling is our oldest and still best illustration of the art of judging quality by "looking at the inside from the outside." Its origin is associated with the invention of artificial incubation of eggs which traditionally is credited to the Egyptian priests of the ancient Temple of Isis. Somehow, these remarkably perceptive priests learned to hold eggs to the sunlight streaming from the apertures of their mud incubators and judge egg fertility from the vague shapes which they observed.

Down through the ages, this practice has changed little beyond substitution, first of candles—hence "egg candling"—and then artificial lamps for sunlight. Overnight this ancient art developed into a modern food process because it was found that the visible light transmitted through the egg could be interpreted electronically and made to activate an automatic quality-sorting device.

It was the idea for such a device that stimulated Engineer Karl Norris and Scientist A. Wade Brant to join forces in the early 1950's at the Agricultural Research Center, Beltsville, Md. They started on a specific problem in egg candling, the automatic detection of

∴ ∴ ∴

CALVIN GOLUMBIC *is Assistant Deputy Administrator, Marketing Research, Agricultural Research Service.*

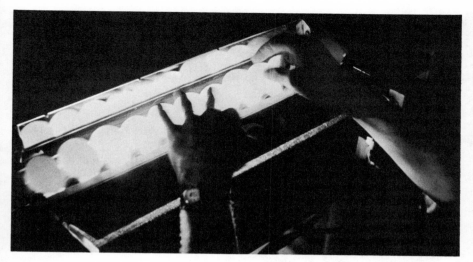

Eggs are candled in Lillington, N.C., during processing for human consumption.

bloodspots in the intact egg. Norris and Brant knew that blood pigments absorb certain wavelengths of visible light. They found that these rays passed through a blood-free egg without difficulty, but were held back to a considerable extent by the eggs which contained blood.

The difference in light transmission was ample to activate an accept-reject mechanism and thus provide an automatic means of sorting out defective eggs. The method worked well with white-shelled eggs, but was less accurate for off-white and brown eggs because they contained shell pigments similar though not identical to blood pigments. By use of a combination of wavelengths that maximized this difference, Norris eventually solved the problem. The commercial version of this detector was capable of screening up to 7,200 eggs per hour. On a commercial grading line, designed and constructed to incorporate its use, the detector decreased the error in bloodspot detection some 90 percent.

It also increased grading line production about a half a case—or 180 eggs—per hour.

At about this time, the idea occurred to Norris that internal characteristics of other commodities could be studied by applying this nondestructive light-transmittance technique. To fund such an investigation required my concurrence. At that time, I had administrative responsibility for quality evaluation research needed by the USDA's Agricultural Marketing Service.

My first reaction to Norris' proposal was skepticism. One would hardly expect that visible light could be transmitted through intact apples, oranges, potatoes, and other fruits and vegetables. But one demonstration in Norris' darkroom convinced me he had broken ground on a new phenomenon decidedly worth exploring. He impinged strong beams of each of the colors of the spectrum on one spot of fruit, causing the whole unit thereby to glow with transmitted light.

He began this new work by devising a fairly simple basic instrument consisting of a light source, precision monochromator, integrating sphere to collect light from the product, a highly sensitive phototube to measure the transmission at each wavelength, and a graph designed to record the spectral response curve.

This transmittance instrument was soon labeled the "Rephobiospect" for *r*ecording *pho*tometer for *bio*logical *spect*ral transmission. During the next

297

USDA Engineer Karl Norris places a potato in "difference meter." Two light frequencies passed through it will reveal whether the potato has hollow heart.

10 years (1953–1963) Norris constantly updated the instrument, incorporating into it the myriad electronic and photometric developments that occurred during this period.

The instrument that has emerged is a versatile, unique, and highly sophisticated recording spectrophotometer. The spectral curves it provides are largely a function of the composition and the light scattering properties of the sample.

Normally the desired measurement for a special problem can be reduced to a simple optical-density-difference measurement. Optical density is a measure of light absorption which in turn is the inverse of light transmittance. A number of abridged instruments for practical application using this difference principle were devised by Norris' colleague, Gerald S. Birth. These "difference meters" are now available commercially and are used in many research laboratories. In general, they comprise a visible light source, rotating filter monochromator, phototube detector in close proximity to the sample, and precision electronics for measuring the difference in optical density between two wavelengths of light.

A wide range of quality evaluation problems can be handled by these instruments by direct measurements on the intact commodity. These include mold damage in corn, degree of milling of rice, smut on wheat, color of red tart cherries, maturity of apples and peaches, color of tomatoes, detection of water core in apples, and evaluating greenness of oranges.

Where the economics of the quality evaluation problem justify it, any of these detection measurements can be incorporated into an automatic sorting device. The maturity problem of apples is a case where a commercial sorting device based on the transmittance principle seems feasible. Norris teamed up with Horticulturist John Yeatman to devise a prototype fruit sorter that is capable of sorting apples for fresh market as to their general eating quality. The sorter successfully separated apples into low-chlorophyll and high-chlorophyll fruit. The low-chlorophyll fruit were significantly superior in quality to fruit having a high chlorophyll content.

More Serviceable Leather

JOSEPH NAGHSKI *and* EDWARD M. FILACHIONE

. . . .

Leather is a very unusual fabric. It is strong, supple, soft, warm, and porous. It is also a product with beauty and appeal. These properties arise because of leather's unique structure. A microscope reveals this structure to be a network of intricately interwoven fibers.

The animal hide—or skin—itself is endowed with this same complex structure. In fact, the native skin is even more complicated. It contains hair, epidermis, and numerous other tissues and constituents. We recognize two general regions through the thickness of the skin. The portion next to the hair is called the grain while the deeper portion extending to the flesh is the corium. The demarcation zone between these two structures lies in the region of the hair roots.

In converting the pelt to leather, the tanner removes the hair, epidermis, and other constituents, thereby exposing the grain. The grain becomes the surface of the leather and contributes to its beauty and appeal.

Other properties, such as strength and suppleness, arise from the corium structure. This organization of interwoven protein fibers is stabilized by tanning so that the leather product is no longer putrescible and will remain soft and flexible.

Today there is practically no end to the variety of leathers commercially available. This is due in large part to new technological developments. However, another important factor is that for his raw material, the tanner can draw on hides and skins of different origins and from all over the world.

Practically all the world's supply of animal hides and skins is tanned into leather. Although many features are common to all skins, a number of characteristic differences determine the particular use.

Some of these uses as related to skin structure are outlined below.

Cattle hides are our most important raw material for leather production. The United States produced about 36 million hides in 1966, of which about 23 million were tanned domestically. Cattle hides are quite thick, usually over a quarter of an inch in the shoulder area and along the backbone where the fiber structure is coarsest yet most compact.

When tanned in their full thickness, cattle hides are used mostly to make soles, insoles, belting, and packings. In the belly area, the hides are much thinner, and the fiber weave is more open. The resulting leather is more flexible and best suited for work gloves, linings, and insoles.

In current practice, most cattle hides are split parallel to the surface to produce two pieces a little thicker than calfskins. The most valuable portion contains the grain and is known as top grain cowhide or steerhide leather. This is used for shoe and boot uppers,

∴   ∴   ∴

JOSEPH NAGHSKI *is Chief of the Hides and Leather Laboratory, Eastern Utilization Research and Development Division, Agricultural Research Service, Philadelphia.*

EDWARD M. FILACHIONE *is Head of the Chemical Modification Investigations of the Hides and Leather Laboratory.*

patent leather, garments, upholstery, belts, luggage, cases, and sporting goods. The flesh portion is less valuable and is known as split leather. This is used to make all kinds of lower priced leather goods containing an embossed artificial grain or a sueded surface.

Calfskins are intermediate in thickness between goatskins and cattle hides. The fiber bundles are heavier than in goatskins. Calfskins can be made into leather that is quite firm or quite flexible as the use demands. So they are ideal for shoe uppers, slippers, handbags, and billfolds.

Sheep and lamb skins are quite thin with a comparatively thick grain layer. The fiber bundles are quite loosely packed. Therefore, sheep and lamb skins can be made into very soft and flexible leather suited for garments, shoe linings, slippers, dress and work gloves, hat sweatbands, bookbindings, chamois, and novelties.

Goat and kid skins are also thin, but the grain layer is a smaller part of the total thickness. The fiber bundles are larger and more compactly woven. Goatskins have more strength and elasticity than sheepskins and are very suitable for making leather for shoe uppers, as well as for linings, dress gloves, garments, and handbags.

Pigskin has a very characteristic appearance with a well-marked grain pattern and perforations, which are due to the hair follicles extending through the full thickness of the skin. The grain layer is very firm and tough yet the fiber bundles of the corium are loosely woven. Pigskin leather goes into sueded shoe uppers, dress and work gloves, billfolds, and fancy leather goods. Production of domestic pigskin leather has never been very great because of the difficulty and economics involved in removal of the skin by the meatpacker. Mechanical methods for flaying pigskins have been developed, and these are increasing the supply.

Deerskins are similar to calfskins except for a thinner grain. Deerskin leathers are also very porous and exceptionally supple, which makes them very attractive for garments, dress gloves, and moccasins.

Horsehide is similar to cattle hide, except for a region in the rump called the shell where the grain is deeper and the fiber bundles are very small, quite regular, and very compactly

Clothing manufacturers are adding style to a variety of new leather garments and accessories including ladies' suits, boots, handbags, and gloves.

ather is a popular and durable fabric for
ortswear, *above.* Jackets, coats, boots,
d ice skaters' shoes can be made from
ather that is tanned with glutaraldehyde.
olfer, *right,* shows off golf glove tanned
 this USDA-developed process. It makes
ather more resistant to perspiration and
undering, and allows golf gloves to be
ed for an entire season.

woven. This area yields leather known as cordovan, which has exceptionally good wearing qualities. The exceptionally soft leather made from horse fronts finds uses in jackets, gloves, shoe uppers, straps, and sporting goods.

Reptile skins include snake, lizard, and alligator. These have special surface characteristics which produce interesting designs. These leathers go mainly into shoe uppers, handbags, and other high-fashion leather goods.

Leather is hard to beat for comfortable, healthful footwear; for rich soft garments; and for accessories of beauty and durability. This does not mean that leather cannot be improved. Most leathers today are difficult to launder or dryclean and are susceptible to deterioration by prolonged exposure to perspiration. These and other limitations are yielding to research by Agricultural Research Service chemists at the Eastern Utilization Research

Laboratory in Philadelphia, where a new process for the tanning of leather was developed.

These scientists discovered that glutaraldehyde, a comparatively simple petrochemical related to formaldehyde, was a very efficient and effective tanning agent. This new tanning agent is most easily used, and to its best advantage, with chrome—a tanning agent used by practically all tanners.

Besides working out the process for using glutaraldehyde in tanning, the ARS chemists also showed how it improved the leather and extended its utility. Glutaraldehyde gives a pleasing softness to the leather. This property is responsible for its use in tanning of certain types of sheepskins into garment leather.

Glutaraldehyde makes the leather easier to lubricate, color uniformly, and finish in the normal finishing operations. For this reason many tanners

Trimmed sheepskins make bedpads that protect hospital patients against bedsores. Tanned with glutaraldehyde and chrome, the sheepskins are now easy to machine launder. A doctor, *left*, at Chestnut Hill Hospital, Philadelphia, discusses tanning process with William F. Happich of USDA, who helped develop it.

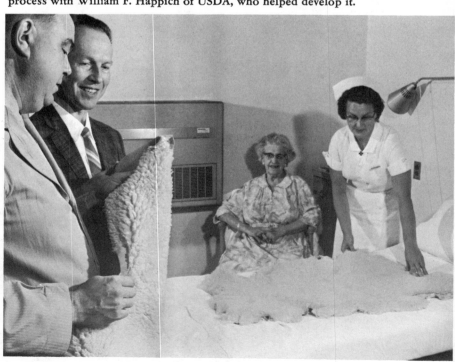

use it today in the tanning of many kinds of hides and skins into leather.

Glutaraldehyde greatly improves leather with regard to two of its deficiencies, resistance to hot soap solution and resistance to perspiration. A service test demonstrated that golf gloves made from glove leather tanned with glutaraldehyde had marked superiority in their resistance to deterioration from perspiration and from washing in soap and water.

The greatest success of all, however, arose because of this new leather's remarkable resistance to perspiration, which is especially desirable in footwear. This notable property led first to commercial use of glutaraldehyde for tanning workshoe uppers. Field tests substantiated the ARS findings. Workshoes made with this leather gave excellent as well as comfortable service to workers in dairy barns, papermills, cement plants, and other places where perspiration and alkaline agents rapidly deteriorated normal leather. Use of glutaraldehyde was soon extended by many tanners to the tanning of upper leather for dress shoes as well.

Today glutaraldehyde is probably most widely used by tanners who produce shoe upper leather from cattle hide. We estimate that approximately 75 million square feet of such leather, valued at over $45 million, was produced in 1967. In recognition of this successful research, ARS chemists M. L. Fein, E. H. Harris, Jr., Joseph Naghski, W. Windus, and Edward M. Filachione received the U.S. Department of Agriculture's Group Award for Superior Service in 1963.

This research suggested glutaraldehyde be used in tanning shearlings. Shearlings are sheepskins with the wool trimmed but not removed and are used in hospitals to prevent bedsores and to aid in curing them. Shearlings were not easily accepted for this purpose because they were not able to withstand the rigorous conditions of laundering and sanitizing. ARS chemists found that shearlings tanned with glutaraldehyde and chrome could be successfully laundered and disinfected. Good results have been obtained in a number of hospitals experimenting with these bedpads.

Shearlings once were used widely as paint roller covers. But with the advent of water-based paints, they gave way to synthetic roller covers which were more resistant to chemical attack.

The glutaraldehyde-tanned shearlings, being more resistant to attack by such chemicals, can be used effectively with water-based latex paints. This added bonus from shearling research has resulted in the gradual regaining of a lost market.

Leather fibers have a strong affinity for water, and this phenomenon is the basis for maintaining foot comfort. Perspiration released by the foot is absorbed by leather in the shoe and passed to the surface, thus keeping the foot dry and comfortable. Paradoxically, this quality of leather is also one of its greatest weaknesses. Leather is rather ineffectual in keeping water from entering the shoe when worn in rain or snow. Much effort has been spent to develop processes for making leather waterproof. The more effective treatments are relatively expensive.

ARS chemists have also been concerned with the development of more economical processes. Their research has resulted in a process for making water-repellent agents more effective and better suited to tannery practice. The process involves use of an alkenyl succinic acid as a leather lubricant, which proved to be compatible with silicone and other types of water-repellent agents. The chemists found a way to apply the lubricant to leather in a conventional drumming process.

Chrome-tanned leather lubricated this way requires only half the usual amount of silicone. The leather can be retanned with glutaraldehyde to achieve even better repellency. This new process promises to be helpful in making leather more competitive with its many substitutes. Most of these have been promoted for their weather and water resistance compared with leather's easy wettability.

Vitamin Plays Key Role In Flavor of Milk

MARK KEENEY

. . . .

A cold glass of milk—in Albuquerque, Bangor, Kansas City, or Seattle—we take it for granted—in the airport, factory, or school. Surely, this is one of the great testimonials to agricultural progress. Milk, the most perishable of all agricultural products, is distributed anywhere you travel in the United States.

What is behind this remarkable saga? Art and science—pure art and science. The ancients developed the art of making cheese and butter from that perishable product of their herds, milk. These were the major products of milk until the 20th century when the newly developing sciences of bacteriology and biochemistry began to be applied to milk utilization.

Concepts of Louis Pasteur, the 19th century father of bacteriology, were applied in the first two decades of this century in developing the heat treatment of milk known as pasteurization. This was the key breakthrough leading to the present wide availability of a glass of milk. Pasteurization not only destroyed pathogenic organisms like those causing tuberculosis, scarlet fever, and typhoid, it also prolonged the keeping quality of milk, from a flavor standpoint, from a few hours to a few days at refrigerator temperature. This was so because pasteurization inactivated the natural nonpathogenic micro-organisms and enzymes of milk which, if left unchecked, would result in sour, putrid, and rancid flavors.

The advent of pasteurization, supplemented by the parallel development of mechanical refrigeration, spawned the modern dairy industry. During this development, many new technical problems appeared. The early pasteurized milk was plagued by an objectionable flavor—variously described as cardboard, cappy, metallic, or tallowy. Scientific study of the flavor defect revealed that it resulted from oxidation of the lipid (fat) components of the milk. Major catalyst of the oxidation was found to be the trace amounts of copper picked up in the milk from the copper alloy utensils commonly used at that time to handle milk. A shift to the use of stainless steel and glass to handle milk eliminated the source of copper contamination.

Despite the great improvement in flavor stability from the elimination of copper contamination, unpredictable outbreaks of oxidized flavor still occur. During the past two decades, it has been demonstrated that copper contamination is not the only factor involved in flavor development. Milk from certain individual cows will develop a strong oxidized flavor within 1 day even when it is known from careful analysis that there is no copper contamination.

Variations in the normal biochemical components of milk have now been implicated in this problem.

∴ ∴ ∴

MARK KEENEY is Professor of Dairy Science at the University of Maryland, College Park.

A radical change has taken place in the method of handling milk in recent years. When the milk was stored and moved from the farm to the dairy plant in 10-gallon cans, it was picked up every day. Now, with the complete conversion to cold wall farm tanks for storing milk, it is picked up every 2 or 3 days. The milk is older by the time it reaches the processing plant. This is a significant factor, too often overlooked by those searching for causes of modern milk quality problems.

This factor of the extra age of raw milk, coupled with the evidence that oxidized flavor development is related to feed-dependent biochemical milk components, presents a new type of problem requiring new solutions. Historically, there has been sharp division between the interest of the milk producer and the milk processor. Milk production was considered a separate discipline from that of dairy manufacturing. It was reflected in many land-grant universities where there were separate curriculae, faculties, and departments in these two areas. The Government laboratories followed the same division, and there are still different laboratories for production research and utilization research. The oxidized milk problem is a classic example of one that cannot be solved with this sharp division of production and product research.

Raymond L. King became interested in the problem of oxidized milk flavor while a graduate student at the University of California in the mid-1950's. He has maintained an intensive research program on the problem since joining the University of Maryland faculty in 1958. He brought the intellect of a Phi Beta Kappa graduate in chemistry to bear on the problem. His chemical attack on the problem kept leading him back to the cow, and things that were happening before the milk was produced.

The Dairy Science Department at Maryland never has had a sharp division between the production and product specialists, so he was in a good environment to go beyond the cow to look for answers. Other scientists had similar experiences, so the Dairy Products Laboratory of the U.S. Department of Agriculture gave King a research grant in 1965 to pursue this problem of the effects of milk production practices on the susceptibility of milk to develop oxidized flavor.

A research herd of 22 Holsteins was selected from the first calf heifers over a 6-month period. The herd was housed the year round in a stanchion barn at the university's Agronomy-Dairy Forage Research Farm, where control could be exercised over feeding and management of the herd.

Initial work with this herd confirmed the widely held belief that dry feed (hay and grain) produces milk susceptible to oxidized flavor development, while green feed (pasture and silage) produces resistant milk. In trying to find the reason for the distinct difference, the first lead has paid off with remarkable success. Krukovsky of Cornell had shown in the early 1950's that vitamin E is an important variable in the forage crops. It is now generally believed that the major function of vitamin E is to serve as a biological antioxidant in both plants and animals. With this background information, King made a thorough study of the role of vitamin E in the oxidized flavor problem.

He found that the addition of alpha-tocopherol acetate, a stable form of vitamin E, to dry rations increased the vitamin E content of the milk in direct proportion to the amount fed and that such milk was resistant to oxidized flavor development. Removal of the vitamin E supplement from the dry ration resulted in rapid decline in the vitamin E content of the milk and reappearance of oxidized flavor. Further study by King of the vitamin E content of various feeds showed conclusively that those feeds which result in oxidized flavor are poor sources of vitamin E and conversely that the feeds which result in stable milk are good sources of vitamin E.

He has made the important practical observation that methods of harvesting

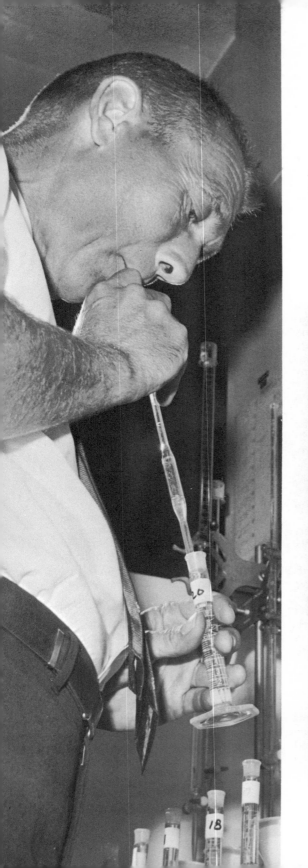

Prof. Raymond L. King analyzes mil
left, for vitamin E content. University
Maryland graduate student, *below,* scor
milk samples for flavor and odor.

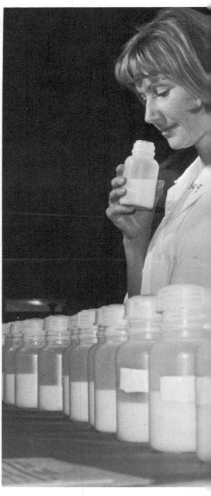

and preserving forages have a profound effect on the vitamin E content.

Some green forages were excellent sources of vitamin E while others were poor. Alfalfa appeared to fall into both categories. The first cutting of the season was a relatively poor source of vitamin E while a late cutting was an excellent source.

Alfalfa hay loses most of its vitamin E during conventional curing, even in barn curing. Ensiling should be an effective means of storing vitamin E-rich forage for winter feeding. Commercial dehydration is also an effective means of preserving the vitamin E content of forages.

The current status of King's research indicates that oxidized flavor can be controlled by providing sufficient vitamin E in the dairy ration. A daily intake of 1 gram is sufficient. This amount can be provided by proper selection of natural feeds or by supplementation with alpha-tocopherol acetate or a combination of both. Alfalfa hay and probably most hays are poor sources of vitamin E. But dehydrated alfalfa and grass or alfalfa silages are likely to be good sources of the vitamin.

An oxidized-flavor problem can be corrected within 2 or 3 days through providing a large single oral dose of alpha-tocopherol acetate (7 grams) followed by regular daily intake of 1 gram of the vitamin. There appears to be no significant storage of vitamin E in the dairy cow; therefore, a constant daily intake is required. King suggests that oxidized milk flavor may be the cow's way of expressing a need for vitamin E.

Mountain Climbing in a Laboratory

B. JEAN APGAR

. . . .

Have you ever wished you could be an explorer? Be the first person to climb a mountain, explore a wilderness, or maybe reach the moon?

Being the first person to do something has a certain fascination, but it isn't an experience most of us expect to have. If I had not had the good fortune to be a member of a research group led by Dr. Robert W. Holley at the U.S. Plant, Soil and Nutrition Laboratory, I might never have had such an experience either. Our group determined the structure of a nucleic acid for the first time. That may not sound as exciting as climbing a mountain, but to those of us doing the work it was just as exciting—and just as much work! Besides, it was perhaps even more rewarding when we were finished than being an explorer in a more conventional sense ever would have been.

Undoubtedly, this sounds a little exaggerated, but ours was no routine chemical experiment. Not only had no one ever determined the structure of a nucleic acid before, no one was even sure it could be done, at least not with the available methods. There were, in fact, those who said it couldn't be done. Why, then, did we embark on an adventure whose outcome was so uncertain and which could result in expenditure of much time, energy, and money for nothing? The answer lies in the special nature of the nucleic acids. It was because of the important things these compounds do that it seemed worth the gamble to try to determine the structure of one.

What is it nucleic acids do? Why are they so important? The nucleic acids carry the body's directions for making all the things the body needs. They are the "master plans" telling the body how to make muscles, bones, nerves, and everything else it must have. Determining the structure of one of these molecules would be equivalent to getting the body's own formula for making hair or blood or many other things. Small wonder scientists would like to determine their structure!

But unfortunately, the nucleic acids which provide all these directions are very large; too large to make determining the structure of one of them practical at present. Our plan was to try our luck on something much smaller, one of the nucleic acids which help the body to read the directions the much larger nucleic acids carry. Dr. Holley had just discovered the existence of these smaller "helper" nucleic acids (called the transfer ribonucleic acids) shortly before I joined the group.

This was the first time there were nucleic acids known which were small enough so that a determination of their structure might be possible.

Actually, determining the structure of a nucleic acid was almost a dream at this point. Our first problem was to get some of these nucleic acids to work on. But this isn't something you simply order from the nearest chemical company. First of all, the body has at least 20 different kinds of these "helper" nucleic acids, all necessary for reading the directions. We wanted only one of them. Which one didn't matter, but we had to have one all by itself so we

∴   ∴   ∴

B. JEAN APGAR *is a Research Chemist at the U.S. Plant, Soil and Nutrition Laboratory, Agricultural Research Service, U.S. Department of Agriculture, located on the campus of Cornell University, at Ithaca, N.Y. She holds a Ph. D. from Cornell. Dr. Apgar is married and has three children.*

couldn't be confused by pieces which came from another nucleic acid.

Since no one knew how to go about getting just one of these nucleic acids without all its relatives, our first project was finding a way to purify the nucleic acids. By 1962, we had worked out a method with which we could get three pure nucleic acids.

At last, we were ready for the big adventure—to try to find out how a nucleic acid was put together. From work already done, we knew a little about the general structure of nucleic acids. We knew, for instance, that all nucleic acids were made up of many small units. If we think of the small units as letters of the alphabet and the nucleic acid as a long sentence, the nucleic acid we were interested in had about 70 letters. (The smallest known information-carrying nucleic acid has 1,200 units; a medium-sized one has 5 million units.)

The first thing was to find out what all the letters were. This we expected to do fairly quickly, since we already knew, we thought, what most of the letters were. In reality, this turned out to be one of the hardest parts, chiefly because we found the small nucleic acids had some strange letters in them that weren't easy to recognize, including one which nobody had known was in nucleic acids! Once we knew what all the letters were, we could arrange them in groups similar to words in a sentence. This much we had known we could do, though it had taken us far longer than anticipated.

After we knew what the words were, we found—as we had really expected from the beginning—that there were many ways to put the words together and still get a logical sentence.

But which was right? Was there any way to find out? Success or failure now hinged on whether we could find some way of telling the right order in which to put the pieces.

We had visions of spending years trying to solve this part of the problem; it was the part about which the least was known. There was no way of knowing how many things we would

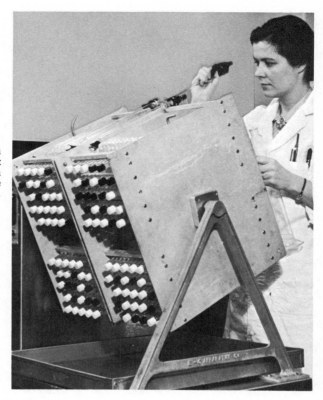

Technician works with laboratory equipment which is involved in determining structure of a nucleic acid.

have to try before something worked—and each thing we tried used up large amounts of our pure nucleic acid. Not that we couldn't get more—we could; but getting it required a great deal of time and effort.

We did try some things that didn't work. But surprisingly, we quickly learned how to break the nucleic acid in half. Fortunately, one half had the equivalent of a capital letter in it, and the other half had the equivalent of a period, so we knew how the halves went together—and in December 1964, we were done.

We had climbed the mountain! We had determined the structure of a nucleic acid for the first time.

Now that we are on top of the mountain, what do we see? Was it really worth the climb? For those of us who did the work, the second question is easy to answer—YES! It was a lot of work, but it was also a lot of fun; so, it was certainly worth it for us. But

what about the rest of the world? Does knowing the structure of a nucleic acid bring us any closer to a solution for more practical problems?

If we think about the nucleic acids and their role as "master plans," we soon begin to wonder whether it might not be possible to change the directions, maybe even put in a new set. It isn't an original thought; viruses have been doing precisely that for a very long time. A virus is nothing more than a big package of nucleic acid which, once it is inside the body, forces the body to stop making whatever it was making and start making viruses, using the directions the virus brought along.

Obviously, it is possible to put in new directions and have the body use them instead of the ones it has.

In theory, such an approach could be used with some forms of hereditary diseases where the body is missing certain directions it needs. And if aging is related to breakdowns in the nucleic acids, as some scientists think, perhaps the "fountain of youth" is a dose of the right nucleic acids. But until we learn to determine the structures of the very large nucleic acids which carry these directions, such ideas are little more than dreams.

Meanwhile, structures of additional nucleic acids are being done; and as we learn more about how these small ones are put together, we will have a clearer idea of how they work. It may be possible, as some scientists think, to influence which directions are read by altering the small helper nucleic acids. In any event, as scientists become more proficient at structure determinations, they come closer to being able to determine the structure of the really big nucleic acids. Perhaps the real significance of having determined the structure of a small one is to pave the way for doing bigger ones.

Tree Has Potential for Treating Cancer

ROBERT E. PERDUE, JR.

. . . .

A tree brought into this country by the U.S. Department of Agriculture produces a chemical substance which has potential value in treating cancer.

Camptotheca acuminata, a native of China, was introduced into the United States in 1934.

The tree's cancer treatment potential was discovered when an extract of a sample of twigs and leaves was tested in a screening program of the National Cancer Institute. This program tests plant extracts in cancer-bearing rodents to detect plant constituents of potential drug value. The *Camptotheca* sample was one of some 14,000 samples USDA has provided for that program.

The new drug is called camptothecin. It occurs in all parts of the tree in minute amounts, but is most abundant in the wood. Camptothecin was isolated and chemically identified by a research team at the Research Triangle Institute, Durham, N.C., that was supported by a National Cancer Institute contract.

Chemists will attempt to synthesize camptothecin. If they are unsuccessful or if synthesis cannot produce the drug economically, American agriculture is able to produce unlimited quantities of raw material.

Camptotheca grows rapidly from seed. Production is now being expanded at the U.S. Plant Introduction Station, Chico, Calif., which has a seed source in two mature trees. This will provide raw material for more camptothecin for research. The plantings will also give a basis for evaluating the tree as a new crop for American agriculture.

Camptothecin is one of the potential rewards to be gained in new drugs and other useful products through USDA's systematic search of the world's plant resources, a search that has evaluated some 50,000 plant accessions from all continents and most countries.

∴   ∴   ∴

ROBERT E. PERDUE, JR., *Botanist, is Leader of Plant Resources Investigations, Crops Research Division, Agricultural Research Service.*

Cool and Carefree Cotton Seersucker

GEORGE J. KYAME *and* JOHN T. LOFTON

. . . .

Those among us who are old enough to remember the "roaring twenties," approximately two generations ago, will recall that man's most comfortable dress wear during hot, humid, summer months was a gray-and-white striped suit that not only looked cool, but felt cool as well. We could wear the suit in relative comfort for hours on end. What made this possible? It was the unique structure of the fabric from which it was made, a structure of alternating flat and crinkle (puckered) stripes. The cool secret? The pucker stripe—it kept the fabric from clinging to the body, thereby allowing air to circulate between the body and the garment.

The fabric, commonly known as seersucker, is easily woven on any textile loom adapted to weaving light and medium weight cotton goods. To make the fabric, two loom beams are needed instead of the single beam used in weaving most other fabrics. One beam carries warp yarns for the flat stripe; the other, warp yarns for the pucker stripe. During weaving, adjustments are made to make the pucker stripe warp yarns feed forward faster than the flat stripe warp yarns. This results in localized buckling of the fabric in the areas of the fast-feeding yarns, first one way, then the other. This produces the pucker in the pucker stripe.

Despite its comfort advantages, the popularity of seersucker began to wane. By the early thirties, men's seer-sucker suits were fast disappearing. Why? Perhaps it was the wrinkling and bagging of the suit, making laundering necessary after even short periods of wear. Or it might have been the use of "plissés"—seersucker-type fabrics with chemically produced pucker stripes—which failed to hold shape or size in the garment. In any event, a market for cotton was lost.

The problem, then, was one of preventing wrinkling and maintaining pressed-in creases. In 1928, the first patent in this field was granted to Foulds, Marsh, and Wood, three British scientists, for a chemical treatment which would reduce the wrinkling tendencies of cotton and cottonlike fabrics. Ever since, researchers have been seeking better treatments which would ease the care of cotton garments. Their goal was, and still is, a treatment which would produce a launderable cotton garment that would come out of the clothes drier wrinkle free and ready to wear without ironing.

Many treatments and new chemical compounds have been developed, some good, but none ideal. The treatments

∴   ∴   ∴

GEORGE J. KYAME *is a Research Physicist and Project Leader with the Southern Regional Research Laboratory, Agricultural Research Service, New Orleans.*

JOHN T. LOFTON *is a Research Textile Technologist and Project Leader with the Southern Regional Research Laboratory.*

311

were effective in preventing wrinkling, but usually caused major losses in the strength of the treated fabric. Here then was a target for research, namely, what to do to minimize or prevent these strength losses.

In June 1964, the Southern Regional Research Laboratory at New Orleans attacked the problem from the standpoint of fabric structure. The authors of this chapter set out to find what part fabric structure played in the ease-of-care picture, and how structure could best be used to counteract undesirable effects of the new chemical treatments.

As a starter, we tackled the revival of the seersucker suit of old, as this offered a great potential market for cotton in men's suits. We designed an all-cotton seersucker fabric with sufficient initial strength so that, when it was given wrinkle-resisting and crease-retaining properties, it would still retain strength sufficient to withstand all the rigors of repeated wear and laundering.

We made yarns for the fabric from the strongest American-grown cotton we could get (Pima S–2) and subjected them to a special mercerizing treatment developed at this laboratory by A. L. Murphy and coworkers. Two hundred yards of the woven fabric were sent to the National Cotton Council of America to be treated and service tested. We treated and tested 50 yards of the fabric to determine its performance in the washing machine. For this test, we made short-length, cuffed trouser legs which were washed and tumble-dried 30 times in home-type laundering equipment. Despite all this washing and drying, each trouser leg still retained its creases and wrinkle-free appearance and developed from one to not more than three tiny holes, mostly at the cuff corners.

In the meantime, the Cotton Council had their 200 yards of fabric treated by a textile mill and tailored into suits by a garmentmaker. The suits were distributed among staff members and others for testing in everyday use.

New cotton seersucker garments developed for modern living.

| Fabric identi-fication | Kind of yarn [1] | | | Mercerizing treatment | Average number of holes per cuff after 55 launderings |
	Flat stripe	Filling	Pucker stripe		
A	ply	ply	ply	special	0.5
B	ply	ply	singles	conventional	1.7
C	singles	ply	singles	conventional	2.2
D	ply	singles	singles	conventional	7.8
E	singles	singles	singles	conventional	4.5

[1] Yarns for fabric A were made from expensive, Pima S-2 cotton. Yarns for fabrics B through E were made from a shorter staple cotton of moderate cost.

The preliminary results were so encouraging that the Council initiated a test-marketing program as part of its research and promotion activity on cotton suits in the summer of 1966. They had a textile mill weave and treat 3,500 yards of seersucker fabric made substantially to specifications set up by the Southern Regional Research Laboratory. The treated fabric was fashioned into about 700 men's suits which were put on sale in six major cities in the United States.

Response of the public was favorable; not a single complaint was received. Several well-known converters (fabric finishers, garment manufacturers, etc.) became interested and wanted to add seersuckers to their lines. In fact, one of these converters placed an order for 10,000 yards of all-cotton seersucker fabric for suits that were to be marketed in the spring of 1968. The future of our old friend looks quite rosy.

Our research did not end there. Our next step was to reduce fabric production costs. You will remember we made our yarns from the strongest cotton we could buy and mercerized them in a special way. Not only that, but we had also plied our yarns, i.e., twisted two strands of the singles yarns together to form a single strand of two-ply yarn. All this added to the cost of producing the fabric. Consequently, we were interested in finding out whether we could use singles yarns made from less costly cotton and mercerized in conventional manner and still produce an adequate fabric. So, we wove four different fabrics, all with singles yarns in the pucker stripes, but differing as to the type of yarn—singles or two ply—in the flat stripe and in the filling.

As before, we treated the fabrics, made test trouser cuffs from each, and subjected the cuffs to 55 cycles of laundering and tumble drying in home-type machines. To make a long story short, we found that each substitution of singles yarns for ply yarn reduced the strength (breaking, tearing, and bursting) of the fabric and reduced its resistance to wear in laundering.

The table shows how these fabrics performed during the repeated laundering tests.

Fabric A, made from plied, Pima S-2 yarns was obviously the best of the fabrics, but that was to be expected. Fabrics B and C averaged less than three holes in 55 launderings. This would indicate that an adequate fabric could be made from less costly cotton and cheaper mercerizing procedures. It should be mentioned that other tests showed all five fabrics to have about the same wrinkle-resisting and crease-retaining properties.

Although our research was slanted toward seersuckers for men's suiting, the new durable-press fabric and the production techniques that produced it are applicable as well to women's and children's wear. One converter's interest in all-cotton, durable-press seersucker has prompted him to embark on a marketing program of his own. Others are bound to follow. The entire family will soon enjoy the comfort of cotton seersucker and benefit from its newly acquired, ease-of-care characteristics.

Dextran Helps Save Lives

ROBERT J. DIMLER

He might have died—not from the injury itself, but because he went into a state of shock.

Yet he lives—because of dextran, a product of research after World War II. The life saved by dextran has been on the battlefield, in the emergency room of a hospital, and on the operating table where the operation itself causes shock.

Dextran is a welcome partner to the blood bank. Blood still must be ready for use, but clinical dextran can take over as a first emergency treatment to serve as a blood-volume expander.

Behind the story of clinical dextran is the hand of a soft-spoken woman from Texas, Allene Jeanes, whose scientific abilities in carbohydrate chemistry were combined with a concern about the needs of America. To her research we add teamwork and inputs from other workers, including early leads from Sweden and England.

Shock. My first aid handbook reads: "Any severe injury can cause shock . . . the skin is quite pale and feels clammy (cool and somewhat moist)."

That pale skin tells the story. His blood is not circulating. Maybe the victim lost a lot of blood through the injury. There is not enough left for the heart to pump out to other parts of his body. But a state of shock is not necessarily caused by bleeding. Instead, the bloodstream loses fluid into the rest of the body. Again, there is not enough volume of blood to go around in the blood vessels.

So the doctor must put fluid (liquid) back in to restore the volume.

Simple, you say? Give a blood transfusion. But many times it is not so simple. What is the patient's blood type? Is there time enough to find out? Is his blood type on hand? Battlefields lack the refrigerated storage needed for a blood bank. There may not be enough blood on hand for an unexpectedly large number of casualties. Furthermore, blood has a short storage life, and the supply must be replaced at least every 3 to 4 weeks.

Even blood plasma, the fluid part of the blood, has limitations. While it does not require blood typing and its storage life is somewhat longer, still it cannot be kept for long periods unless freeze-dried. Then it still presents problems. Sterile water must be added, a time-consuming act at best and quite difficult under many emergency conditions, such as on the battlefield.

What about water, alone? No, but why not? Something has to be added to help hold the water in the veins and capillaries. And that is where dextran comes into the picture.

Dr. Jeanes, U.S. Department of Agriculture chemist at Peoria, Ill., started working with dextran at the Northern Regional Research Laboratory in 1942—but not for treatment of shock. Her project was cornstarch, its chemistry and molecular structure. In particular, she was trying to find out more

⁖　⁖　⁖

ROBERT J. DIMLER *is Director of the Northern Regional Research Laboratory, Agricultural Research Service, Peoria, Ill. He was a member of the dextran team recognized by the U.S. Department of Agriculture with its Distinguished Service Award during 1955.*

about the branch-point linkage in the starch molecule.

What a job that was! Only 5 percent of the linkages in starch was this special kind. Where might she find an abundance of this linkage? Dextran was the answer—a polysaccharide made by a harmless bacterium when it grew on sucrose (cane sugar or beet sugar). Dextran and starch are polysaccharides in which the building blocks are dextrose units. Both give dextrose (corn sugar) when broken down completely by hydrolysis. Dr. Jeanes knew from the work of others that almost all of the linkages in the molecular structure of dextran were like the few special ones in starch.

Soon after Dr. Jeanes turned her attention to dextran, fate played into her hands, although the full import was not to be seen until much later.

A bottle of root beer went bad; it became thick and sirupy (sometimes called ropey). The merchant brought it to the northern laboratory to see if anyone could tell him what had happened. The bacteriologists quickly saw that an abundant growth of the organism *Leuconostoc mesenteroides* was changing the sugar to dextran to give the viscous character to the root beer. This particular strain of *L. mesenteroides* was entered into the ARS Culture Collection at the Peoria laboratory with the number NRRL B–512.

Dr. Jeanes was eager to work with the new dextran. The organism grew exceptionally well and produced a dextran in good quantities. This dextran was easier to separate than any she had worked with before.

Meanwhile the atom bomb had been dropped; atomic warfare was a reality. Preparedness and the threat of an atomic bomb attack on the United States became an increasing concern.

Then a number of pieces fell into place. Dr. Jeanes, with her feeling for human lives, turned her thoughts to a question several high-level people had asked. How could the United States prepare for treatment of masses of people injured in an atomic attack, people who would suffer from a state of shock, people who would need a blood transfusion or require blood plasma? Stockpiling of blood or plasma for such an emergency was impossible.

She saw a ray of hope in reports she had read from Sweden and England where solutions of dextran had been injected for emergency treatment of shock. Although the results were not perfect, lives were being saved.

Most important, she and her fellow workers had been studying dextran. They had found that there was an array of different dextrans, each produced by a different strain of the same micro-organism. Dr. Jeanes had confidence that one dextran could be found that would be better than the material used in Sweden and England.

How right she was! And how fortunate that in 1950 she took the lead in urging that the U.S. Department of Agriculture turn its attention to the problem of a blood plasma volume expander that could be stockpiled for emergency use.

It was a big job. Many things had to be worked out. Discoveries were made. High standards of quality were met. Processes were devised which could be depended on to give the product needed.

Cooperation was the word—within the USDA laboratory at Peoria; with other Government agencies including the Department of Defense, the National Bureau of Standards, and the National Institutes of Health; with research scientists in universities and medical schools; and with industrial companies that went into production of dextran as a blood plasma volume expander.

The dextran team at the northern laboratory in Peoria numbered some 50 people. It included bacteriologists, biochemists, chemists, and engineers. They were filled with enthusiasm and inspired by the urgency of the problem.

The timetable was breathtaking: Into action in 1950. Experimental commercial samples produced by one company early in 1951. Four companies producing clinical dextran by the end of 1951. Armed services award

Dr. Allene Jeanes, with life-saving dextran produced in the research she supervises.

Next, exactly how do you tailor dextran for use as a blood plasma volume expander? The size of the molecules is critical in this area. Neither too large nor too small. The micro-organism makes molecules that are too large. Methods were worked out for breaking the molecules down and separating out just the right fraction. These procedures were the pattern for the first commercial production of clinical dextran in the United States.

Then the discovery of how to use an enzyme preparation (called dextransucrase), instead of the micro-organism itself, gave a more economical method of making clinical dextran with the correct narrow range of molecular size.

Woven through these developments was the perfecting of methods for measuring the size of the molecules. These, and other analytical methods, were used by the Government in its specifications for purchase of clinical dextran.

Careful clinical testing went hand in hand with the work on making dextran. Initially on animals, then on people, the safety and effectiveness of clinical dextran NRRL B–512 were established.

The speed and the smoothness with which all of these things, and many more, were accomplished is a tribute to the teamwork and dedication of research people. As might be expected, special tributes have come to Dr. Jeanes. Among them are the Garvan Medal and the Federal Woman's Award. Her leadership was strong throughout the work. She devoted personal interest and time to all the phases, far beyond what was expected. Her experiments were meticulously planned, precise, and accurate. All these attributes influenced others working on the team and contributed to the speed and success of their research. Such personal leadership often is at the heart of great accomplishments. Yet—as in all such research—the key to success is many people working together.

Of course, the lifesaving story of

of contracts for 1 million injection units by the midpoint of 1952. The battlefields of Korea were the proving grounds for dextran. In May 1953, the Army announced that dextran (NRRL B–512) would be used in large measure in place of blood plasma for all needs at home and overseas.

Finally, sales for civilian use became possible in 1954.

What were some of the problems and steppingstones to success? First, which dextran? More than 100 different ones were prepared, but results with the dextran produced by the NRRL B–512 strain (the one found in the sirupy root beer) were so good that an all-out effort was placed on it.

dextran is not over. Clinical dextran is stockpiled for use in national emergencies, both civilian and military. It has become a standard item in many civilian hospitals in the United States. The Vietnam conflict again brought quantities of dextran onto the battlefields. During 1967, total civilian and military purchases of clinical dextran (6 percent solution in physiological saline for intravenous injection) were valued at $2 million.

Clinical dextran does not replace the blood bank. Many patients still must have blood transfusions. But dextran can tide them over until the blood can be administered.

So—He might have died
But he lives
Because of dextran.

The Many-Splendored Potato, A Marvel of Convenience

BERNARD FEINBERG and MERLE L. WEAVER

. . . .

There is one field in which the average Russian does better than the average American—eating potatoes. The Russian eats over 400 pounds a year, the American little more than 100. Back in 1910, we were pretty good potato eaters; we ate about 180 pounds per person. However, by 1952, this had dropped to about 100 pounds.

One reason for this drop in potato consumption was the growing concern of the public with calorie intake and the mistaken belief that potatoes are high in calories. It is unfortunate that potatoes acquired this undeserved reputation. It is not the potato, but the added butter, gravy, or the absorbed frying oil which account for most of the calories in our favorite styles of cooked potatoes.

Another reason for the decline in potato consumption was growing competition from other starchy foods like rice and macaroni. Just as important was the fact that American housewives became time-conscious and impatient with the task of food preparation. Peeling, cutting, boiling, and frying potatoes just took too much time.

Other processed foods which were already prepared, cooked, and flavored, and therefore provided convenience, pushed potatoes out of the shopping basket of Americans.

The only processed potato product readily available in the supermarket up until about 1950 was potato chips. Potato chips still qualify as the ideal convenience food because they can be eaten directly from the bag. Chips remain one of the most popular processed potato products. Indeed, until 1965 when frozen french fries production topped 1.5 billion pounds, chips were the most important processed potato product.

Beginning around 1950, a variety of new processed potato products began to appear on the market.

∴ ∴ ∴

BERNARD FEINBERG is Assistant to the Director at the Western Utilization Research and Development Division, Agricultural Research Service, Albany, Calif.

MERLE L. WEAVER is Head of Potato Investigations at the Western Utilization Research and Development Division.

317

They included instant mashed potatoes, dehydrated potato slices au gratin, frozen french fries, and many other products.

Per capita consumption of potatoes began to climb from its low point in 1952. Fresh potato consumption, however, has continued to decline so that in 1966 we consumed only 65 pounds of fresh potatoes per person. Fortunately for the potatogrower, another 45 pounds or so were consumed in the form of processed potatoes. It is estimated that by 1970, 50 percent of the potatoes we eat will be consumed in some processed form.

With the high cost of labor today, restaurants are just as interested in "convenience" foods as the housewife. More than two-thirds of all mashed potatoes served in restaurants are now made from dehydrated potato flakes or granules. And more than two-thirds of the 1.5 billion pounds of frozen potato products—primarily frozen french fries—packed in 1966 were used in restaurants.

The Department of Defense has long recognized the advantages of dehydrated foods from the standpoint of convenience, shipping weight, stability, etc. In 1966, Defense purchased some 22 million pounds of dehydrated potatoes. The savings in transportation and storage alone from the use of dehydrated potatoes are evident in the fact that 22 million pounds of dehydrated potatoes are the equivalent of 179 million pounds of fresh potatoes. And unlike his father in World War II, today's fighting man finds mashed potatoes made from dehydrated products a most acceptable item.

That potato processing is big business is illustrated by just one plant in Idaho which makes frozen french fries.

Processed Potato Products

Frozen Products

French fries, regular and crinkle cut	Au gratin	Dumplings
Patties	Delmonico	Knishes
Shredded	Scalloped	Blintzes
Diced	Dutch potato salad	Pirogen
Hash brown	Small whole potatoes	Hashed in cream
Mashed	Vegetable stew mix	Soup
Whipped	Roasted	Potatoes and peas in
Stuffed baked	Cottage fried	cream sauce
Rissole	Boiled	Dehydrofrozen: Diced
	Pancakes	

Dehydrated Products

Instant mashed: Granules, flakes, "buds"

Diced, for preparing hash brown potatoes, general purpose dishes, and for remanufacture in canned hash and stews

Slices, chiplets, shreds, for preparing salad, hash brown, casserole, and other general purpose dishes

Scalloped; salad mix; pancake mix; cream of potato soup; au gratin

Flour, for potato bread, doughnuts, crackers, and other specialty baked goods and breading material

Starch

Regular and chemically modified potato starches for use in paper manufacture, textile sizing, and food processing

Potato Chip Products

Regular and crinkle-sliced chips; shoestring or julienne; barbecue-, cheese-, onion-, and smoke-flavored chips; dip chips; crackers

Prepeeled Products (for fresh delivery to the restaurant trade)

Whole potatoes; hash brown; oil blanched; salad; french fry cuts

Canned Products

Whole potatoes; stew; soup; sliced potatoes; shoestring potatoes; salad (American and German style); potato pancakes; hash; chowder; au gratin; strained (baby food)

Each working day this plant processes the equivalent of a trainload of 100 cars of potatoes and a 10,000-gallon tank car of vegetable oil.

Food processors have found the potato a most versatile raw material, adaptable to a wide variety of products. The accompanying table is only a partial list of processed potato products available today. Most can be found in the supermarket, but some are used only by restaurants or by manufacturers making items such as beef stew or corned beef hash.

The diversity of products made from the potato is equaled by the diversity of processing equipment. Potato cubes have been experimentally shot from specially designed guns so that after drying they cook much faster than conventionally dried cubes. The pieces of potatoes are first dried in hot air to about 25 percent moisture, then loaded into the gun where they are quickly heated to a temperature that superheats the moisture in the piece above its atmospheric boiling point. When the pressure is suddenly released, the pieces explode from the gun and steam escapes from the pieces and leaves a porous texture.

After final drying in a hot-air oven, the dry, porous cubes can now rapidly reabsorb moisture during cooking.

Several potato chippers are using microwaves, a kind of high frequency energy much like TV and FM radio waves, but at higher frequencies, to make a better potato chip.

The chips are taken from the conventional fryer just as they begin to develop a golden brown color. Since they are not dry and crisp enough at this stage, the drying is completed by evaporating the remaining moisture with microwave energy.

This technique permits the use of potatoes which would make objectionably dark-colored chips if cooked to dryness in the conventional fryer. Microwaves selectively heat water by molecular agitation throughout the chip, not just at the surface. In microwave drying, the chip does not get hot enough for further browning.

Dehydrofrozen potatoes, based on a process developed at USDA's Western Utilization Research and Development Division, are made by precooking potato cubes or slices, evaporating sufficient water to reduce their weight by 50 percent, and freezing. The resulting product is a potato chunk both larger and quicker cooking than that which can be made by conventional dehydration. Yet it still retains the advantages of weight reduction.

Newest of the many varied forms of processed potato is the extruded french fry. This ingenious product is made from a dry mix of dehydrated potato granules with added starch, vegetable gum, and flavoring and is designed primarily for restaurants or hamburger stands. The mix can be packed either in a metal can or in a paper bag and held without refrigeration. To use the mix, the cook adds sufficient water to make a dough which is placed into a cylinder and extruded into noodlelike ribbons with the same general cross section as conventional french fried potatoes. A knife cuts the ribbons to the desired length, and they fall into hot fat to become french fries within 2 minutes.

The development of instant, dry potato flakes offers an excellent example of the path that a U.S. Department of Agriculture development can follow from the laboratory to industrial use. For the past 17 years, USDA has sponsored a series of National Potato Utilization Conferences at various potato-growing areas around the country. These conferences are attended by growers, processors, distributors, and others interested in the growth of the potato industry.

During the Sixth National Potato Utilization Conference held at Cornell University, Ithaca, N.Y., in 1954, USDA's Eastern Utilization Research and Development Division announced development of a method for making potato flakes by drum-drying mashed potatoes. In this process, the potatoes are first cooked and cooled under carefully controlled conditions and then spread onto a heated drum. The dried

Freshly-harvested potatoes at a processing plant in Presque Isle, Maine.

potatoes come off the drum in a thin sheet which is broken into flakes.

To determine whether this product was a feasible commercial venture, a carload of Maine potatoes was processed into flakes at the Division's research laboratory pilot plant in Philadelphia. In 1956, a market test of the finished product was conducted by USDA's Marketing Economics Division. This test demonstrated that consumers would buy potato flakes.

The first commercial production of potato flakes began in 1957, and annual production is now more than 100 million pounds.

Yet another form of instant mashed potatoes is dehydrated potato granules. Potato granules are one of the most unusual of all processed vegetables. Every granule is a dry, whole, unbroken plant cell. The potato cell resembles a kind of Easter basket, the cell wall being the basket and the starch grains the "eggs." If the cell wall is broken during processing, the starch grains escape, and the reconstituted mashed potato has an undesirable sticky texture.

Learning how to separate the individual potato cells and to dry them so they remain intact and unbroken proved a difficult task. The secrets of how to do this were still being learned

even as late as the Korean war. The consistency of mashed potatoes produced at that time left much to be desired. GI's in that conflict often found reconstituted mashed potatoes to be rubbery and sticky, a far cry from the fresh mashed potatoes they were accustomed to at home. But the instant mashed potato of 1968 has come a long way and has been readily accepted by housewives and restaurants as well as by soldiers.

The Western Utilization Research and Development Division at Albany, Calif., made many technical contributions to development of a high-quality potato granule. One of these contributions was adaptation of the fluidized bed dryer to granule processing. Various types of this dryer are now used by most potato granule manufacturers.

The fluidized bed dryer consists of a long box or trough with a porous ceramic bottom. Warm air is blown up through the bed at a velocity which is sufficient to suspend the granules. Drying is rapid and gentle under these conditions.

Restaurants, cafeterias, hospitals, and others in institutional feeding now find that the use of dehydrated mashed potatoes is an economical—and highly acceptable—method for preparing mashed potatoes.

Wood Can Protect
You From Fire

HERBERT W. EICKNER

. . . .

Man and wood formed a partnership centuries ago—and wood is still performing its role as servant and protector to man today. This partnership is particularly interesting in relation to fire.

Wood usually becomes an intermediary between man and fire. Wood was probably man's first fuel for fire. Conversely, experience and research have shown us how wood can be used to protect man from fire.

Wood's resistance to fire is particularly impressive in large buildings where big timbers or laminated beams or arches provide the framework. Because wood burns slowly and does not soften or become weakened by intense heat, large timbers retain a large part of their original strength for several hours of fire exposure. The structure itself will stand even if contents and covering materials are damaged.

By comparison, noncombustible materials, such as structural metals, do not always perform well under similar conditions. They are such efficient conductors of heat that they rapidly transfer the heat throughout the member and lose much of their strength at 1000° F.

A bizarre idea to the uninitiated is the use of wood coverings to protect steel from fire! In Europe, wood slabs have been tried over steel structural members in large buildings. With the wood to insulate the steel from heat, the steel retains its strength for a longer time.

A further example of wood protecting you from fire is the fire door, used in buildings to confine fires to the area where they start. Because of wood's low thermal conductivity, slow rate of fire penetration, and general integrity under fire, solid wood doors 1¾ inches thick generally meet fire code requirements for three-quarters of an hour protection.

However, reducing the flammability of wood can increase the number of the ways in which wood can serve—and protect—you. Fire-retardant treatments for wood have been developed for this purpose, and they are gaining increased acceptance.

In short, the fact that "wood burns" doesn't figure too heavily in the amount of protection it offers man from fire. More important are such questions as how do building fires get started? What burns first? How fast does wood burn? How does wood compare with other building materials in fire performance? All of these questions should be considered as well as the point that wood does burn.

Most building fires start in the contents of the building—not in the structure itself. This is true whether the building is a home, a store, a manufacturing plant, or a warehouse.

Paper, clothing, draperies, furniture,

⋰   ⋰   ⋰

HERBERT W. EICKNER *is Supervisory Chemical Engineer in Charge of Fire Research at the Forest Products Laboratory, Forest Service, Madison, Wis.*

machinery, and processing materials—when combined with human carelessness or negligence—are typically involved in starting fires in buildings.

Research shows that burning a small amount of combustible contents in the center of a room or end of a corridor soon creates enough heat and toxic gases, and removes enough oxygen, so that humans cannot survive. Suddenly "flashover" occurs. The gases ignite, spreading fires to remote areas. This flashover time appears to be unrelated to the combustibility of the wall coverings. Sometimes combustible wall linings do not even ignite until the gases flash into flame.

The expanded burning results in extreme heat which may weaken even noncombustible structural members. This is well illustrated by the conflagration that destroyed Chicago's huge McCormick Place in January of 1967. There the contents caught on fire and their intense heat caused the noncombustible structural members to fail. The roof then collapsed and the building was virtually destroyed.

In contrast, wood structural members may hold up the roof assemblies long enough to permit firefighters to attack and extinguish the fire within the structure. Furthermore, automatic sprinklers can provide additional protection for the structure and can help control fires started by combustibles in the building.

Wood's resistance to the penetration of fire starts with its good insulative value—heat passes through wood very slowly. Moreover, as burning wood decomposes and chars, the layer of charcoal adds insulation. Burning may even stop at the surface if sufficient external heat does not get through the insulative layer to continue decomposing the wood beneath.

Even when there is enough external heat to keep the wood surface at 1200° to 1700° F., the exposure of new wood to flammable gases is a slow process. Despite these high surface temperatures, the inner portion of the char layer is heated only to about 550° F. Furthermore, a quarter of an inch inward from this layer the temperature of the wood is less than 360° F.

How fast fire penetrates through wood depends on the species of wood, its density, and its moisture content. In general, the rate is about $\frac{1}{30}$ to $\frac{1}{50}$ inch per minute. Thus, it is easy to see why the thicker wood members retain their strength for a considerable time when exposed to fire.

For example, a 12- by 12-inch wood member, after continuously burning for 1 hour on all four sides, will still be stronger than a 9- by 9-inch wood member never touched by fire.

Besides the natural protection wood gives us against fire, fire-retardant treatments to wood are gaining greater acceptance. Production of fire-retardant wood has almost tripled between 1960 and 1965.

Wood can be treated with fire retardants by two methods. The more common consists of injecting solutions of fire-retardant salts into wood under pressure. In the other, paints containing fire-retardant chemicals are applied to the wood surface. Pressure injection usually is more effective and lasting, but wood must be treated in a closed cylinder; this limits the pressure treatments primarily to materials before they are installed in a building or structure. Fire-retardant paints are used principally to upgrade the fire performance of materials already installed in structures.

Of primary importance in public acceptance and use of fire-retardant-treated wood is the extent to which fire-performance characteristics have been improved over those of untreated wood. The principal advantage is that surface flammability is decreased. When treated wood is exposed to fire, it decomposes and chars much the same as untreated wood. However, it releases less combustible gases and tars, thus reducing flame spread along the wood surface and spread of fire to other parts of the room.

A second advantage of fire-retardant-treated wood is that it contributes less heat, especially from volatile products, during the initial stage of a fire. Thus,

Interior of church, *above,* was destroyed by fire, yet framework remains intact. Laminated wood beams can be resurfaced and refinished in place because little strength was lost, and beams did not twist or sag under high temperatures. *Right,* a fire with temperatures of 1,000° to 1,600° F. has licked at opposite side of this 1¾-inch-thick wood door for 45 minutes—and still the door is intact! In test, temperature on this side of door reached only about 250° F.

fire-retardant-treated wood is less likely to aid in propagating a small fire started from combustible contents.

A third advantage is that commercial fire-retardant treatments, which include either formulations with ammonium phosphate or boric acid, retard the afterglow of wood. Thus, treated wood is self-extinguishing once the primary source of the fire has been removed or exhausted.

This is extremely important in buildings in which fires may start within concealed spaces and be difficult to extinguish without completely demolishing walls and ceilings. If the wood is treated with extinguishing chemicals, that is not necessary.

For further reading:

American Institute of Timber Construction, *What About Fire?* Washington, D.C., 1965.

Bruce, H. D., and Fassnacht, Don, "Wood Houses Can be Fire-Safe Houses." *Forests and People,* Fourth Quarter, Southern Forest Experiment Station, 701 Loyola Ave., New Orleans, La. 70113, 1958.

Canadian Wood Council, *Wood: Fire Behavior and Fire-Retardant Treatment.* November 1966.

Eickner, Herbert W., "Fire-Retardant-Treated Wood." *ASTM Journal of Materials,* Vol. 1, No. 3, 1966.

Hamre, R. H., "How Good is Wood in a Fire?" *Forest Farmer,* July 1961.

National Lumber Manufacturers Association, *Comparative Fire Test of Timber and Steel Beams.* Technical Report 3, Washington, D.C., 1965.

National Safety Council, *Fire-Retarding Treatments for Wood.* Data Sheet 372, 1960.

Very Important People

RUTH M. LEVERTON

....

Everyone who benefits from the science of food and nutrition, and that includes all of us, is indebted to a very special group of people who are sometimes facetiously referred to as "human guinea pigs." Actually, they are healthy normal people—elementary schoolchildren, teenagers, and young, middle-aged, and old adults—who voluntarily help with the progress of science through being "subjects" on detailed nutrition studies.

How the human body uses food, how much it needs of the different nutrients—proteins, minerals, and vitamins—how it reacts to different foods and combinations of foods, and its response to different sources of nutrients are some of the questions for which answers are sought.

For many types and at many stages of research, the small laboratory animal such as the rat, mouse, guinea pig, or chicken is almost ideal. It lives fast and so it can be studied through its lifetime and several generations can be studied within a few years. It is economical. It eats only small amounts, it doesn't take up much room, and many test animals can be studied at the same time. Its environment can be controlled and changed as desired. Its blood and tissues can be studied in detail after an experiment has been completed. Pigs and pigeons and, in certain specialized studies, monkeys are also useful for some types of scientific research.

Most laboratory animals used for nutrition studies have digestive tracts, enzymes, metabolic patterns, and requirements that are similar to those in the human. Research with these animals has greatly increased our understanding of human nutrition. But much as we have learned from studies with animals, we cannot be sure that the human will respond in exactly the same way and to the same degree. We cannot be sure that a dietary recommendation made only on the basis of results from studies of animals will be completely satisfactory for people.

This is the time in the progress of most human nutrition research when we must study the human subject directly. At this stage, the researchers begin to look for some volunteers who will contribute to science by being subjects on a nutrition study. Sometimes a group of children is needed, sometimes young adults, or older ones, sometimes men, other times women. Whatever the specific requirements of age and sex, there is usually the general one that they must be healthy. It is this requirement that makes the cooperation of these subjects rather unique in scientific studies.

We are accustomed to people being subjects and helping with medical research. Usually these are people with a medical problem—sometimes a very serious one. When people are ill, they are willing, cooperative subjects in the search for successful treatment and cure. But when people are sailing along in good health, they have no disease problem and no reason to seek scientific aid. Then it is rather special for them to be willing to devote time and attention to the search for facts about healthy people and how they can stay that way. These are truly volunteers who are motivated to contribute to scientific knowledge.

In the broad field of agriculture and home economics, the focus of food and nutrition research is on how food can contribute to the health and well-being of all of the population throughout a lifetime. This means studying healthy normal people. In order to identify what conditions are abnormal and how to correct them, we must know what is normal, what factors are associated with normalcy, and how they can be maintained.

∴   ∴   ∴

RUTH M. LEVERTON, *a professional nutritionist, is an Assistant Deputy Administrator, Agricultural Research Service.*

Where can healthy, normal people be found who would be interested in contributing to science by being a subject on a nutrition research study? There are many places, and these are best known to the researchers who have need of human cooperators. Institutions such as orphanages or retirement homes that assume responsibility for the care of healthy people (even penal institutions) have been sources of fine subjects. University and college communities are probably the best source of interested, science-oriented people of every age, whether one needs college-age students, faculty-age adults, or their children.

Willingness and interest on the part of would-be subjects do not guarantee that they will be selected for a specific nutrition study. All of the volunteers are carefully screened with regard to their physical condition, health, character, and habits. In addition to being normal and healthy, are they stable emotionally? Are they likely to see a project through, even if the rigid routine becomes tiresome or inconvenient? Are they absolutely honest people who will make every effort to conform to the routine, but if they should make a mistake, will they report it so the records will be accurate? Does their schedule of activities and responsibilities permit the time needed to be a good subject, because it does take time to follow directions and make reports? Also, if the would-be subjects are minors, will the parents give wholehearted consent and cooperation to their children being subjects?

Some of the most valuable and also the hardest kinds of studies that are done with human subjects are called "balance or metabolism" studies. A balance study is based on the principle that if we know the amount of a nutrient such as calcium that goes into the body in the food and the amount that leaves the body in the excreta, we can calculate what has been used. The amount that has been used reflects the amount that was needed.

Being a subject on a balance study means giving up all freedom of choice

Students eat controlled diet in USDA study of effect of the kind of carbohydrate on metabolism. They are from William and Mary College and the University of Maryland.

of what and how much to eat and when and where to eat it. The kinds and amounts of the food components in the diet are rigidly controlled as are the times and the place where they are eaten. Often even drinking water has to be especially prepared—distilled to free it from any minerals it may contain. In addition, collections must be made of urine and feces for analysis. Blood samples may be taken during the study. Usually the subject keeps records of his activities and sleep. Above all, he must remember not to eat or drink anything any time except what his controlled diet provides or permits. The length of such a study can vary from 2 or 3 weeks to 2 or 3 months, sometimes longer.

The diet may be mildly distasteful and almost certainly it will be monotonous. Repetition, however, is necessary in order to be sure that every subject's response is adequately measured. Often it is necessary to supply the specific nutrients being studied in a pure form not combined with other nutrients.

Purified cornstarch, sugar, fat, plus vitamins and minerals, form a basic diet when protein or amino acids requirements are to be studied. These may have quite a different taste than when the nutrients come from our usual good-tasting foods. For instance, instead of supplying generous amounts of amino acids in the usual food forms of milk and milk products and all the

Two of the girls from a group of coed volunteers prepare muffins to be eaten by the group in a test of whether mealtime routines have an effect upon weight gains.

groups of meats, they may be supplied in their crystalline purified chemical forms. In this form, the amino acids may cost as much as $25 per person per day, but they are not as tasty as if they had come from the much less costly forms of steak and ice cream or hotdog and milkshake.

In one study, it was necessary to have the same food components in the same ratio in every mouthful that was eaten. The solution was to combine all the food for a person for a day and to bake it into a dozen muffins! These, plus small amounts of orange juice, butter, and jelly, made the daily menu for 8 weeks. It was a completely adequate diet, but tiresome in the extreme.

Research subjects could challenge the people who promote "algae" for human consumption on the basis of its high nutritive value and its low cost. They doubt that the promoters have eaten this product three times a day for several weeks in the amounts they recommend. To date, algae are extremely distasteful to most people.

What does a person get out of being a subject on a balance study? You can't put a price on cooperation and integrity in a subject and pay him accordingly. But you can pay him for the extra time it takes to be on a study. Moneywise, this doesn't amount to much. Of course, he doesn't have to spend any money for food while he is on a study. Also he gets excellent medical supervision and stays in good

327

health. But anyone who has been a subject will tell you that these benefits are only secondary to the experience of being an essential part of a scientific project. Being a subject carries along with it a certain status and recognition. But again this is secondary to the satisfaction that comes from having accomplished a difficult task.

There have been at least 1,500 of these very important people who have been subjects on balance studies over the last 20 years. There were about twice as many girls and women as there were boys and men. The youngest was 8 years old, the oldest 92.

Here's just one example of the contribution of human subjects:

The laboratory rat was a fine tool for determining which amino acids the body can make from the materials supplied by our food (called "nonessential") and which amino acids the body cannot make, but must have completely formed and ready to use (called "essential"). The rat was also a good tool for determining how much of each essential amino acid was required. The findings gave good leads on what and how much humans might need. College students, first men and later women, became the subjects for nitrogen balance studies to measure amino acid needs.

The value of different foods as the sources of protein depends upon how well they supply the kinds and amounts of the essential amino acids required by the body. Knowledge of requirements is also a guide in combining foods which have differing kinds and amounts of amino acids so that the combination will be better than any one of the ingredients alone. Sometimes it is possible to add an amino acid that is in particularly short supply in a food in order to improve its protein value. Basic to whatever use we make of knowledge of amino acid requirements is the contribution of some very important persons in being human subjects.

Miracles From Cotton, and Lace for Milady

J. DAVID REID *and* ROBERT M. REINHARDT

. . . .

A good-sized brick building sprawls near the bank of Lake Pontchartrain in New Orleans, La. It appears somewhat out of place in its luxurious surroundings between a city park and expensive homes. This is the U.S. Department of Agriculture's main headquarters for research to improve cotton textiles. Within its walls is the foremost scientific center in the world for such research, and a tremendous store of fundamental knowledge has accumulated here. Year after year, new developments pour out for the benefit of the cotton farmer, the consumer, and industry.

The uninformed visitor to this amazing complex is likely to ask, as he surveys the intricate instruments and maze of laboratories, "But what can you do to change cotton for the better? Isn't cotton just the same as ever?"

When the authors of this chapter are asked this question, they do not point out the durable-press cotton shirt the visitor is wearing. Neither do they mention his water-repellent cotton raincoat. They do not refer to flame-, rot-, or soil-resistant cottons. They ask, "Would you believe cotton cloth that dissolves in water?"

This little anecdote about a dissolving or disappearing cotton is told because it shows what can be done to completely change the nature of cotton. Also, it is illustrative of a solution to a textile problem, together with the joys and frustrations of research.

The case of the disappearing cotton began during World War II at a time when England suffered nightly under a rain of incendiary bombs. Firehoses were needed desperately in the Battle of Britain, but they were in short supply. Rubber had gone to war, and hoses were made of linen until this supply failed, too. Linen has a unique property in that it swells mightily when wet; thus, firehoses made from linen do not leak because the wet yarns swell and plug the holes. In an effort to help the British, textile chemists at our laboratory were presented with the problem, "Can cotton yarns be chemically treated to make them swell like linen for firehoses?"

When the southern division was established in the early 1940's, the principal objective was to help the farmer to sell more cotton by devoting a major proportion of the research effort to improve the position of King Cotton. One promising approach was to alter the cotton fiber to give it specific desirable properties. Competing manmade fibers were being "tailormade" into whatever the buying public wanted: Synthetics could be made elastic or nonelastic, water repellent or absorptive, or given whatever property was most salable. Could the same be done for cotton? This was a "64–million–dollar question."

⁂   ⁂   ⁂

J. DAVID REID *is the Chemist in charge of Wash-Wear Investigations at the Southern Utilization Research and Development Division of the Agricultural Research Service, New Orleans, La.*

ROBERT M. REINHARDT *is a Senior Research Chemist of the same group.*

Cotton fibers, like linen, silk, wool, fur, milady's hair, and all the other fibers in nature, are composed of clusters of long, thin molecules. These long "chains," as they are called, are held together by a sort of magnetic attraction. In cotton, these chains are the cellulose molecules. Cellulose is the chemical building block of which both cotton and linen are made and is also the principal component of trees and most other plants.

To tailormake new types of cotton fibers, it was visualized that the research worker would attach the various chemical groups onto the tough cellulose backbone to change the character of the fiber.

For example, attachment of long, waxlike molecules would make cotton resistant to wetting so that comfortable, porous rainwear could be made—or other chemicals could be attached to prevent it from burning. Use of still other chemicals would change its properties to make it more desirable for many uses.

To prepare a cotton that would swell like linen, we decided to attach water-loving groups to the cellulose chain. We hoped to retain the normal fibrous appearance of the cotton yet, by this chemical modification, produce a material that would attract water like a sponge and swell when it was wet.

Theoretically, there was basis for such a hope. We already knew that purified cellulose made from woodpulp could be made into a soluble material. When such cellulose reacts completely with chloroacetic acid in the presence of strong sodium hydroxide solutions, water-loving organic acid groups are attached to the cellulose chain. The product is called CMC (a shorthand way of saying *C*arboxy *M*ethyl *C*ellulose). It is a soluble starchlike powder that is widely used to strengthen cotton yarns for weaving, as an additive in washing powders, and even as a smoothing and nonfattening agent in food products.

We reasoned that the same process could be applied to the cellulose of the cotton fibers, but we would try to add

329

only a limited number of the water-loving groups. In the attack on a research problem, this is the first step—the development of an idea for a possible answer. This is the inspiration. It's trite but true, however, that successful research is 10 percent inspiration and 90 percent perspiration. Much experimental work is necessary.

We made a trial experiment using strong solutions of reactants to treat the cotton fabric and then left the treated fabric to wash in running water. But when we came back to inspect our product, there was nothing to inspect. The fabric had disintegrated, and gone down the drain!

Too many water-loving groups had been attached to the cellulose in our initial experiment; we had made a soluble material, just as had been done with purified cellulose. However, the basic principle of tailoring the cotton cellulose had been established, and we could proceed with further experiments—the laborious preparation of a large number of chemically treated yarns covering the effects of all practical variations of conditions. Finally, to our satisfaction, some of the treated yarns swelled beautifully when wet, just as they should in the theory.

Unfortunately, however, it was soon evident that the CM-Cotton, as we called it, could not be used for the manufacture of firehoses. But we had overlooked one important point. You have probably noticed that water does not pass through a canvas tent unless the fabric is wetted by rubbing. Similarly, water will not pass readily through a small-mesh dry screen. This resistance to passage through small holes is due to a phenomenon called "surface tension." If an agent, such as a soap or synthetic detergent, is dissolved in the water, it decreases the surface tension, the holes wet, and the water flows through the screen.

In our CM-Cotton, the yarns did swell adequately when wet, and the holes in the fabric did become much smaller, just as we had planned, but the same chemical groups that caused the cotton to swell also decreased sur-

330

Lace embroidered by machine on soluble cotton backing cloth, *top,* and after an alkaline wash removed backing, *below.* This cotton lace is inexpensive since it does not have to be hand woven.

face tension, and the water poured on through the treated fabric. There would be no cotton firehose for Britain from this development. Fortunately, about this time England won the fight against bombing so that firehoses made from cotton were no longer a necessity.

What to do? A new kind of cotton fiber had been produced, but it wasn't suitable for the purpose intended. We began to survey other possible uses. At the same time, we published details of the preparation and properties of the new fiber in scientific journals.

Our new water-soluble fiber got some unwanted attention. As a "disappearing cotton," it was incorporated into a science-fiction story.

There were, of course, some serious proposals covering a wide gamut of possible uses. CM-Cotton was evaluated as an absorbable suture for surgeons to use in sewing up wounds, but it disintegrated too readily for this purpose. Industrial chemists tried to modify it for use in tying skinless frankfurters during cooking, but this too proved unsuccessful. One proposed use was promising, however. This was in the manufacture of lace.

In the Schiffli process, a special machine produces lace by embroidering it onto a backing cloth, which is later dissolved to free the lace. Originally, the process used silk backing cloth, which could be dissolved in alkali. Later, less expensive cloth of acetate rayon—which dissolves in acetone—was used. CM-Cotton appeared a "natural" as an easily removable and inexpensive backing cloth.

A simple modification of our original process was all that was necessary to give a product that was insoluble in water containing a little acid, but that dissolved quickly and completely if the water contained alkali. This product was adopted by industry. The CM-Cotton acted as a temporary scaffold to hold the lace for treatments such as bleaching, dyeing, texturizing, and washing. The lace could then be freed simply by dissolving the backing material in an aqueous alkaline solution. At present, about a million yards of such backing cloth are used each year in the manufacture of cotton lace. You have probably seen this lace at a store.

We had set out to develop a research product to help in the Battle of Britain; instead, it is used to produce feminine adornment. But the case of the disappearing cotton was only our first commercially successful chemical modification of cotton. In the years since then, we have participated in a whole series of modern miracles with cotton. Chemists at the southern division have modified cotton chemically to make durable-press garments, water-resistant rainwear, rot-resistant awnings, flame-resistant uniforms and work clothing, and soil-resistant garments.

Safe Milk in the Atomic Age

WILBUR I. PATTERSON

. . . .

In 1959, testing of nuclear weapons had created worldwide fear of the dangers to health from radioactive fallout. Some governments urged their scientists to find ways to eliminate fallout from foods. Frightened citizens added their voices to the clamor.

Scientists developed first a laboratory technique to remove radioactive fallout from milk. This technique with the aid of milk technology and engineering knowledge was converted to a successful commercial scale process.

In the United States, three agencies had responsibilities connected with fallout. The Atomic Energy Commission controls the use of radioactive materials in the United States. Several agencies of the Department of Health, Education, and Welfare have duties to protect people from foods which may contain hazardous substances. And the U.S. Department of Agriculture is responsible for food production, including the processing of food into a safe form for eating.

The element considered most dangerous in food contaminated with fallout is radioactive strontium, which acts like calcium in the body and therefore seeks the bones. The radioactivity is a potential cause of cancer.

Radiostrontium persists for a long time; after 28 years only half of it has changed to a harmless state.

Radioactive iodine is also formed in nuclear explosions. Since half of its radioactivity is lost every 8 days, its danger exists for a much shorter time than the strontium hazard. Only 3 percent of radioactive iodine is left after 40 days.

However, iodine concentrates in the thyroid gland, and the radioactive kind could damage this organ or possibly cause cancer here, too. So, any treatment to make food contaminated with nuclear fallout safe should remove both strontium and iodine.

A nuclear accident in Great Britain in 1957, with resultant contamination of pastures and milk, necessitated the discarding of milk from a 30-square mile area.

Sam R. Hoover of the Agricultural Research Service initiated experiments in USDA to remove radionuclides from milk.

Other laboratories had already experimented with ion exchange treatments of milk to remove radioactive elements. B. B. Migicovsky at the Canadian Government laboratories in Ottawa first demonstrated in the laboratory the principle of removing radioactivity from milk with ion exchangers in a way designed to preserve its normal mineral composition, taste, and appearance. Later, the procedure was refined and adapted to commercial scale milk processing.

Since three Government agencies had responsibilities for protecting the Nation's food supply against radioactive fallout, a cooperative attack on the problem was arranged. Each agency agreed to contribute an equal share of the cost. USDA furnished laboratory and pilot plant space and, most valuable of all, experts in milk technology. The Public Health Serv-

·:·   ·:·   ·:·

WILBUR I. PATTERSON *is Assistant Director for Program Development, Eastern Utilization Research and Development Division, Agricultural Research Service.*

ice carried out chemical tests and sanitation studies on the process at its Robert A. Taft Sanitary Engineering Center in Cincinnati and assigned scientists to USDA's Research Center at Beltsville, Md. PHS scientists also supervised nutritional studies on treated milk to make sure that the treatment had not changed the nutritional value in any way, either through adding harmful substances or removing any essential component, as a vitamin.

By ordinary standards of measuring impurities, the amount of the radiostrontium ever to be expected in contaminated milk is infinitesimally small. The allowable dosage of radiation is related to the amount and type or power of the radiation. One guideline given by the Federal Radiation Council is 200 picocuries of strontium-90 per day; this daily intake of radiation for life is not believed to present any hazard at all. Two hundred picocuries of strontium-90 is equivalent to approximately one million-millionth of a gram, an amount invisible to the eye.

Compared to the radiation we all receive from natural sources such as cosmic rays or the traces of radioactive elements in rocks, the radiation from fallout in foods is small indeed. It is also small compared to the radiation we receive from X-rays of our teeth and other medical treatments.

Finding such minuscule amounts of an impurity in any material as complex as milk may not seem possible, but analytical techniques based on radioactivity are extremely sensitive. To remove these relatively few molecules from a quart of milk may sound absurd. However, background information on the removal of radionuclides from water to make it safe was available. This was an already technically feasible process based on ion-exchange techniques. In similar laboratory tests on milk to which radiostrontium had been added, variable percentages of strontium-90 were removed, usually less than 80 percent.

The calcium in fresh milk is bound to the milk proteins. When milk sours, the calcium is set free. Experiments in the Public Health Service laboratories showed that in slightly sour milk more than 90 percent of radiostrontium is removed from milk by a selected commercial cation exchanger. Charging the exchanger with the right proportion of calcium, magnesium, potassium, and sodium chlorides permitted the removal of more than 90 percent radiostrontium without changing the concentration of those elements. Scientists of the PHS and ARS received a public service patent on the process, thus assuring the public of free use of it.

Yet another problem was created by making the milk slightly sour; if the milk is too sour, the protein will coagulate. This was avoided by the carefully controlled addition of citric acid solution in the right amount. Milk normally contains a little citric acid.

The treatment must produce no appreciable change in flavor. So the sour taste had to be removed by adding a little potash, also a normal constituent of milk. The average consumer cannot taste any difference between the treated and untreated milk.

With a satisfactory laboratory process worked out, a pilot plant was the next step. Automation is desirable in modern food processing. Thus, the pilot plant design included automatic controls and it had a capacity of 100 gallons per hour.

No process can be called commercially successful until actual test on a commercial scale. Knowledge gained from the pilot plant experience permitted design of a commercial scale plant. This meant conversion of the original experiment with ounces of milk through a pilot plant to the commercial scale in which 100,000 pounds of milk were processed in an 8-hour day. The increase in size was accompanied by a host of technical problems not fully realized even on the pilot scale. One of the many problems in such a large scale test was location and cost. Only a few geographical areas could supply the needed milk since their production is geared for normal requirements.

Since this removal process did not

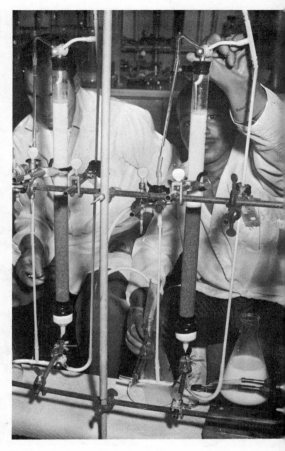

Laboratory tests being made with small columns of ion exchange resin to determine effectiveness of process in removing radioactive elements from milk.

have official clearance to permit use of the treated milk for human consumption, the milk was dried and then used in animal feed.

Such large tests were considered essential before the process could be recommended as suitable for use in commercial milk plants.

When to use the removal process has resulted in lengthy discussions. One view is that any contamination from fallout, no matter how minute, should be removed. This extreme view has not been accepted.

A number of factors determines the extent of radioactive contamination allowed in milk before removal would

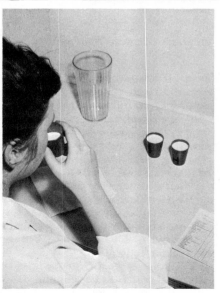

Processed milk samples being tested for radiostrontium contamination with a scintillation counter, *above*. Jesse Harris, Public Health Service officer, loads the counter which handles 50 samples at one time. Trained taster, *left*, checks for any flavor changes in milk that has been put through all of the steps to remove radiostrontium.

be recommended. The Federal Radiation Council was set up to establish levels of radiation in food above which removal might be necessary.

Besides giving efficient removal of radionuclides, the process must not change to any significant degree the composition of milk or its nutritive value or cause bacterial contamination. The acidification and neutralization steps do increase the citrate and potassium contents of the treated milk; but these changes are considered unimportant.

Extensive feeding tests with rats and pigs showed no difference in nutritive values between the treated and untreated milk. Conditions were devised to control bacterial contamination.

If practical ways could be found to keep radioactivity out of milk so its removal would not be necessary, this would be preferable to removal. Since most radioactivity in milk obviously comes from the cow's diet (very little comes from air), feeding a diet free of fallout radioactivity would solve the problem. But removing the fallout from pasturage and other feeds, at the moment at least, is far more difficult than removal from milk itself, with one exception: Iodine-131 has a half life of 8 days. Thus, storage of contaminated hay and feed for 40 days before feeding the cow should result in milk with safe levels of iodine-131. With the long-lived radioisotopes, like strontium-90, feed storage has no appreciable value in reducing milk contamination. The cow secretes only one-fifth to one-tenth of the ingested strontium-90 into her milk.

Another version of the storage method of avoiding iodine-131 consumption in milk is through processing milk into a sterile product or into dry milk (preferably nonfat milk which can be recombined later with the milk fat). Such a procedure would increase cost.

Although the ion-exchange process is semicontinuous, today's trend to completely automated and continuous processing prompted further engineering research on equipment design. Again, there was already available for other purposes ion-exchange equipment with automatic cycling. On a pilot scale (10 gallons per hour), this apparatus was successfully used to remove radionuclides from milk. However, certain problems—especially sanitary design of some parts—still have to be resolved for commercial size equipment.

For a temporary emergency, cost may not be critical. But if treatment over an extended time should ever be required, cost becomes extremely important. To remove both radiostrontium and iodine, the cost for the commercial test was about 6 cents per quart. The actual cost will depend upon the quality of chemicals used in regenerating the ion exchanger. This cost is believed to be acceptable in an emergency. For the removal of only strontium-90, the cost is about 2 cents per quart.

Development of this process from laboratory to commercial scale cost the government somewhat more than $1 million. The annual value of milk on the farm is about $5 billion.

In 1962, when fallout from testing nuclear weapons was at its highest, the iodine-131 content reached a level in a few areas which prompted Government officials to recommend the use of stored feed (free of radioactivity) for dairy cows. This was continued only for a few weeks until the radioiodine had changed into substances with no radioactivity.

So far, the level of radioactivity in milk has never reached a figure for which widespread removal has been recommended. If this time should ever come, the technical knowledge is available. Estimates of the time period which would be required to equip dairy plants vary from 6 months to a year. Research to date shows the job could be done should it ever be necessary. With the increasing proliferation of nuclear weapons despite international efforts to prevent their spread, the potential danger still exists. Further knowledge on removing radioactivity from food is important for the continued welfare of mankind.

New Stone Fruit Varieties Add Zest to Our Diet

HAROLD W. FOGLE

. . . .

Peaches, nectarines, cherries, apricots, and plums provide some of the most delightful but also most perishable treats which enliven our diet. These fruits, mostly of Chinese and southwest Asian origin, have been luxury items available for a few weeks of the summer. Their delectable flesh surrounds a single hard stone, hence their group name. Now, however, one buys peaches in the local supermarket from May through October. The frontiers of the peach ripening season have been pushed both earlier and later.

An almost-complete revolution of varieties has occurred. The soft white-fleshed peaches have been replaced by yellow-fleshed ones. Older yellow-fleshed varieties have given way to firmer, more highly blushed, more attractive ones. New standards of firmness have eliminated many of the older varieties. Only 'Elberta'—a truly outstanding peach originating almost a century ago in Georgia—and 'J. H. Hale' have survived the revolution. Neither is favored for new plantings: The former lacks fruit attractiveness of its competitors, and the latter has a weak tree.

A comparable expansion of the ripening limits is occurring in nectarines. Larger, firmer, yellow-fleshed, freestone varieties have replaced the small, soft, white-fleshed ones. These "fuzzless peaches," which mutated from peaches over 2,000 years ago, rather suddenly have evolved into a popular novelty item. Private breeders have realized the potential and contributed many of the attractive new varieties.

Similar changes, although less perceptible, are occurring in the other stone fruits. More new varieties have been introduced in the last 25 years than in centuries previously.

One significant milestone in the revolution of peach varieties was the introduction in 1940 of 'Redhaven' by Prof. Stanley Johnston of the South Haven Experiment Station in Michigan. This variety set the standard of attractiveness by which new varieties are judged. Few varieties have adapted so widely as 'Redhaven.'

Basic information on the inheritance of commercially important characteristics in peaches was amassed by New Jersey researchers. New varieties specifically adapted to New Jersey conditions were introduced. Some are commercially important today, and others have been supplanted by improved varieties from the continuing program. The most significant contribution, however, was the blueprint of how desired characteristics could be combined.

The U.S. Department of Agriculture played a major role in recognizing industry needs and in "tailoring" new varieties to those needs. USDA fruit breeders embarked upon an extensive

∴　　∴　　∴

HAROLD W. FOGLE is Leader for Stone Fruit Investigations, Agricultural Research Service, at Beltsville, Md. From 1949 to 1963, he was in charge of the cooperative Federal-State stone fruit breeding program near Prosser, Wash.

freestone peach breeding program at Beltsville, Md., in 1936. This was expanded to central Georgia, the San Joaquin Valley of California, and the Yakima Valley of Washington to meet divergent objectives in the Southeast, California, and the Pacific Northwest producing regions.

Dr. John Weinberger has been responsible for introduction by USDA of 17 peach varieties, one nectarine, one plum, one apricot, and one peach and almond rootstock. His research has spanned the more than 30 years of the Department's current stone fruit breeding program.

Weinberger helped make the initial peach crosses at Beltsville in 1936. He evaluated these and later peach hybrid populations totaling some 37,000 seedlings at Fort Valley, Ga., during the years 1937 to 1954.

From this effort 'Dixigem,' a high-quality variety ripening a full month before 'Elberta,' in 1944 became the first of 12 varieties selected by Weinberger for the Southeast. 'Dixired,' named the next year, permitted the southeastern grower to market a yellow-fleshed peach 5 or 6 weeks before 'Elberta.' This was soon utilized in other producing areas to spread the harvest season, thus becoming the second important milepost of the peach revolution.

'Cardinal,' introduced 7 years later, pushed the harvesting date barrier a few days earlier. Three other varieties, 'Hiland,' 'Redcap,' and 'Maygold,' with similar maturity season, but with lower chilling requirements for normal blossoming, were introduced the next year. These were of particular value in the southern extremes of the peach producing areas.

Despite its high quality, 'Dixigem' failed to attract growers to plant it. Thus, the USDA in 1953 introduced 'Coronet,' an extremely attractive variety as a replacement. Despite difficulties with productiveness in some areas, 'Coronet' is replacing 'Cardinal.' 'Keystone' was introduced in 1954 and 'Suwanee' in 1962 to provide slightly later-maturing compan-ion varieties replacing an earlier introduction ('Southland').

The standard peach variety, 'Elberta', has been losing favor with growers for many years. Because of this, USDA introduced 'Dixiland' to fill this varietal gap for southeastern growers. It appears to be adapted for other areas as well.

In 1966, 'Sentinel,' which showed much improved resistance to bacterial spot disease, was introduced.

The mark of an outstanding plant breeder is his ability to see and realize the significance of unusual phenomena in his plots. This sometimes is called serendipity. Weinberger has this characteristic and therein lies his success as a peach breeder.

A prime example of this was the development of 'Nemaguard,' now widely used as a peach and almond rootstock. Rootstocks in use were subject to damage by nematodes—tiny worms which attack roots of fruit trees and other plants. Realizing the need for increased resistance to the *javanica* root-knot nematode, Weinberger remembered published reports of resistance in the peach relative, *Prunus davidiana*. He obtained nursery seed of the latter with the goal of combining this additional resistance with existing good resistance to another root-knot nematode.

The seedlings obtained were not typical *P. davidiana*, although they resembled hybrids of that species and peach. However, one seedling showing unusual productiveness was evaluated for resistance and showed good resistance to both nematodes. None of the other seedlings had so great resistance. This observation saved perhaps 15 to 20 years in reaching the goal of resistance to both nematode species.

Likewise, Dr. Weinberger's serendipity was responsible for the short-chilling peaches which made possible peach breeding programs in the Deep South and in Brazil. He obtained a few seeds of a Hawaiian rootstock from a nurseryman. One seedling, which bloomed at Christmastime but had small, white-fleshed, bitter fruits, was crossed with

'Southland.' The hybrid seedlings gave a few selections with low chilling requirements and lack of bitterness, but all were small fruited and soft.

Successive crosses and backcrosses to superior yellow-fleshed varieties retained the low-chilling characteristic and increased the fruit's economic desirability. This material was made available to others interested in developing low-chilling varieties. The adaptation range of peaches thereby was pushed farther South.

Weinberger in 1954 accepted the challenge of breeding new stone fruits for California as well as USDA's grape breeding effort for the west coast. These fruit for long distance shipment must be firm enough to reach the east coast markets in good condition. The program is located near Fresno and is primarily concerned with the irrigated interior valleys, principally the San Joaquin.

Since he was placed in charge of this station, some 34,000 peach and nectarine, 17,000 plum, and 7,000 apricot seedlings have been planted.

Weinberger was quick to recognize the needs of the California freestone peach industry and the potential of material already in his plots. In 1958, 'Regina' was introduced as a replacement for the 'Redhaven' variety. The latter, although perfectly acceptable in shape in northern areas, tended to a long, pointed shape in California and other Southern States. 'Regina' and 'Coronet' have been slowly replacing 'Redhaven' in California.

In 1959, the 'Suncrest' peach reaffirmed the Department's success in breeding for flesh firmness. 'Redglobe,' introduced from the Beltsville program 5 years earlier, and 'Earlihale,' 1 year earlier, had set the standard for firmness in new varieties. 'Suncrest' also filled a ripening gap between the midseason and Elbertaseason varieties. It is becoming a leading variety in California and is highly regarded in all producing areas where bacterial spot is no problem.

The naming of 'Redtop' in 1961 added another very attractive, unusually firm variety developed for California, but widely adapted. It ripens between 'Redhaven' and 'Redglobe' seasons and is becoming a leading variety in its season.

In 1965, 'Summerset' moved the late-ripening frontiers of nonpatented peaches. Ripening between 5 and 6 weeks after the latest standard variety ('Rio Oso Gem'), this variety permits the California grower to supply firm, attractive peaches to west coast markets for this extended period.

Most recent of the Fresno peach introductions is 'Fayette,' which ripens in a previous gap about a week before the 'Elberta' ripening season. The two varieties, 'Summerset' and 'Fayette,' appear to be taking over the acreage which formerly was planted to 'Redglobe.' The latter is not being planted to any extent because of a fruit apical (tip) softening which has occurred in recent years in California.

Collectively, the 17 peach varieties which Weinberger selected and other USDA varieties constitute between 70 and 80 percent of all peaches planted in California for the past dozen years. Probably an even higher percentage are Department originations in the Southeast. USDA varieties are important in all producing areas and dominant in most. Breeders at all four locations have promising selections in all stages of testing to systematically replace varieties as the need arises. Weinberger, for example, has some 5,200 peach and nectarine seedlings which have not yet fruited.

Nectarine breeding by USDA is more recent, but definite progress has been made. Early nectarines, which arose as "sports" on peaches, were mostly small, white-fleshed, very soft, and clingstone. Numerous crosses of nectarines to peaches and backcrosses to nectarines have added larger size, yellow flesh, and the freestone characteristic. An outstanding selection was named 'Independence' in 1965 because it ripened at Fresno about July 4. Other similar selections ripening at intervals will be named when they are tested sufficiently.

Weinberger realized the potential of this specialty fruit and was responsive to the industry need for reliably tested freestone varieties. A sequence of similar varieties over a period as long as for peaches is envisioned.

As was true with peaches, main crop apricot varieties were static for many years. As a consequence, the varieties, mostly of European origin, became less well suited to changing market demands. Commercial drying of fruit became less prevalent, and the need for larger fruit and for resistance to pit burning—browning of flesh adjacent to the pit—became more important as more fruit was shipped fresh or canned.

Weinberger realized the need for greater resistance to pit burning, improved firmness, and larger size in varieties similar to the major varieties. In 1963, 'Castleton' was introduced by USDA because it fulfilled these objectives. The other selections which promise to complement this variety are in various stages of testing. Over 2,100 seedlings have not yet fruited, and additional crosses are made each year. There is reason to expect a complete replacement of present varieties.

Weinberger's interest in improving Japanese-type plums led to a resumption of breeding for new varieties. An earlier, very productive, cooperative program between the USDA and the California Agricultural Experiment Station at Davis had developed 'Burmosa,' 'Redheart,' 'Nubiana,' 'Laroda,' and several other varieties which became important to the industry.

Using these and other varieties as parents, Weinberger produced over 17,000 hybrids and now is testing many promising selections. One was named 'Frontier' in 1967. It combines the high quality of the leading red-fleshed variety with much better exterior color, thus increasing its market appeal. 'Friar', an amber-fleshed and black-skinned variety, was introduced in March of 1968. Other selections are undergoing rigorous plot and commercial testing. Weinberger is growing some 3,200 plum seedlings which have not yet fruited.

Penicillin: Breakthrough to the Era of Antibiotics

FRANK H. STODOLA

. . . .

To many, scientific research is an impersonal and forbidding pursuit. This notion is something of a myth, perhaps never more so than for penicillin. Its story abounds in drama and human interest.

Forty years have now passed since Alexander Fleming was led by a "curious concatenation of circumstances" to the discovery of this astonishing substance at St. Mary's Hospital in London in 1928. This discovery was a highly improbable event and involved two elements of luck. The right kind of mold spore had to come in contact with the right kind of disease germ and thereby produce an unusual effect. And this effect had to be observed by someone who knew its meaning.

Fleming was such a man: A highly trained and acute observer who had devoted his whole career as a medical bacteriologist to the search for nontoxic agents for the treatment of disease. It would be hard to find a better example of fortune favoring the prepared mind.

Not only did Fleming make the original observation on penicillin—he sensed the importance of his discovery. He preserved the mold; and he carefully described its behavior in a paper entitled "On the Antibacterial Action of Cultures of Penicillium." Beautiful in its simplicity, this paper was to become one of the classics of medical literature. It was the opening gun in the victorious battle against the infectious diseases. It ushered in the Era of Antibiotics and altered the whole course of modern medicine.

In his paper, Fleming wrote "A certain type of penicillium produces in culture a very powerful antibacterial substance. . . . The action is very marked on the pyogenic cocci and the diphtheria group of bacilli. . . . Penicillin is nontoxic to animals in enormous doses and is nonirritant." He suggested, "It may be an efficient antiseptic for application to, or injection into, areas infected with penicillin-sensitive microbes."

Everything of importance is in these few sentences! Yet, who would have guessed what a profound effect this modest account was to have upon human welfare.

Knowing that chemical studies on penicillin were next in order, Fleming was pleased when Harold Raistrick of the London School of Hygiene and Tropical Medicine undertook the isolation of penicillin. Being a careful and experienced worker on the chemistry of mold products, Raistrick took the necessary first step in such work by establishing with certainty the identity of the penicillin organism. On April 29,

1930, he sent a subculture of Fleming's mold to the U.S. Department of Agriculture's Bureau of Plant Industry at Beltsville, Md., to be examined by Charles Thom, a world authority on fungi, including the Penicillia. The result of this first visit of the penicillin organism to America is recorded in Thom's notebook as follows:

5112 H. Raistrick
Rec'd 5–14–30
5112.1 *P. rubrum* (?) isolated by Fleming.
British collection No. 3127. Culture on
Dox-glucose agar Apr.25.30
= *P. notatum*

Thom's assignment of the mold to the correct species (*P. notatum*) was invaluable. It identified the culture with a cosmopolitan series of molds and, later, gave direction to the search for more productive strains.

Valuable contributions were made by the Raistrick group to the production and chemistry of penicillin. Unfortunately, the work was not continued beyond 1932 because of the accidental death of the Mycologist Charles and the departure of the Bacteriologist Lovell. Although temporarily discouraged by this setback, Fleming did not lose faith in penicillin. In lectures and publications, he continued to point out its virtues and its possibilities.

The scene next shifts from London to the Sir William Dunn School of Pathology at the University of Oxford. There Howard Florey, a medical man who had extensive experience with the antibacterial enzyme lysozyme discovered by Fleming in 1922, joined forces in 1939 with Biochemist Ernest Chain, Organic Chemist E. P. Abraham, and Bacteriologist Norman Heatley in a new and determined attack on the penicillin problems. Aided by a $5,000 grant from the Rockefeller Foundation, they succeeded by late 1940 in taming the previously intractable penicillin by converting it into a stable, dry powder.

So effective was this purified material in the treatment of some human infections that by early 1941 Florey and his associates were convinced that

FRANK H. STODOLA *has been in charge of the Pioneering Laboratory for Microbiological Chemistry at the Northern Utilization Research and Development Division, Agricultural Research Service, Peoria, Ill., since 1957. He worked for 15 years before that in the Fermentation Division, whose members received the Lasker Award in 1946 for penicillin research.*

if penicillin could be made available in quantity, its use in the treatment of war wounds would result in a marked physical and psychological advantage over the enemy. Unfortunately, it was not possible at that time for the already overburdened British chemical and drug manufacturers to undertake large-scale production of penicillin, so in July 1941 Florey and Heatley came to this country to take advantage of the more favorable conditions and the American knack for mass production. They were not to be disappointed.

Their first stop was at New Haven, Conn., where Florey's children had been staying at the home of J. F. Fulton during the bombing of London. There, R. G. Harrison, chairman of the National Research Council, advised the English visitors to see Thom. He promptly recommended the newly established Northern Regional Research Laboratory (NRRL) at Peoria, Ill., where USDA investigators were already familiar with industrial fermentation processes and where a large collection of molds was maintained. The following telegram on July 9 from P. A. Wells, acting head of the Bureau of Agricultural Chemistry and Engineering, to O. E. May, director of the laboratory, was to set in motion a series of events of utmost importance to the war effort.

"Thom has introduced Heatley and Florey of Oxford. Here to investigate pilot scale production of bacteriostatic material from Fleming's penicillium in connection with medical defense plans. Can you arrange for shallow pan setup to establish laboratory results in metal?"

To which May replied the next day: "Pan setup and organisms available Heatley and Florey experimentation. Details of work of course unknown and suggest they visit Peoria for discussion. Laboratory in position to cooperate immediately."

The meeting was held in Peoria on July 14, and laboratory work was underway 2 days later. By November 26, 1941, Andrew J. Moyer, the laboratory expert on the nutrition of molds, had succeeded, with the help of Heatley, in increasing the Oxford yields tenfold by the use of corn steep liquor, a byproduct of corn starch manufacture.

On December 17, this highly encouraging result was disclosed by Robert D. Coghill, head of the Fermentation Division at NRRL, to representatives of four companies (Merck, Squibb, Pfizer, and Lederle) at a meeting called in New York by A. N. Richards, a friend of Florey's, chairman of the Committee on Medical Research of the Office of Scientific Research and Development. This meeting established a vital link between government research at NRRL and the chemical and pharmaceutical firms capable of large-scale production and led to a fruitful collaboration that was to continue throughout the war.

The simplest and quickest way of producing penicillin in quantity in 1941 was by the "surface" method, in which the mold grows as a mat on the top of a nutrient solution. Pilot plant production of penicillin by this process was slow at first because of contamination and isolation problems. By March 1942, only enough penicillin was available in the United States for the treatment of one case.

Prospects were vastly improved, however, when K. B. Raper, a former collaborator of Thom, found a superior strain of *P. notatum-chrysogenum* at NRRL, which doubled the yield of penicillin, raising it to 150 units per milliliter of nutrient solution compared to the two units of the Oxford group. This yield left no doubt that the surface method was suitable for mass production. Factories were built here and in England that could process in one day the culture liquor from 30,000 milk bottles. It was by this means that almost all the penicillin used to establish its clinical usefulness was obtained.

Still another means of producing penicillin was available in 1941. The mold could be grown as a suspension in stirred and aerated tanks of nutrient solution, as was being done in the

Sir Alexander Fleming, *right*, when he visited USDA's laboratory in Peoria, Ill., the year he received the Nobel Prize for discovering penicillin. *Below,* Andrew J. Moyer of the Peoria lab whose steep liquor-lactose medium made possible the mass production of penicillin.

commercial production of gluconic acid. This so-called "submerged" process offered tremendous advantages over the surface method in reduced space and labor requirements, one 10,000-gallon tank being the equivalent of 70,000 bottles. However, the Fleming organism was unproductive in tanks. It was not until strain 832 was developed at NRRL that the submerged process was assured of industrial adoption.

By 1943, the War Production Board was convinced of the need for greatly increased production of penicillin for military use, and 21 submerged process plants were rushed to completion at a cost of about $20 million. Through the use of a succession of improved strains (NRRL 1951–B25, Carnegie Institution X–1612, and University of Wisconsin Q–176), these factories raised the 1943 production of 28 pounds to 14,000 pounds for the year 1945, enough to meet all military and some civilian needs. With yields of 16,000 units per milliliter, not uncommon in 1968, it is amusing to recall the state of mind of early workers, as revealed in a letter of November 24, 1941, from NRRL to the bureau chief which read in part:

"Recent experiments have also indicated that penicillin can be prepared in submerged culture with yields of 3 to 4 units per cc. This was just a preliminary experiment, and probably does not represent the ceiling for this type of culture."

Within 25 years, yields increased more than 4,000 times.

It would be hard to overestimate the contribution of penicillin to the war effort through the saving of countless lives and limbs.

The American share in this cooperative venture was acknowledged by the Oxford group as follows:

". . . too high a tribute cannot be paid to the enterprise and energy with which American manufacturing firms tackled the large-scale production of the drug.

"Had it not been for their efforts there would certainly not have been sufficient penicillin by D-day in Normandy in 1944 to treat all severe casualties, both British and American."

And it is not amiss to add that the American industrial success would not have been possible without the prompt and sustained support of Government administrators and research workers.

All during the war, studies on the chemistry of penicillin were actively pursued in England and in the United States. It was hoped that the makeup of the penicillin molecule could be established and that a practical synthesis could be devised which would give unlimited amounts of the drug without recourse to fermentation. Only the first hope was realized. Before the war was over, the arrangement of the carbon (C), hydrogen (H), oxygen (O), nitrogen (N), and sulfur (S) atoms with respect to one another was known and could be pictured in the shorthand of the chemist as:

$$
\begin{array}{c}
\overset{O}{\overset{\|}{R-C}}-NH-CH-CH \overset{S}{\diagdown} C(CH_3)_2 \\
O=C-\!\!-N-\!\!-CH-COOH
\end{array}
$$

where R represents any of the five different groups of atoms found in the natural penicillins produced by the mold. In the common commercial penicillin G, R is $C_6H_5-CH_2-$.

By 1946, the conditions of use, dosage, and standardization of penicillin were essentially worked out. The drug was known to be remarkably effective in the treatment of hemolytic streptococcic infections, such as tonsillitis, scarlet fever, puerperal sepsis, erysipelas, cellulitis, and wound infections; subacute bacterial endocarditis; gonorrhoea and syphilis; anthrax and gangrene. And happily, mass production had placed the lifegiving medicine within the reach of almost everyone. One would have guessed that after such a hectic and precocious adolescence the "queen of drugs" had a right to look forward to a placid lifetime of service. This desirable state was not to be—yet.

In 1945, reports began to appear that hinted of a disturbing situation.

With increasing frequency, new forms of the dreaded *Staphylococcus aureus* were being encountered that did not yield to the magic of penicillin. Soon these "bandit" strains were being spread by cross-infection to hospitals, and by 1950, the situation was almost out of control. Distressing as it was, it had to be admitted that the status of penicillin in 1950 was actually less satisfactory than it had been in 1945. Fortunately, cooperative scientific research was again able to meet the challenge in dramatic fashion.

The breakthrough in the battle against the resistant strains came from workers at Beecham Research Laboratories in England, who took advantage of a clue supplied in 1950 by Sakaguchi and Murao in Japan. An enzyme was found that would remove the R—$\overset{\overset{\textstyle O}{\|}}{C}$— group from commercial penicillin G, leaving the "nucleus," which could easily be converted by the chemist into new penicillins with different R—$\overset{\overset{\textstyle O}{\|}}{C}$— groups. Hundreds of these semisynthetic penicillins were prepared and tested. One of them, methicillin, proved to be remarkably effective against staphylococci resistant to penicillin G. Thus, the penicillins were restored to their former position as the agents of choice for treating communicable infections like sore throat, scarlet fever, and rheumatic fever.

Research workers have also been active in other directions, seeking to circumvent the shortcomings of penicillin. One of the most successful of these has been the development of the oral penicillins to eliminate the inconvenience of intravenous injection. The problem was to produce a stable penicillin that would not be destroyed by stomach acids as penicillin G is. One of these, penicillin V, was discovered in 1948 by Behrens and his associates of Eli Lilly and Co. It was produced by alteration of the R group in penicillin, through the use of the proper nutrient for the mold.

Penicillin V came into clinical use in 1953 and has had wide application since. But hopes that it would replace penicillin G entirely were not realized when its range of activity proved to be somewhat limited. However, the success of this modified penicillin encouraged a further search, and still better oral penicillins were later found among the many semisynthetic penicillins prepared by the workers at the Beecham laboratories.

Another problem of great concern to medical men is the ability of penicillin to produce hypersensitivity reactions, which can vary in severity from a skin rash to death from anaphylactic shock. The problem is doubly serious because no wholly satisfactory method for determining penicillin hypersensitivity has yet been developed. The incidence of the reaction varies from 2 to 15 percent, depending on the patient's previous history of allergy. In 1964, it was estimated that 100 to 300 fatal reactions to penicillin occur each year in the United States.

The gravity of the situation has prompted many attempts to determine the cause of the reactions and to devise means of eliminating it. Only recently have promising results been obtained. It appears that penicillin itself is not responsible, but rather a protein impurity. There is now some evidence that this impurity can be removed to give purified penicillins of greatly improved properties with regard to hypersensitivity. If this encouraging lead works out, it will be a boon to those now denied penicillin's benefits.

So, despite some limitations, penicillin remains the most valuable of the available antibiotics, with annual production in the United States approaching 2 million pounds. Its usefulness has not been limited to human therapy; large amounts are used in veterinary medicine and for the promotion of growth in animals. From humble beginnings in 1941, the production of penicillin has spread all over the world, with manufacturing facilities in 27 countries. Truly a great and lasting tribute to Fleming and his successors.

Getting the Beat on Rhythm— New Way to Pest Control

W. N. SULLIVAN

. . . .

Ever since the world began, night has followed day in an unfailing rhythm. The ebbing and flowing of the tides have been subject to a monthly cycle. The seasons have come and gone in regular order through the years. These are dominant rhythms in our world, dependent on the daily turning of the earth upon its axis, the monthly revolution of the moon about the earth, the yearly journey of the earth around the sun.

All the creatures on earth developed under the sway of these primordial rhythms and are adapted to them. Most animals including insects and man have alternations of sleep and wakefulness which are rhythms with periods of about 24 hours. Activity occurs during the warmth of the daytime and rest during the cool of night in diurnal species. Nocturnal species reverse the procedure and are active during the night.

A few animals, particularly those inhabiting tidal waters, have rhythms which are geared to the tides and also lunar rhythms of about 28 days. Many species of insects in temperate climates that have several generations each year have seasonal rhythms. Growth and reproduction occur when the summer daylight hours are long, and diapause—a state like hibernation— occurs during the short days of winter.

Man has many aids (clocks, calendars, etc.) for telling the time of day and the season of the year. How does a lower and less intelligent form of life like an insect know when it is time to become active each day; when to go into diapause in the fall, and when to resume growth and development in the springtime?

Since 1920, when Garner and Allard of the U.S. Department of Agriculture discovered photoperiodism (or the response of an organism such as by growth to the relative length of day), scientists in many countries have sought the answer to this basic biological phenomenon. It will be a long time before all the answers are in, but a great deal has already been learned. We know that for insects the daily and seasonal changes in the length of daylight and darkness—mathematically precise events in nature—serve as a guide in telling time. Day length can apparently be measured by insects to about ± 15 minutes per day and seasonal length to about ± 3 days. Some scientists have suggested the term "biological clock" for the timing mechanism of insects.

The "biological clocks" control the cicadian (about 24 hours) rhythms in behavior and in physiological processes such as enzyme activity. These rhythms are endogenous, since they are caused by the insect itself. The "clocks" are not identical with the

∴   ∴   ∴

W. N. SULLIVAN is a Research Entomologist with the Pesticide Chemicals Research Branch, Entomology Research Division, Agricultural Research Service.

rhythms, but are like built-in computers that measure day length, temperature, and so on.

These clocks are inherited by the insect and occur at all levels of organization (organs, glands, and tissues) down to the cell level. The clocks run continuously and are synchronized with the environment by the daily rhythms of light and darkness. They are synchronized to a lesser degree by the daily temperature fluctuation rhythms.

Dickson (University of California) and Lukefahr of USDA studied the oriental fruit moth and the pink bollworm which have several generations a year and found that they are synchronized to the rhythm of the seasons. This is true of many lepidoptera (moths and butterflies), which include some of our most serious agricultural insect pests like the corn earworm, codling moth, and cabbage butterflies.

When daylight in spring lengthens to 13 to 15 hours, the endocrine glands cause the insect to start growth and development. As the days shorten in the fall to less than 13 to 15 hours, the insect goes into diapause. This happens while food and temperature are still favorable for growth and reproduction and protects the last generation each year from being killed off by cold and lack of food. It is one of nature's ways of assuring survival of the species.

Diapause is characterized by a number of general physiological features, of which the most essential is a lowering of metabolism. The following features are also typical: A decrease in oxygen consumption; a decrease in the total amount of water in the body; the accumulation in the tissues of abundant deposits of reserve food material, by means of which the vital processes are maintained during the resting period; and the absence—or an extremely low level—of feeding and movement.

A group of Agricultural Research Service scientists (physicists, chemists, biochemists, and entomologists) at the Agricultural Research Center, Beltsville, Md., are investigating the physical and chemical aspects of biological rhythms to see if they can be manipulated to damage harmful agricultural insects.

The colors or wavelengths of light most effective in breaking larval diapause of the codling moth (*Carpocapsa pomonella*) are being investigated. Test insects are grown in the laboratory on a synthetic diet at 80° F. and a regimen of 8 hours light and 16 hours darkness. This short day conditioning causes the full grown larvae to spin up in cocoons.

After 1 to 3 months in diapause, the larvae are placed in the cells of an aluminum block. The aluminum block is then centered in a constant temperature cabinet (80° F.) so that each vertical row of insects receives a different wavelength of the spectrum. The daily light regimen in the cabinet is white light (8 hours); colored light (8 hours); darkness (8 hours).

While the 8 hours of white light would keep the insects in diapause, the additional 8 hours of colored light are sufficient to add up to a total of 16 hours of light and thus will break diapause at wavelengths to which the insect is sensitive. Additional groups from the same lot of insects are subjected to 8 and 16 hours of white light as experimental controls.

In the initial tests, the peak effectiveness of light in breaking diapause (the larvae changed to pupae) occurred at the shorter wavelengths (blue-green) of the spectrum. We are now attempting to make more refined measurements of the exact wavelength(s) of the visible spectrum involved in inducing growth and development. Pigments in the insect that absorb light at the appropriate wavelengths will then be investigated.

At present, we believe that light acts directly on a pigment in insect nervous tissue (eye or brain) in synchronizing biological rhythms in insects. This light action (at appropriate day lengths) then triggers the synthesis or release of hormones that induce growth and development.

The Beltsville group is also exploring the possibility of using chemicals to either block diapause or initiate diapause and thereby upset the rhythm of nature.

It has already been shown by Bunning and Barker in their work with the cabbage butterfly larvae that light flashes of short duration applied during certain sensitive periods during darkness will cause biological clocks of insects to misinterpret short days as long days. After further basic work on the use of light as well as chemicals, it may become possible for the farmer in intensive agriculture to prevent the diapause of insects in the fall by: (1) the use of high-intensity lights for short periods of time during darkness or (2) spraying a naturally occurring material which is harmless to plants and animals and which will block diapause or put insects into diapause at a time unfavorable for their existence. In this manner, natural processes will be modified for the benefit of mankind.

Halberg and associates reported in 1960 that the same dose of a bacterial toxin killed 85 percent of mice at 4 p.m. and only 10 percent at midnight. The mouse kill was dependent on the phase of the cicadian rhythm (oscillation with a period of about 24 hours) at the time of injection. That is, there was a high kill during susceptible phases of the rhythm and a low kill at nonsusceptible phases. This important work suggested that insecticides might be more effective if applied during the time of day when the target was most susceptible.

Entomologists have found that cockroaches, boll weevils, mites, and crickets have a cicadian rhythm in susceptibility to insecticides. Prof. Perry Adkisson of Texas A&M University reported that under a photoperiod with a 10-hour light cycle the same dose of methyl parathion killed approximately 10 percent of the boll weevils tested at dawn, but almost 90 percent of those tested when applied only 3 hours later.

In 1966, at Beltsville, we investigated the cicadian rhythm in susceptibility of the house fly (*Musca domestica*) and Madeira cockroach (*Leucophaea maderae*)

to the widely used pyrethrum aerosol. Twin 1,000 cubic feet blackout chambers were used at a temperature of 29° C. (84° F.) and with light from 5 a.m. to 8 p.m. and darkness from 8 p.m. to 5 a.m. to simulate long day conditions in summer.

One chamber (A) was used to rear and condition the test insects.

When the house flies reached the adult stage, they were placed in cylindrical wire cages and conditioned for several more days.

Large nymphs and adults of the cockroach were placed in open glass dishes and further accustomed to the given temperature and light conditions.

During the 8 test days, separate but comparable groups of caged flies and cockroaches were transferred to the test chamber (B) each hour on the hour for a 24-hour period. Each group was subjected to the same measured dosage of aerosol (40 milligrams pyrethrins per 1,000 cubic feet) for a half hour period.

The "knockdown" of the insects was then recorded, and the air in the chamber exchanged several times with a blower before the next hourly test. After exposure to the insecticide, the insects were placed in an air-conditioned room and held for 2 days before mortality determinations were made.

Results were analyzed by a computer program. Peak susceptibility for both species of insects studied occurred at about 4 o'clock in the afternoon. A possible explanation for the agreement in crest values for the fly and the roach is that the fly reaches a peak of activity during the same time that the roach is commencing activity.

From these results, it would appear that the best time to apply insecticides in the control of house fly adults and roaches indoors is at 4 o'clock in the afternoon.

The crest movement of house flies, horn flies (*Haematobia irritans*), and the stable fly (*Stomoxys calcitrans*) to the indoors often occurs at 2 to 4 p.m. when the cattle are brought indoors for milking. Since these insects are susceptible to pyrethrum, it would appear

347

that 4 p.m. would be an ideal time to treat dairy barns provided that all three insects have the same peak period of susceptibility.

In human beings, rhythms in cancerous tissue are different from those in normal tissue; and some mental patients exhibit rhythms which deviate from the usual 24-hour pattern. The understanding of such human disorders may be advanced measurably by the knowledge gained from a study of rhythms in insects and how these may be manipulated.

For further reading:

Aschoff, J., *Cicadian Clocks*. North Holland Publishing Co., Amsterdam, Holland, 1965.

Danilevskii, H. S., *Photoperiodism and Seasonal Development of Insects*. Oliver and Boyd, Ltd., London, England, 1965.

———— *Cold Spring Harbor Symposia on Quantitative Biology*. Waverly Press, Baltimore, 1960.

A Water Repellant Through Sheer Chance

M. T. GOEBEL

. . . .

Because a chemist decided to toss a small piece of filter paper into a sink instead of a wastebasket, a water-repellent chemical was born.

This was no ordinary piece of filter paper, however. Before it was discarded, a series of chance circumstances had changed it from the usual into the unusual.

Not the least of these events was the fact that the sink was half full of water. Had it been empty and dry, chances are a real discovery might have gone down the drain.

But the sink was not empty, and the filter paper, instead of sinking to the bottom like it normally would, continued to float upon the surface of the water. To the chemist, this indicated that some chemical reaction had imparted a water-repellent property to the paper. Intrigued, he attempted to duplicate through scientific methods what chance had created.

The result of these efforts was "Quilon" chrome complex, a Werner complex of chromium with a long chain acid, whose unique properties have caused it to be used widely in paper products where water and grease repellancy are desired. It also is used in applications which require a surface with good release characteristics. Paper backings for pressure-sensitive labels and tapes are an example, as are nonsticking meat wraps and board.

A most dramatic application of "Quilon" of some possible advantage in conservation of wildlife is its use in a process to tan chicken feathers, enabling them to replace the waterfowl feathers in low-cost mattresses, sleeping bags, and pillows. Likewise, it can be used in tanning leathers to make them more pliable, softer, and resistant to alkalies and acids, while extending their service life. In the case of suede leather, "Quilon" helps make it drycleanable and resistant to water and staining.

"Quilon" chrome complex was a laboratory accident, but a research

∴   ∴   ∴

M. T. GOEBEL *is Director, Research Division, Industrial and Biochemicals Department, E. I. du Pont de Nemours & Co.*

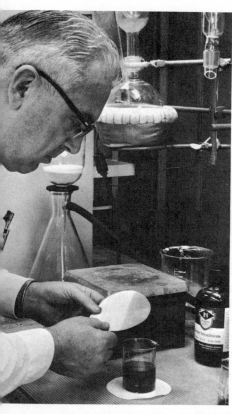

Ralph K. Iler reenacts his chance dis-covery of a new water and grease repellant. After dipping part of filter paper in chromyl chloride, *left,* he heated paper. *Below,* what Iler saw after he discarded paper in sink. Untreated part becomes water-soaked. But beads of water stand out on treated part, showing treatment made it water repellent.

background had prepared its discoverer, Dr. Ralph K. Iler, to take advantage of the chance when it came. His keenness of observation, initiative, and persistence were instrumental in transforming "Quilon" from a laboratory curiosity into a useful material.

Iler is now manager of exploratory industrial research for Du Pont's Industrial and Biochemicals Department. But back in 1940, he was a young chemist who had been working in the Cleveland laboratory of Du Pont's Grasselli Chemicals Department just 3 years.

One day, another chemist at the laboratory approached him with the suggestion that chromyl chloride might make a wood preservative. Knowing the potency of chromyl chloride as an oxidizing agent, Iler informed him that the chemical would cause wood, or paper, to ignite.

To prove his point, Iler put some chromyl chloride on a piece of filter paper from an opened package. Surprised that it did not burn as expected, he put the soaked paper on a hotplate in the laboratory hood, placing a piece of asbestos sheet over it for a few minutes to make sure it was hot.

When the resultant fumes had been driven off, Iler removed the paper from the hotplate and found to his surprise that it was still white and apparently unaffected. By chance, he threw the paper into the sink—"because it was closer than the wastebasket," he recalls. The paper floated. Iler observed that the untreated part of the paper was turning dark as it absorbed the water, while beads of water stood out on the side that had been treated with chromyl chloride. It was obviously water repellent.

Intrigued by his discovery, Iler attempted to repeat the experiment. This time, he used a piece of filter paper from a freshly opened package. The paper immediately sank to the bottom of the sink.

"I was ready to think that the water-repellent effect was just my imagination, or a 'fluke,'" Iler recalls.

But, by chance at that time, he remembered reading how clean glassware will pick up a film of greasy material from the air in a few hours. Wondering whether the water-repellent effect probably had been produced by a reaction between chromyl chloride and a very thin layer of a greasy compound on the filter paper which had been exposed to the atmosphere, Iler decided to "put a little 'grease' on the paper first, to simulate exposure to the air." By chance, he used a long-chain alcohol.

Diluting out some lauryl alcohol with carbon tetrachloride, Iler dipped a piece of filter paper and dried it. As he had hoped, the reaction between the long-chain alcohol and chromyl chloride made the paper water repellent after the excess fumes from the alcohol had been driven off by heating. He notes that "Had I applied paraffin wax—or even stearic acid—there would have been no reaction with the chromyl chloride."

Iler then tried chip paper and newsprint which still contained some natural resin. These became water repellent when treated with chromyl chloride vapor and heated, but it was a clumsy process.

Continuing his efforts to develop a practical approach to the desired reaction product, Iler reacted lauryl alcohol and chromyl chloride in carbon tetrachloride with the idea of getting a solution which could be applied to paper. But the product was a grease on the test tube walls and was not soluble in carbon tetrachloride.

Iler tried to wash out the test tube with water, but found the material was insoluble in water. He then used methanol—and the solids dissolved easily. The resultant solution, however, did not make the paper water repellent.

Iler poured the solution into the sink, some of it going into a beaker of water. The material, previously insoluble in water, did not form a milky suspension or precipitate as one would expect when an alcoholic solution of water-insoluble material is poured into water. Instead, it formed a clear green solution. Concluding that there must have been some further combination with the methanol, Iler applied the solution to paper and dried it over the hotplate. The paper then became water repellent.

Iler concludes, "By chance, I had used the right ratio of lauryl alcohol and chromyl chloride, and by chance, I first dissolved the reaction product in a water-mixable solvent, both things being necessary to obtain a water-soluble product. There was a whole series of fortunate incidents involved!"

Although Iler, with characteristic modesty, emphasizes the happenstance factor in his discovery, the progression from the first observation of water repellancy to the first usable solution was in reality quite orderly and thoughtful.

As Iler succinctly put it in an early technical paper: "Following the discovery that paper could be rendered water repellent by treatment with chromyl chloride vapor, the reaction products of chromyl chloride with certain organic materials were investigated with the objective of finding a water repelling agent that could be applied from aqueous solution."

Moreover, once the discovery had been made, a practical process had to be developed for commercial use. This took about 4 years, and some involved process chemistry had to be pioneered by Iler and his associates. Meanwhile, Iler also became a "salesman," trying to develop uses for the product both inside and outside the company.

The first form of "Quilon" chrome complex was stearato chromic chloride. It was a complex compound in which stearic acid was combined with trivalent chromic cations to form a water-soluble, surface-active product which was strongly absorbed from aqueous solution by negatively charged surfaces like cellulose, proteins, and glass. The adsorbed film is water repellent, and when dried, the complex becomes insoluble in water.

Putting it more simply, when "Quilon" chrome complex is applied, the chromium end of the molecule attaches itself to the negatively charged surface of paper or other materials. The fatty acid groups of the molecule thereby are oriented outward, forming an insoluble water-repellent finish on the surface.

Putting the Heat on
Peaches and Papayas

HAROLD T. COOK

. . . .

Peaches and papayas are delicious fruits, but they used to often decay before they could ripen and reach the people who use them. They would look perfect when picked and shipped, but be decayed and moldy by the time they reached the terminal market.

One spoiled peach in a transparent film-covered tray of fruit could make the whole tray unsalable. The housewife who bought beautifully colored, firm peaches on Thursday expecting to ripen them at home for Sunday dinner dessert would often find they had decayed.

Papayas are exotic tropical fruits which must be transported for long distances to reach city markets in temperate climates. Some come from Florida and California, but the majority come from Hawaii and Puerto Rico. These luxury fruits used to frequently arrive in decayed condition or else decay before they could be marketed.

The monetary losses caused by decay between the farm and the table were large. Besides loss of the fruit, there was the cost of washing, grading, packing, and shipping. Repeat purchases also were affected. Housewives were reluctant to buy again after experiencing excessive decay in fruit they had purchased.

Heat treatments now offer a way to reduce decay in peaches, papayas, and some other kinds of fruits and vegetables. Scientists have shown that if just the right amount of heat is used, the fungi and bacteria which cause decay can be killed without affecting the appearance, flavor, and ripening. The result: Today's consumer gets excellent quality fruit and vegetables that have been treated in this way.

Heat treatments are better than chemical treatments because they kill the decay fungi and bacteria even after these have penetrated beneath the skin. Chemical treatments only kill the ones on the surface. Another big advantage is that heat treatments do not leave residues.

Use of heat to control decay is not new. H. S. Fawcett, a plant pathologist at the University of California Citrus Experiment Station, Riverside, reported in 1922 that washing lemons for 2 minutes in water heated to 115° to 120° F. would control brown rot much better than the copper sulfate bath then being used.

This treatment was immediately put into use by commercial lemon packinghouses, but it was many years before heat treatments were developed for other fruits and vegetables.

∴   ∴   ∴

HAROLD T. COOK *is Director of the Market Quality Research Division, Agricultural Research Service.*

About 30 years after Fawcett's report, heat treatments were developed in Hawaii to control anthracnose decay in papayas. For many years, this disease caused widespread decay of papayas shipped from Hawaii to the mainland of the United States. Papayas are often diseased when picked, but the decay does not spread until the fruit is just about ripe. Chemical treatments after harvest are ineffective.

E. K. Akamine and T. Arisumi, at the University of Hawaii Agricultural Experiment Station, experimented with vapor-heat and hot-water treatments. In 1953, they reported that treating fruits for 20 minutes in water heated to 110° to 120° F. gave excellent control of decay in laboratory tests. Then, they tested the treatment in shipments from Honolulu to San Francisco.

Control of anthracnose was as good in the commercial shipments as in the laboratory tests. There was no decay in the treated fruit when unloaded in San Francisco after 6 to 7 days in the ship's hold, while about 17 percent of the untreated fruit was decayed. The vapor-heat treatments also controlled decay, but they took much longer and sometimes injured the fruit.

About 10 years later, Wilson L. Smith, Jr., a U.S. Department of Agriculture plant pathologist at Beltsville, Md., prompted by Fawcett's success, decided to try heat treatments to control brown rot and rhizopus rot of peaches. These diseases sometimes caused whole carloads of peaches to be dumped because of excessive spoilage on arrival at the terminal markets. Brown rot and rhizopus rot of peaches after harvest had defied the efforts of generations of plant pathologists to find practical and effective methods of control. Smith, himself, had already tried numerous chemical treatments, but none reduced spoilage enough to be commercially worthwhile.

Smith gave the heat treatment a severe test. He made shallow cuts in peaches and dipped them in water containing hundreds of thousands of spores of the brown rot and rhizopus

Wilson L. Smith, Jr., *foreground,* conducts a test with portable heat treating tank which he took into peach packing areas.

fungi. He even waited for 24 hours to allow the rot fungi a headstart before he dipped the fruit in hot water. He experimented with temperatures from 120° to 140° F. for 2, 3, and 7 minutes to find how high a temperature and how long a treatment was necessary to reduce the spoilage and how high a temperature could be used without injuring the fruit.

His laboratory tests showed that, even under very extreme disease conditions, peaches treated for 3 minutes in water heated to 130° F. or for 7 minutes in water heated to 120° F. had 70 percent less decay than untreated fruit. And these treatments did not injure the fruit.

But would the hot-water treatment work as well in commercial packing sheds as in the laboratory? Smith was not long in finding out. In 1963, he had a portable heating tank mounted on a trailer and went into the peach-growing areas of Georgia and South Carolina to run tests in commercial packing sheds. He treated peaches and sent them to eastern and midwestern markets in 27 commercial loads. The treatment worked as well in these practical shipping tests as it did in the laboratory experiments.

The results were so convincing that one packing shed operator in Georgia installed a hot-water tank that season and treated around 40 commercial loads. Other packing sheds used the treatment the following year.

Treatment for 2 to 3 minutes in water heated to 125° to 127° F. is recommended now.

Smith's experiments with peaches and Akamine's tests with papayas stimulated other plant scientists to try heat treatments for market diseases of various fruits and vegetables. If hot water worked for lemons, peaches, and papayas, why wouldn't it for other fruits and vegetables?

W. Pennock and G. Maldonaldo, at the University of Puerto Rico Agricultural Experiment Station, and J. J. Smoot and R. H. Segall, at the USDA Horticultural Field Station, Orlando, Fla., independently experimented with heat treatments to control anthracnose on mangoes. This disease is so common that it is often difficult to find a ripe mango on the market not blackened by it. Chemical treatments are useless because virtually all mangoes already have nearly invisible pinpoint anthracnose spots when they are picked.

Both teams had good results with hot-water treatments. Pennock and Maldonaldo obtained good control of anthracnose by dipping the fruit in water heated to about 123° to 125° F. for 15 minutes. Smoot and Segall found that only a 5-minute treatment was necessary if the water was heated to 130° to 132.5° F.

T. T. Hatton and W. F. Reeder at the USDA Horticultural Field Station, Miami, Fla., tried the hot-water treatment under commercial conditions in a mango packing shed that had a hot-water tank which could handle 50 bushels of fruit in an hour. They reported that treating for 5 minutes at 131° F. controlled anthracnose well.

Texas bell pepper shippers were plagued with severe losses from bacterial decay until H. B. Johnson, a USDA plant pathologist at Harlingen, Tex., tried hot-water treatments. Losses up to 50 percent occurred in some shipments. The bacteria that cause decay infect the peppers through the broken stems during picking, washing, and packing, but the decay does not become evident until peppers reach the market. Johnson had found that decay could be reduced considerably by washing the wax applicator brushes frequently with chlorine. But he was not satisfied. There was still too much decay. Maybe Smith's hot-water treatment would be as good for peppers as it was for peaches and mangoes.

Johnson gave the hot-water treatment a stringent test. He cut the stems of freshly harvested peppers, smeared them with a mixture of water and decayed pepper, and kept them in a plastic bag for about a day to give the bacteria a good start. Then he treated them for 2½ minutes in water heated to 123° F., 1½ minutes in water at 128° F., and three-fourths of a minute in water at 133° F. The 1½-minute treatment at 128° F. was best.

Seven days after treatment, only 19 percent of the treated peppers were decayed compared to 73 percent of the untreated and 59 percent of the peppers waxed with chlorine-treated brushes. The Texas shippers were impressed. Now, many of their peppers are treated in hot water.

Texas cantaloup shippers were hav-

ing troubles, also. Cantaloups they harvested during wet periods became moldy en route to market. Sometimes the molds caused decay at the stem end.

Johnson's success with hot-water treatment for peppers prompted him to try it on cantaloups. His experiments in 1965 showed that moldiness and decay were greatly reduced by dipping cantaloups for only a half a minute in water heated to 135° to 145° F. Commercial tests were as successful as the laboratory experiments, and by 1967, hot-water treatment was being used in seven packing sheds in Texas and two across the river in Mexico.

Smith and Akamine's rediscovery of the usefulness of hot water to control spoilage of fruits and vegetables after harvest also stimulated investigations overseas. R. T. Burchill, an English plant pathologist, successfully used hot-water treatments to control Gloeosporium rot, a serious storage disease of apples. On the other side of the world, K. M. Harrow and R. Foster at Auckland, New Zealand, reported excellent control of peach decay by dipping the fruit for 10 minutes in water heated to 122° F.

Heat treatments hold promise of even wider application. Hot-water treatments have been used successfully on raspberries and blueberries, and vapor-heat treatments have shown considerable promise for strawberries and fresh figs.

Experiments indicate that hot water combined with gamma irradiation may be more effective than either treatment alone for some products.

The treatments must be developed specifically for each kind and each variety of fruit or vegetable and for each disease. Treatments which are good for peaches may injure some kinds of fruits or vegetables and not be effective against some diseases. Also, it is important to protect the fruit or vegetable following heat treatment. Benefits of the treatment would be quickly undone if the fruit or vegetable were cooled afterward in water that was not clean.

354

Sleeping Sickness Wakes Again

ROBERT J. BYRNE

....

Sleeping sickness of horses was, as recently as the 1930's, the most devastating livestock disease in the United States. Horses died by the hundreds of thousands in the Midwestern United States, in California, and along the Atlantic seaboard at a period which coincided with the beginning of the sharp decline in the use of horses on the farm. Losses were so severe in some areas that the inevitable process of farm mechanization, particularly the use of tractors, was accelerated.

Today, the owners of horses, ponies, mules, and burros can take steps to protect their animals from this continuing disease threat.

As used in this chapter, sleeping sickness refers to equine encephalitis, a virus disease of American horses. It should not be confused with African sleeping sickness of human beings which is caused by a blood parasite and spread by bites of tsetse flies.

While severe outbreaks of equine encephalitis had been observed during early periods of American history, the most significant milestones weren't reached until the 1930's in determining its cause, in witnessing its most devastating effects, and in developing control methods.

Credit for recognizing equine encephalitis as a virus disease, and one that is transmitted to horses by mosquitoes, belongs to veterinarians, physicians, and entomologists serving in the U.S. Department of Agriculture

and various biomedical research institutions. Among those who figured prominently were K. F. Meyer, formerly of the University of California and presently Director Emeritus of the Hooper Foundation. USDA veterinarians who contributed to early research on equine encephalitis included H. W. Schoening, M. S. Shahan, and L. T. Giltner.

Investigators soon found that equine encephalitis was due to two different viruses, both producing a similar disease. They were designated as the eastern and western strains of virus. The western virus affects horses generally west of the Appalachians. The eastern attacks horses along the Atlantic seaboard and in the Gulf States. Subsequently, it was found that the two viruses and the disease they produce overlap considerably in their geographic distribution.

Another type of equine encephalitis, affecting horses in South and Central America, is Venezuelan equine encephalitis. However, this disease has not been recognized in horses in the United States.

Meyer was also the first to speculate that the virus causing equine sleeping sickness might also cause encephalitis in human beings. His theories proved out, as it was soon established that

ROBERT J. BYRNE *is Chief, Research Reference Reagents Branch, National Institute of Allergy and Infectious Diseases, National Institutes of Health, Bethesda, Md.*

both man and horses are victims of the same disease resulting from exposure to a common source of infection which is found in nature.

Responding to the devastating effect of virus equine encephalitis on American horses in the early 1930's, USDA scientists mounted an intensive research program to understand the disease's nature. They also needed to get this information to veterinarians and animal disease regulatory officials and to develop a control program. Fortunately, the program was highly successful. A satisfactory vaccine emerged by the end of the 1930's.

Pioneer work in the study of vaccines for horses was done by USDA. Development of the most practical vaccine resulted from later discoveries that equine encephalitis virus multiplies readily in developing chick embryos. From these embryos a virus-rich material is obtained which can be made into a potent, safe vaccine.

This finding resulted in commercial production of vaccines which are in present-day use. The vaccines contain both eastern and western strains of virus, since one strain does not protect against the other.

Despite these advances, however, the disease is still a threat to the health of animals and man. To explain this paradox, we need to examine the nature of the virus, the type of disease that it produces, and how it survives in nature and spreads to its victims.

Equine encephalitis is caused by a virus considerably more lethal than viruses causing the common cold, chickenpox, or measles. Like other viruses, it is so small it can't be seen under the ordinary microscope. The virus multiplies in the cells of intact living animals or insects, although it can also be propagated in living cells grown in tissue cultures in the laboratory. As with most other viruses, the equine encephalitis virus is not damaged or killed by penicillin or other antibiotics, so the disease in animals cannot be cured or prevented by using antibiotics. However, chemical agents commonly used as disinfectants do kill the virus and are used in laboratory procedures and in disinfecting.

In the laboratory, the virus can infect and cause disease and death in a variety of experimental animals including mice, guinea pigs, and rabbits. Certain birds, and in particular English sparrows and pheasants, are highly susceptible to the virus and die within days following exposure.

Newly hatched (baby) chicks are highly susceptible, but older chickens are resistant. The virus attacks primarily the brain and so is much more lethal when injected directly into the brain of an animal than, for example, when injected into the muscle or under the skin. This is even true with horses. Only a fraction of horses injected under or into the skin with the virus, or bitten by infected mosquitoes, develop the disease and die.

The virus strains causing western and eastern forms of sleeping sickness are in the family of arboviruses—not to be confused with tree viruses. Arbovirus is a shortened form of arthropod-borne animal virus. Arthropods are members of the animal kingdom having an external skeleton and jointed body and legs. They include mosquitoes, ticks, and mites.

Equine encephalitis virus strains are intimately linked to arthropods since they can multiply in mosquitoes which have obtained a virus-containing blood meal from an infected bird or animal. The virus then migrates to the salivary glands of the mosquito where it again multiplies. Thus this mosquito becomes capable of spreading infection, by biting, for the rest of its life. The mosquito spreads infection without being adversely affected itself. The relationship of yellow fever, another arbovirus, and the *Aedes aegypti* mosquito was worked out at the turn of the century by U.S. Army scientists led by Maj. Walter Reed.

Since infected human beings and horses don't have enough virus in their blood to infect mosquitoes, considerable research was needed to determine how mosquitoes become infected in nature. Results of this research revealed the complexity of the equine encephalitis threat.

It was found that mosquitoes picked up the infection from a variety of wild birds and rodents, some of which reside in almost inaccessible swamps and forests. In these remote areas, the virus can be maintained in a bird-mosquito cycle without doing any apparent harm to domestic animals or man. Because of this, the virus almost defies elimination from the environment.

Under certain circumstances, such as heavy rains and a resultant increase in mosquitoes, the virus breaks loose from its natural surroundings and spreads to birds and other mosquitoes in closer contact with man. The natural cycles for western and eastern forms are not identical nor are the specific mosquitoes that cause their spread. But the basic involvement of wildlife reservoirs presents the same problem in controlling the disease.

A localized outbreak of eastern equine encephalitis which I observed in 1960 will illustrate a number of factors influencing the number and distribution of cases of disease. In mid-August of that year, a few cases of encephalitis in horses in tidewater Maryland were reported and subsequently confirmed by laboratory tests. The disease continued to occur in Maryland horses and ponies until late September. The population of mosquitoes during this period was quite high. Rainfall was above average during August. Hurricane Donna left very heavy rain along the coast on September 12. No cases of the disease were observed in vaccinated animals.

After several weeks with no new cases being reported, the disease broke out again in the pony herds on Chincoteague and Assateague Islands in Virginia. Most of the deaths were among foals born in the spring of 1960. Many of these young animals had been held past the regular "pony-penning" sale and were used in the filming, during July and August, of

Pony, *right,* starred as young Misty in the movie "Misty" and died afterwards from equine encephalitis. Many ponies in the film were from wild herds on Virginia islands.

the motion picture, "Misty." A pony which had portrayed young Misty in the film was one of the first to die from the disease in October. At least 30 ponies, none of which had been vaccinated, died on Assateague and on Chincoteague from October 10 to 20.

This outbreak of equine encephalitis had two phases. The first phase represented scattered deaths in tidewater Maryland among horses exposed to the high concentration of mosquitoes resulting from above average rainfall and continued warm weather through much of September. The second phase, the outbreak on Chincoteague and Assateague, followed by 2 to 3 weeks a deluge of rain, from Hurricane Donna. This, plus continued warm weather, resulted in a new wave of mosquitoes—many of which had obtained the infecting virus. The crop of young, susceptible ponies on the coastal islands of Virginia was thus vulnerable to this situation.

Horses infected with encephalitis virus from the bite of a disease-carrying mosquito may react in a number of ways. As previously stated, a significant number show no ill effects—in fact such horses probably become immune to the infecting virus for life.

Other infected horses develop only a slight fever and recover to normal in a few days.

The most severe form is encephalitis or inflammation of the brain. In this form, the disease is commonly recognized, and more than half the horses which develop brain inflammation die.

Early indications of disease which would attract the owner's attention are signs of depression, lack of appetite, and drowsiness—hence the name sleeping sickness. Animals frequently grind their teeth and stagger slightly when moving. While the disease progresses, animals become reluctant to move and are inclined to lean against walls, fences, or other structures. In the final stages, affected horses stagger blindly and finally fall. When down, they continue an aimless, running motion until they die or are killed.

Sometimes an animal with equine encephalitis doesn't reach the severe stage and may recover completely and probably be immune for life. Those which are most severely affected, and yet survive, are likely to be left with permanent brain damage—the so-called dummy horses. Little can be done to treat sleeping sickness of horses once recognizable signs occur.

However, a veterinarian should be called when the disease is suspected. First of all, the veterinarian may determine that the suspect horse has a disease other than equine encephalitis, and this may be a disease that can be treated successfully. Second, it is important that veterinarians obtain confirmation of equine encephalitis cases in order to inform the animal disease control authorities.

Control measures, including vaccination and mosquito suppression, can be launched or intensified and the lives of other animals saved.

Since there are no specific treatments of any value for equine encephalitis, great emphasis should be placed on preventing the disease. In most U.S. areas, the owners of horses, ponies, mules, and burros should have their animals vaccinated. This is particularly desirable in the areas where the disease is known to occur. Vaccination also is strongly recommended for any horses moved from place to place for shows and races.

Because of the overlap in distribution of eastern and western types of equine encephalitis, bivalent vaccines are recommended, containing a protection against both types.

Horses and other equine animals in risk areas should be vaccinated annually several months in advance of the usual time of the disease's occurrence. August and September are the months equine encephalitis is most frequently observed, so vaccination should take place toward the end of spring. If vaccination has not been carried out due to oversight, it is still worthwhile, even in the face of an outbreak.

A necessary part of prevention is mosquito control, which is primarily in the hands of State or local government. Mosquito control measures are most beneficial if applied early in an outbreak of equine encephalitis and when directed at the particular mosquitoes implicated in its spread. Mosquito control efforts are highly effective in preventing the spread of yellow fever which is carried by the *Aedes aegypti* mosquito, an urban area dweller. But the complex natural history of eastern and western types of equine encephalitis makes mosquito control measures against this virus more difficult. Continued research may solve some of the problems.

The individual horse owner can apply mosquito control measures in horse stables and transportation vans. Recommendations for safe, effective sprays can be obtained from county agents and local mosquito control authorities. Bringing pastured animals indoors during the night reduces exposure to mosquitoes that carry and spread the infection.

Although man and horses are both victims of the same disease, it is not spread from horses or man. Both contract the disease from a common source in nature. If you compare the number of people in the United States with the number of horses and then examine the frequency of the disease in each, it becomes quickly obvious that the disease in man is quite rare. In horses, the attack rate is higher because they are openly exposed to heavy concentrations of mosquitoes in areas where equine encephalitis occurs.

In summary, the health of animals and man have benefited from research on equine encephalitis (sleeping sickness) virus. Effective vaccines have been developed. The mosquito control measures have been strengthened. And improved laboratory techniques have speeded diagnosis of the disease so that quick action can be taken to save lives. More advances will come through the coordinated efforts of physicians, veterinarians, entomologists, microbiologists, and other scientists who make up the research team.

Knock on Any Door: Consumer Research

THEODORE R. CRANE

. . . .

Household surveys of consumer opinion, studies of reactions to new foods and fibers, all help bridge the gap between the farmer and his ultimate customers. It is a distance that may span hundreds or even thousands of miles, a marketing system that includes a crowd of intermediary handlers and processors.

Mrs. McCann, with her six kids, husband, one dog, and an occasional stray cat, lives in a comfortable rambling house on the edge of the small western town where her husband runs a prospering hardware store.

When she thinks of food—which is often, with a family her size—she thinks first of food that the entire family will like.

Mrs. Hoffman's home, a modest brick structure, is in a development not far from the shores of Lake Michigan. The house seems a bit crowded, especially now that little Anne has joined the other two children of the family. But things have been slow at the factory, and her husband Jim says they can't think about a bigger place just now.

When Mrs. Hoffman goes to market, the price of food is at the top of her shopping list. Thus convenience takes second place.

Shopping, for the recently married Lowes, is a sometime thing, since both work and often they stop for dinner on their way home to the apartment.

Mrs. Lowe puts a premium on convenience, figuring any time saved in routine kitchenwork is worth the price.

The McCanns, the Hoffmans, and the Lowes are miles apart in their ways of life, further apart in their tastes, their needs, and their desires. When they shop for food, they are meeting quite different requirements.

The families represent one of the central problems of merchandising in these days of mass production leading to—and depending on—mass purchases. They live in cities hundreds of miles from the producer, and they are the unknown but all-important customers in the sales charts.

Helping the producer get to know the needs and the opinions of these families is the job of consumer surveys, opinion research.

In the U.S. Department of Agriculture, much of the work on consumer opinion and attitudes is done by the Special Surveys Branch of the Statistical Reporting Service. This group of social scientists gives the consumer a chance to say what he—more likely she—thinks about a given food or fiber. Such research gets the word back to the producer.

The need for information of this type is increasingly important. Not only is the pressure of competition keener these days, it is costlier, with the proliferation of mixes and processes and instant substitutes.

∴   ∴   ∴

THEODORE R. CRANE *is Acting Chief of the Special Reports Division, Office of Information.*

Studies of consumer opinions and reactions take some of the guesswork out of the hazardous business of merchandising farm products. The surveys are a necessary step in evaluating the consumer's opinion of the basic merits of products developed by USDA's utilization research laboratories. And in general, the work helps to guide the technical studies which provide farm products in a form that more closely satisfies consumer demands. Recent work with citrus fruit is a case in point.

About three out of every five crates of citrus fruit end up in processing plants. With a predicted increase in the per capita supply of processed citrus products, the industry needs to increase its share of the beverage market. Thus, the industry is constantly in search of new products which can serve to expand the market for citrus fruit.

One of the most promising recent developments is a dehydrated base for citrus juice. Crystals from a foam-mat drying process are an attempt to capture more of the true citrus flavor than other drying techniques. The crystals can be stored for months on end without refrigeration.

This powderlike product resulted from USDA's utilization research, a function of the Agricultural Research Service, with the cooperation of the Florida Citrus Commission.

The first step in finding out what the consumer might think of the citrus powder would be a series of taste tests, more accurately known as sensory evaluation studies.

Headquarters for the taste tests is a small room off a busy corridor of USDA's South Building in downtown Washington, D.C. The laboratory provides an environment in which participants can react, under controlled conditions, to a number of qualities of a given food.

The tests, for example, measure reactions to differences in such characteristics as flavor, sweetness, texture, or even the effect of months of storage on the shelf.

Such tests can help to determine whether there is any hope at all for the

In USDA taste test laboratory, volunteers sample a new fruit juice, giving it a rating that can range all the way from "like extremely" to "dislike extremely." Separate booths, special lighting, pass-through to the kitchen, all are part of environmental controls that help keep test reactions free of extraneous influences.

grapefruit juice crystals and find it out before the product undergoes the vastly more expensive household surveys of consumer opinion.

For the powdered grapefruit juice there were specific questions to be answered. One set of tests checked out the consumer preference for different concentrations of peel oil in the reconstituted juice. Peel oil contains most of the ingredients that give the juice a natural flavor.

Other tests in the sensory evaluation laboratory provided a rating of the reconstituted juice when compared with canned grapefruit juice and frozen concentrate. In time, an improved formula was considered ready to try out against the wider range of consumer preferences that would show up in a household survey.

The dried grapefruit juice is just one of scores of different food products that have been put to the laboratory's simulated consumer vote. One study tested two variations of a low-fat dairy spread to find out whether volunteers could

distinguish between the two. Answer: They could.

The Special Surveys Branch is presented with problems and test products from a number of sources. Many of the new foods, like the grapefruit crystals, come in from the utilization laboratories. State colleges and universities may also ask to have one of their products run through the sensory evaluation laboratory. The dairy spread was an example. And farm associations—dairy producers, citrus growers, livestock men—may ask USDA to provide an objective, unbiased test of their product's consumer appeal. When such a group does request a study of one of their products, often they help to pay for part of the work.

There comes a day, however, when the new food must move out of the laboratory, when it is time to distribute samples of the product to selected households. It's part of the field survey work which will evaluate consumer opinions of the product as it might actually be used in the home.

First step in working out a survey of consumer acceptance of the dehydrated grapefruit juice was to put together a set of specifications for the kind of data wanted and the manner in which they should be gathered.

The specifications, for example, called for the survey to be held in a metropolitan area—it would be easier to find the necessary number of families who use grapefruit juice. And the work was kept out of a citrus region to avoid possible bias.

After a questionnaire has been written, it is pretested. The pretest helps the researchers find out how the questions will sound in the actual interview. Can the interviewer read the questions aloud easily? Are they understandable to the respondents? Do they avoid antagonizing the respondents? These are a few of the problems that can be removed during such a trial run.

When the questionnaire is ready, when all necessary changes are made in trial runs, the interviewing force is ready to move out into the streets and begin the business of knocking on doors. The grapefruit study was a fairly small one. Some 18 interviewers were used to gather the voluntary information from families in 400 Pittsburgh houses and apartments.

The interviewer carries a sizable package of material. For the survey of grapefruit juice crystals, she had a letter of introduction, forms for the initial interview and the two followup questionnaires, a page of questions for each household member who would try the juice. All together, there were 20 or more pages of interviews, questionnaires and rating forms, instructions and visual aids in the form of scale cards, not to mention a supply of the product to distribute.

As the questions unreel, the profile of the potential user of the dehydrated grapefruit juice begins to build up: How old are the members of the family? How large the family income? What juices does the family use? How often? In what form? Canned? Frozen? What advantages would there be to a powdered grapefruit juice? And what disadvantages?

In a half hour or so, this first questionnaire is complete. It is time to leave packets of the crystals—either a sweetened or unsweetened formula—and make an appointment for the followup visit, with further questions.

On the return visit, the interviewer asks what the family thought of the grapefruit crystals. How did they like the reconstituted juice? Was it easy to mix? Were the instructions clear?

A week later, the last interview. There's another report on the packets of grapefruit crystals used, then the final wrap-up interview.

How did the crystals compare with the family's usual grapefruit juice? In taste? Ease of preparation? Even in texture or color? Did the homemaker follow directions exactly? In what way could the package be improved?

And then on to expectations in the marketplace.

Would the housewife buy the grapefruit crystals if she found them at her store? And how much would she expect to pay? More, or less, than grapefruit juice in other forms? And on and on, until the last line has been filled in, the last question answered.

Then the painstaking work begins. There will be weeks of preparing the information for the computers, analyzing results, discarding less important tables and figures, and, finally, putting together the report for publication. This is the payoff point for everyone, the moment when the researchers and the farmers get the results from the homemaker's ballot.

Was a new convenience food born? Or has the promise faded from another new formula, sending it back to the laboratory?

Each study poses different problems. One study, for example, cataloged consumer opinion of the all-American broiler-fryer, documenting the fact that chicken is just about everyone's dish. Some 97 percent of the homemakers interviewed had used chicken during the survey year. Why? The report indicated that the price usually

362

attracted customers. And the national pastime of outdoor cooking in the summer helped to boost the popularity of chicken.

Farms grow more than food. Other surveys have given the consumer a chance to voice her opinion of such products as cotton and wool clothing. One study concentrated on the teen-age population, the buyers just starting to do their own shopping, developing loyalties that could last for a lifetime of purchases.

Studies of the consumer's whim of iron, measures of attitudes that shape a market, all have long been part of USDA's research program. And the need to test the winds of opinion will continue for a long time to come, as long, in fact, as competition exists in the marketplace.

As the stakes get bigger, as the distance between the consumer and the producer widens, consumer opinion studies will help make it possible for the farmer—and the entire marketing system—to hear the voice of the Lowes, the Hoffmans, and the McCanns.

Selenium—Vital but Toxic Needle in the Haystack

W. H. ALLAWAY

. . . .

Selenium is essential, in very small amounts, to animal life. Yet, this same element is more toxic than arsenic, and it is less abundant in the earth's crust than gold. If cows and sheep are wintered on hay that contains less than two one-thousandths of an ounce of selenium per ton, their lambs and calves may die from "white muscle disease." But if forage for cattle and sheep contains more than two-tenths of an ounce of selenium per ton, growth will be depressed, their hooves may break off, and their hair fall out. Still higher levels of selenium in the feed may cause death.

People in the United States have been interested in selenium since 1857, when some cavalry horses at Fort Randall, S. Dak., got sick while grazing certain pastures near the fort. Similar problems occurred in range livestock in various localities in the northern Plains during the years that followed. It was not until 1933 that the cause of these troubles was found to be an excess of selenium in the plants in these localities.

Interest in selenium took a sharp change in direction in 1957 when scientists at the National Institutes of Health found that selenium would protect rats from liver degeneration when they were fed diets low in vitamin E. Within 2 years, other groups found that small amounts of selenium would prevent some critical diseases of lambs, calves, chickens, and pigs.

In 1961, a small group of us at the U.S. Plant, Soil and Nutrition Laboratory at Cornell University in Ithaca, N.Y., started to look into the soil and plant factors that might be involved in occurrence of the selenium-responsive diseases of livestock.

∴ ∴ ∴

W. H. ALLAWAY *is a Soil Scientist and Director of the U.S. Plant, Soil and Nutrition Laboratory, Agricultural Research Service at Cornell University, Ithaca, N.Y.*

Alfalfa sample is burned in oxygen-filled flask as first step in measuring amount of selenium present. Balloon acts as safety valve.

We asked ourselves several questions. First—was selenium moving from soils to plants to animals in some localities, but not in others, in sufficient quantities to protect animals from selenium-responsive diseases? It seemed that it probably was, but these diseases were usually found where a double deficiency—selenium and vitamin E—was present, and there was evidence that some unknown factor in certain feeds increased the animal requirement for either selenium or vitamin E.

Occurrence of the selenium-respon-sive diseases could, then, have been controlled by factors affecting the distribution or stability of vitamin E or by factors controlling the distribution of some unidentified inhibitor.

We prepared a map of the United States showing the distribution of cases of white muscle disease as these cases were reported by State veterinary diagnostic labs and by animal nutritionists at the State experiment stations. Then we plotted on this map the distribution of soils formed from geological materials known or suspected to contain selenium. This phase of the study was based upon findings about the geology of selenium by scientists at Wyoming, South Dakota, the U.S. Department of Agriculture, and Columbia University who were working on selenium toxicity in the Plains States following the 1933 discovery.

When the two features—white muscle disease and our estimated distribution of soils formed from materials containing selenium—were plotted on the same map, it was quite evident that white muscle disease was very rare wherever naturally occurring selenium was a probable part of the soil. So, we were confident that soil and plant selenium was involved in the problem.

At this point, we had to develop a reliable method for measuring the selenium content of plants and animals. This was difficult because selenium is volatile, and it might be lost from the biological material during the ashing process so essential to removing the selenium from proteins and other organic components. This difficulty was met by burning the material in an oxygen-filled flask. We finally pieced together certain parts of selenium methods developed in England and New Zealand and developed a technique that would reliably measure as little as one one-hundredth of a part per million (three ten-thousandths of an ounce per ton) of selenium in dry plant or animal tissue. Thus, we could, indeed, find a needle in a haystack! The method was cross-checked with a technique called "neutron activation analysis," in which the selenium in the sample is made radioactive by placing it in an atomic reactor.

With this method, we set out to measure the selenium content in the feeds on the farms where white muscle disease had been a problem and to compare these selenium levels with those on farms where white muscle disease had never occurred. A number of county agents and extension workers helped us locate these farms. We found less than 0.1 part per million of selenium in forages and feed crops in regions where white muscle disease had occurred. There were other broad regions, such as the western part of the Corn Belt, where white muscle disease has been very rare and where all the feeds examined contained more than 0.1 part per million of selenium. We concluded that the selenium moving from soil to feed crop was responsible for the broad regional patterns of occurrence of white muscle disease.

Within the low-selenium regions there were, however, some farms that had never experienced white muscle disease problems. It appeared that in these low-selenium regions, the farm-to-farm occurrence of the problem was probably due to practices influencing the level of vitamin E in the feeds during the critical late winter months.

The next question was—just how effective in animal nutrition is the selenium in plants? Different chemical compounds of selenium were known to vary widely in their value for prevention of liver degeneration in rats, so it seemed there might be differences in nutritional value of the different selenium compounds in plants. For this work, we got help from some of our neighbors on the Cornell campus who were working on nutritional aspects of selenium. Using plants grown in our greenhouse in soil treated with selenium or in solutions containing radioactive selenium, we found that most of the selenium in alfalfa is combined with the protein fraction in an amino acid called "seleno-methionine." The New Zealanders had found substantial amounts of this compound in other forage plants.

When pure seleno-methionine or selenium in alfalfa was fed to chicks, rats, or lambs, it was digested at about the same rate and was as effective in preventing diseases as was sodium selenite, an inorganic source of selenium that had been used in many controlled experiments. So—the data on selenium requirements developed in these controlled experiments could be applied directly to judging the adequacy of selenium in farm-grown feeds.

From some of our work, plus data

from other scientists working on this problem, it appeared that lambs and calves needed at least 0.05 to 0.1 part per million of selenium in their feed in order to prevent white muscle disease, if the feed supply was also low in vitamin E. Chicks and turkeys required a little higher level of selenium.

During work on the selenium toxicity problem, it had been found that about 4 parts per million of selenium were necessary to cause toxic effects in animals. Feeds containing 0.1 to 4 parts of selenium per million should then protect animals from selenium-responsive diseases without causing any detrimental effects. Even though this "proper" range of selenium concentration seems narrow, it was obvious there were broad regions in the United States where the feeds naturally contained about the right amount.

Our next step was to prepare a map of the United States, attempting to show regions where feed crops were deficient in selenium and the regions where the feed crops contained an adequate level. We made use of a great many measurements of the selenium content of wheat and feed grains made 20 years earlier during studies of selenium toxicity in the Plains States.

We traveled over the rest of the country taking samples of forages from Miami to Okanogan, Wash., and from New Hampshire to the Imperial Valley. We usually sampled alfalfa because it grows in so many States, and we knew it would take up selenium if there was any in the soil. Altogether, over 3,000 samples of plant material were collected and analyzed in making this map. Major regions where feeds are low or very low in selenium are found in the Pacific Northwest, the eastern Corn Belt, and the Northeast and also along the South Atlantic seaboard. In the West Central and Southern United States, there is a large area where over 80 percent of the samples collected contained more than the critical level of 0.1 part per million of selenium.

We didn't find any samples of alfalfa

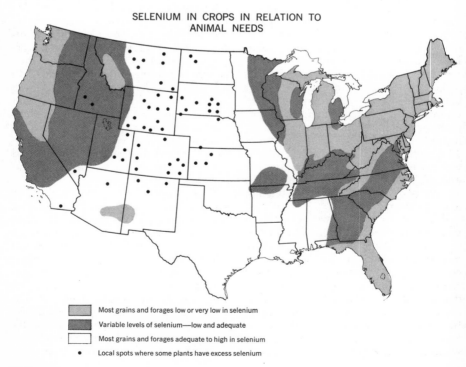

SELENIUM IN CROPS IN RELATION TO
ANIMAL NEEDS

Most grains and forages low or very low in selenium

Variable levels of selenium—low and adequate

Most grains and forages adequate to high in selenium

• Local spots where some plants have excess selenium

containing toxic levels of selenium, but local spots where toxic levels might occur—especially in some "selenium-accumulator" weedy plants—had been pretty well identified by the earlier workers. One thing that became obvious as the map took shape was that shipment of feed grains from the West Central United States to the Northeast has helped, almost accidentally, to meet the selenium needs of dairy cattle and poultry in the Northeast.

The next question was—would it be possible to add selenium to soil of the selenium-deficient areas in order to produce feeds with adequate, but nontoxic, levels of this element?

To answer this question, we joined forces with scientists at Oregon State. White muscle disease has been a serious problem in central Oregon for some time, and scientists at Oregon State had shown it could be prevented by adding small amounts of selenium to feeds grown there.

We rented an alfalfa field on a central Oregon ranch and applied 2 pounds of selenium per acre to half the field. Samples of the alfalfa, and of tissues from the lambs born to ewes that ate this alfalfa, were sent to the lab at Ithaca for analysis. Every lamb in the experiment was carefully examined in the clinical laboratory.

It worked. Over half the lambs born to ewes fed alfalfa from the untreated part of the central Oregon field developed white muscle disease, and about 20 percent of them died from it. But there was no white muscle disease among lambs born to ewes that were fed alfalfa from the selenium-treated half of the field. Levels of selenium in the edible meat from these lambs were well below amounts that might be toxic to people who ate this meat. Protective effects of one application of selenium lasted for 3 years of hay production and for three lamb crops and might have lasted longer—we didn't follow it after the third year.

Only about 2 percent of the selenium added to this central Oregon field was taken up by the alfalfa in the first 3 years after the selenium application.

We needed to know what had happened to the rest of the selenium.

Was it still in the soil and might it become available to plants all at once and give rise to toxic levels of selenium in the crops?

We tackled this question by "tagging" a number of different soils with radioactive selenium on them for a year, growing alfalfa in pots in our greenhouse and then hunting for the selenium left in the soils and finding out what chemical combinations it was in. It turned out that most of the selenium left in the soil was in one of two forms, both of which are quite inert and unavailable to plants. We found neither of these would change rapidly to forms that can be taken up by plants. So, addition of selenium to soil does offer possibilities as a way of improving nutritional quality of the feed crops produced, and if the rate of application is controlled, the danger of selenium toxicity is low.

But, before one tampers with the amount of any element which might become toxic as it circulates from plants to animals to people, it is a good idea to know how much of this element is normally circulating to humans. In the case of selenium, this knowledge was doubly important, because some early work on selenium toxicity indicated the continued feeding of toxic levels of selenium might cause cancer in rats. More recent work from Oregon State has shown there is little danger of cancer in rats fed for a long time on protective, nontoxic, levels of selenium. Still, we needed to know the normal selenium status of people.

So we obtained small samples of human blood from blood banks scattered across the United States and analyzed them for selenium. Selenium was present in every one of 210 samples of blood from 19 different cities, and the amounts present were remarkably uniform. We could barely measure the difference in selenium in blood of residents of Rapid City, S. Dak., in the selenium-adequate area and residents of the low-selenium area in the Northeastern United States.

367

Just at this time, we received some interesting data from Vanderbilt University, where a research team had measured the amount of selenium in the blood of Guatemalan children suffering from the nutritional disease called "kwashiorkor." Selenium concentration in the blood from these Guatemalan kwashiorkor patients was about half of the average we had found in our study of U.S. blood donors. Less than 3 percent of our donors were as low in blood selenium as were the kwashiorkor patients.

There were no available data on the levels of selenium in the blood of people exposed to excessive levels of selenium. But, if it is safe to reason from data on the levels of selenium in the blood of sheep suffering from selenium poisoning, none of our blood donors were even close to the danger level. So, it appears that if selenium is essential to humans as it is for many animals, most U.S. residents are above, although perhaps not far above, the possible required level of selenium.

Consequently, the chance of widespread selenium toxicity in U.S. residents appears remote.

Now, where are we? Although there are still many things to be done, we do know a bit more about the cycling of selenium in our environment. We know that vital amounts of selenium are moving from the soil to the plant to the animal. We know where these movements are keeping up with the needs of the animal and where they are not. We have some understanding of the biochemical processes involved. If it is desirable to increase the amounts of selenium circulating from soils to plants to animals, we have some good leads on how to make these adjustments with safety. In some places, these increases could improve the efficiency of production of animal products. There is a possibility they might also improve human health.

Our next step will be to test soil applications of selenium on small plots located on farms scattered throughout the selenium-deficient regions.

Aiding Mankind's Struggle Against Muscular Dystrophy

LOGAN M. JULIAN

. . . .

A hereditary disease of muscles of domestic chickens is aiding in research on muscular dystrophy of man by providing an experimental model of many of the disease processes which occur in comparable diseases of people.

Research on muscular dystrophy of man has long been handicapped because of the lack of experimental animals which had hereditary muscular dystrophy. It was not until 1955

that such a strain of experimental animals became available. At that time, hereditary muscular dystrophy was discovered in a strain of mice. Then, in 1956 an "inherited muscular abnormality" was found by an agricultural scientist in a strain of New Hampshire chickens at the University of California, Davis. This muscular disorder had a variety of characteristics which strongly resembled a number of the muscular dystrophies of

368

man. Still another hereditary muscular dystrophy was reported in 1962 in an inbred line of Syrian hamsters.

Before 1955, direct research on muscular dystrophy of man was restricted to studying the condition in patients. Family histories were probed and the clinical signs investigated to determine what the common factors of the disease might be. "Experimental" research was restricted to studying the reaction of muscles to interferences such as restriction of nutrients like vitamin E or interrupting the nerve or blood supply. Here the hope was that the study of a muscle that was obviously sick due to a known cause would help explain the detectable responses of a dystrophic muscle that was sick due to unknown causes.

Although much information was gained concerning the incidence of muscular dystrophy and the response of muscles, the availability of strains of animals with hereditary muscular dystrophy—animals in which dystrophic changes could be anticipated and used—has proved a great aid to the further understanding of muscular dystrophy of man. One of these biomedical models, the muscular dystrophic chicken, was developed when two of us doing unrelated work in agricultural research on the University of California's Davis campus put together the experience of our training, background, and interests.

During 1953, a geneticist, Dr. V. S. Asmundson, professor of poultry husbandry, brought some New Hampshire chickens to my laboratory with the question, "Can you tell me why it is that when these birds fall on their backs, they cannot get up?" Dr. Asmundson explained that he had obtained the chickens from a commercial breeder in a southern county of California and that the breeder had been selecting for broad-breasted birds when this mutation occurred. The

∴   ∴   ∴

LOGAN M. JULIAN *is Professor of Anatomy in the Department of Anatomy, School of Veterinary Medicine, University of California, Davis.*

chickens did have large breasts; in fact, the birds were being termed "double-breasted chickens." Dr. Asmundson was working out the inheritance of the abnormality, but wanted to know the cause of the physical disability since it posed a threat to the production of such a strain of chickens. Once they fell on their backs, they soon died of respiratory distress.

Since I am a veterinary anatomist convinced that anatomy is not a dead subject, but rather is living and vital when applied to problems of investigators working in other disciplines, Dr. Asmundson's question posed a challenge to me. I accepted the challenge; however, I must admit that to this day I have not been able to answer in specific detail why it is that the chickens can't right themselves.

Dissecting and then weighing individual muscles revealed some of them to be greatly enlarged. It appeared that the major depressor of the wing interfered, due to its enlargement, with the action of the major elevator of the wing. This might explain the inability of the bird to arise when placed on its back. In some birds, involved muscles did not remain enlarged but wasted away, sometimes to the point of weighing less than half their normal weight.

Microscopic examination of skeletal muscles of affected birds revealed a number of alterations that are typical for a variety of the muscular dystrophies of man. These include an increase of the number of nuclei of muscle fibers and outright destruction of some muscle fibers. Microscopic sections of wasted muscles (atrophied muscles) revealed that large quantities of fat had been deposited between existing muscle fibers.

In the meantime, Dr. Asmundson had determined that the condition was inherited as a simple recessive trait. That is, both parents would have to carry the gene for dystrophy. About one quarter of the offspring of such parents would have two "doses" of the gene, they would be homozygous for the gene, and would be clinically

369

dystrophic. Thus, the domestic chicken clearly had a hereditary disorder of muscles that resembled a variety of alterations that are encountered in one or more of the recognized types of muscular dystrophy of man.

Since that time (1956), work has continued and information has accumulated as to just what it is this chicken, as a biomedical model of muscular dystrophy of man, has to offer that can be of help in further understanding muscular dystrophy of the human being. Much of this work has been made possible through financial support of the Public Health Service of the U.S. Department of Health, Education, and Welfare.

Muscular dystrophy is defined literally as abnormal growth of muscles. Hereditary muscular dystrophy of the chicken is the most mild of the three forms of experimental muscular dystrophy (of the mouse, chicken, and hamster); therefore, it provides an excellent opportunity for study of the various disturbances of muscular growth that are represented.

Gross enlargement (hypertrophy) is the first detectable change that occurs in involved muscles. Hypertrophy is followed by wasting (atrophy). The degree of hypertrophy and the time of onset of atrophy are influenced by the particular muscle being studied and by the hereditary background of a particular dystrophic chicken.

Atrophy is associated with the deposition of fat. Thus, muscle fibers that are lost in the wasting process are replaced by fat. Hypertrophy, wasting, and fat deposition occur in a number of the varieties of muscular dystrophy of man. These changes are particularly prominent in the pitiful "Duchenne" type of rapidly progressive muscular dystrophy of young boys.

Dark muscles of dystrophic chickens are less vulnerable to the dystrophic processes than are the white muscles. Yet, all muscles do become involved sooner or later. This fact has not created a great deal of interest among medical researchers; however, it could be very important. It indicates there is something about the metabolism of dark muscles that delays the development of dystrophic changes.

Possibly the reason why this has not caused more interest is that skeletal muscles of man do not vary in color as they do in chickens. We all know from gustatory experience that drumsticks have dark meat and wings have white meat. In man, the comparative muscles—those of the calf and of the shoulder—do not differ in color. Nevertheless, it is recognized that the muscles of man are made up of two sorts of muscle fibers . . . dark (red) fibers and light (white) fibers.

Chickens that carry the major gene of muscular dystrophy (heterozygotes) show the same structural and functional characteristics of muscular dystrophy that are found in homozygous dystrophic chickens; however, these changes are much milder and occur much later. This situation, which has also been recognized in the dystrophic mouse and has been demonstrated in some human "carriers," permits the investigator to study the individual alterations most carefully, since they are going on more slowly.

All of the experimental models of muscular dystrophy of man . . . the mouse, the chicken, and the hamster . . . promise to aid in the fight against muscular dystrophy. The chicken has some particular advantages that are being capitalized upon. The size of the chicken as compared to a mouse or hamster is of considerable advantage because it permits obtaining a series of muscle samples from the same muscle for the study of structural or biochemical alterations.

The ability to genetically manipulate the chicken easily can be utilized to produce special strains of dystrophic chickens in which particular characteristics of the dystrophic process are concentrated. Dr. Asmundson has produced a line of dystrophic chickens that fail to arise from a flat surface at a very early age. This line has particularly large breast muscles. Another line has been developed in which disability occurs late. Another line has high fat content of the breast muscles . . . another low fat content.

By genetic manipulation, some of these characteristics can be combined.

As stated, hereditary muscular dystrophy of the chicken is the most mild of the experimental dystrophies. We do not know if muscular dystrophy ever kills the dystrophic chicken except in the case of accidental death that results when a bird falls on its back and suffocates. Since the chickens reach reproductive age and survive for a long period, it is quite simple to produce groups of experimental animals of a known genetic type for each of the special lines. This feature is a great advantage to an investigator since dealing with populations of experimental animals of known genetic type avoids the confusion caused by using a mixed population of animals.

None of the three hereditary muscular dystrophies of experimental animals (mouse, chicken, hamster) is an exact image of any one of the many forms of muscular dystrophy of man. Yet, a study of experimental animals may help unlock the riddle of muscular dystrophy of man.

In the case of muscular dystrophy of the chicken, processes of hypertrophy, atrophy, and fat deposition occur, and these are probably the processes which underlie the establishment of "pseudo-hypertrophy" (false enlargement) of skeletal muscles which occurs in some forms of muscular dystrophy of man.

Myotonia, the inability of a muscle to relax properly, occurs in at least two varieties of muscle diseases of man, and it also occurs in the chicken.

Photographers

Most of the pictures in this Yearbook are by U.S. Department of Agriculture photographers. If no organization follows a photographer's name in the credits, this usually indicates he took the photo for USDA. Credit is given to photographers—and in a few cases to photo directors—if their names are known.

Great help in assembling photos was given by USDA's Office of Information Photography Division, which is headed by Albert W. Matthews. Russell T. Forte of the Division was especially helpful, assisted by Mary M. Cowell. Others in USDA who provided photos include Robert C. Bjork, Stuart A. Oring, Bluford W. Muir, and Robert B. Branstead. Prints were made by the Office of Information and the Forest Service photo labs. The Editor is also indebted to other Government agencies, universities, private companies, and authors who furnished photos.

With few exceptions, photos in the Yearbook may be obtained by news media from the Photography Division, Office of Information, U.S. Department of Agriculture, Washington, D.C. 20250. Please refer to the 1968 Yearbook, and give the page number.

Note that roman numeral page numbering begins with the first photo in full color.

C. Wayne Adkins, XXXII.
Air Products and Chemicals, Inc., 270.
William C. Allen, 171.
Ansil Photograph, 264.
Clifton M. Audsley, 86.
Murray M. Berman, 274.
Robert C. Bjork, XI (top), XI (bottom, with Stuart A. Oring), XV (lower left), XX (top), XXV, 5, 97, 259.
Gene T. Bowers, 178.
Robert K. Brigham, Bureau of Commercial Fisheries, 22, 24, 28 (left), 32.
Bill Brown, Jr., XXII.
Hugo Bryan, 182.
Arthur Buckingham, 224 (top).
Albert M. Candido, 6, 7.
Central Soya, 40 (lower left).
Roy M. Clark, IX (upper right).

Erwin W. Cole, XV (lower right).
H. Cooper, 139 (top).
Richard A. Cooper, XXIX (top).
Max S. Corey, 141.
Harry C. Davis, XXIX (bottom).
E. I. duPont de Nemours & Co., 349.
Donald W. Drilling, XXIII (bottom).
Malcolm Emmons, XXIII (top).
Jack Everly, 127.
James N. Felger, 162.
Florida Citrus Commission, 268 (right).
Bob Fowler, Farm Journal, 93.
T. G. Freeman, 187.
Robert E. Garrett, 257.
Herbert Gehr, Life Magazine, 132.
Wallace C. Guy, IX (bottom).
E. P. Haddon, Fish and Wildlife Service, 29.
Harris Laboratories, Inc., II.

H. M. Hull, XIX (bottom).
Edwin C. Hunton, 39.
Starr Jenkins, 227.
George B. Kelez, Fish and Wildlife Service, 28 (right).
Kitchens of Sara Lee, 268 (left).
Harold A. Laney, 100, 101.
W. H. Lathrop, XLIV, 129.
George Lavris, New York State College of Agriculture, 67.
Murray D. Lemmon, VII (bottom), XVI (top, with Stuart A. Oring), XXI (top 2, with Stuart A. Oring), XXVI, 3 (bottom), 9, 12, 56, 59 (bottom), 66, 76, 90 (with Stuart A. Oring), 96, 102, 106, 144, 145, 297, 326, 373 (photo of USDA photographer Murray M. Berman).
Long Reach Manufacturing, XXIV (bottom).
Los Angeles County Air Pollution Control District, 143.
Wilford Mead, XXXIX, 238.
Merck & Co., Inc., I.
Ralph Mills, North Carolina State University, 34.
William G. Murray, 266.
Olin Myers, 31.
Ronald Nelson, 162 (bottom).
William P. Nye, XVI (bottom), 111.
Terence K. O'Driscoll, 83.
John H. Ohman, 8.
Martin M. Onishuk, 195 (upper left).
Stuart A. Oring, XI (bottom, with Robert C. Bjork), XVI (top, with Murray D. Lemmon), XVII, XXI (top 2, with Murray D. Lemmon), 90 (with Murray D. Lemmon), 159.
Carl E. Ostrom, XIII (top).

James E. Pallas, Jr., XVIII (top), 214.
Ernst Peterson, 209.
Hermann Postlethwaite, 3 (top).
Leland J. Prater, 173, 224 (bottom).
Vance Price, 222.
Lawrence Rana, X, 134, 291.
Lloyd W. Richardson, 298, 333, 334.
Frank Roadman, 185.
Thomas C. Roberts, 206.
Jerry Rodgers, University of Arkansas, 174, 175.
James E. Russell, National Geographic Society, 45.
Jack S. Schneider, 361.
H. F. Scholz, end sheet.
Earl R. Shade, 140 (bottom).
Kevin Shields 1, 10, 11 (top, right), 160 (bottom), 301 (bottom), 306, 320.
Richard S. Shomura, Bureau of Commercial Fisheries, 26 (right).
Southern Pulpwood Conservation Association, 50.
Southern Railway System, 243, 244, 245.
Robert M. Steele, 140 (top).
L. F. Steiner, XXIV (top).
Dale Swartz, 375.
Dan O. Todd, 49, 53, 183, 234.
20th Century Fox, 357.
John D. Tynes, 262.
University of Arkansas, 172.
University of Pennsylvania, 200.
David F. Warren, VII (top), 68, 80, 250, 302.
Jack Washichek, 188.
M. Woodbridge Williams, National Park Service, 218.
Fred S. Witte, 287.
Leep Zelones, 280, 282.

374

Index

381